MACHIN

THEIR HISTORY AND
TACTICAL EMPLOYMENT

(BEING ALSO A HISTORY OF THE
MACHINE GUN CORPS, 1916–1922)

LIEUT.-COLONEL G. S. HUTCHINSON
D.S.O., M.C.

The Naval & Military Press Ltd

Reproduced by kind permission of the Central Library,
Royal Military Academy, Sandhurst

Published by

The Naval & Military Press Ltd

Unit 10, Ridgewood Industrial Park,

Uckfield, East Sussex,

TN22 5QE England

Tel: +44 (0) 1825 749494

Fax: +44 (0) 1825 765701

www.naval-military-press.com

© The Naval & Military Press Ltd 2004

MACHINE GUNS

From the painting by Lt.-Colonel G. S. Hutchison, D.S.O., M.C.

"THE DEVIL'S WATERING-POT"

Vickers Machine Gun under Battalion command

DEDICATED

WITH GRATITUDE

TO

Brigadier-General SIR JAMES EDMONDS

C.B., C.M.G., D.LITT.

FOREWORD

THE compilation of the History of Machine Guns is a
task considerably greater than I had anticipated when
I decided to essay the task. The early history of
mechanical development, the tracing of the growth of
fire-power and of the development of tactical ideas as
to its employment, covers a wide field of invention,
experiment, and warfare. The sources of information
here have proved to be widely scattered and far from
complete; while no official record has ever been
prepared.

The development of machine guns and their tactics
can be conveniently presented in three cycles. The
first lies within the period around the Franco-German
War, 1870–71 ; the second around the Russo-Japanese
War of 1904–5 ; and the third, in the Great War,
1914–18, with its transcendence in November 1917. At
this date, it can be said that knowledge as to machine
guns and their relation to artillery weapons, automatic
rifles and other arms, had been perfected : though this
is not to suggest that, subsequent to 1917, machine
guns were always tactically disposed and exploited in
battle in the light of this accumulated knowledge.

If sources of information in regard to the early
history of machine guns are few, the mass of detail in
regard to their use, and misuse, during the third cycle
of their development is overwhelming. Throughout

this period is to be found the narrative of the birth and rapid growth of a complete arm of the Service, the Machine Gun Corps, embracing a history of 159,000 men, innumerable battle actions, important developments in technical use and tactical employment, machine gun companies and battalions, staffs, training depots, personalities, in addition to matters concerning organization and tactics, of vital importance for future consideration. Nevertheless, though the material is overwhelming — official and regimental histories, diaries, and staff publications during the War—I have found it difficult, indeed, to separate and select the matter incorporated in this work. I have been obliged to omit many records of heroic achievement and other matters of deep interest to those who served as machine gunners during the Great War in order to keep this volume within the bounds of reasonable length. Moreover, a History of Machine Guns must be objective in its purpose ; and the selection of actions has been to illustrate the use of machine guns and the science of their tactical employment in the field.

The work might have been arranged in a different manner, in order to enable the military critic and student to use the book more easily as a text-work, under headings of Attack, Defence, Trench Warfare, and so forth. I have chosen rather to present the story in its historical sequence, the chapter headings providing the clue as to the content. Necessarily, as the history proceeds, the narrative pauses while points of important technical and tactical interest are discussed. I much regret that it is not suitable to underline such points in order to convey their emphasis to the reader. There may be found, also, some repetition. This is unavoidable in a work which necessarily compares the

technique and tactical methods of one battle with another, and perhaps the desirable emphasis is conveyed
thereby.   Field-Marshal   Lord   Wolseley,   a   noted
student, advised the younger officers of his day " to
read and re-read the history " of former campaigns.
Reconsideration may, therefore, serve the ends of
knowledge.

It is unfortunate that a number of documents
relating to the formation and disbandment of the
Machine Gun Corps have not come to light.   At the
Fifth Machine Gun Conference held at General Headquarters, British Armies in France, on 25th November
1918, it was agreed that " all information possible on
" the work of machine guns, and the Machine Gun
" Corps during the War, should be collected in order
" that such information might be examined thoroughly,
" and placed on record at the Machine Gun Training
" Centre, Grantham, both for instructional and histori-
" cal purposes."   There is, however, no evidence that
this was done.   I have no doubt that in a history of this
character there will be omissions.   Some of these have
been necessitated by the limitation of space ; others are
due to the lack of records.   I do not think, however,
that any omissions can be important, excepting those
which may fail to record a conspicuous battle action
and a notable achievement of arms.

Only one map is included among the illustrations,
which may appear to be a defect.   Two alternatives
presented themselves—a map or plan to illustrate each
action discussed, or no maps.   The student is advised
to use the maps issued with the Official History of the
War for the corresponding period, and those included
with the reports of military attachés for campaigns
prior to 1914.

In recording my generous appreciation of the loan of diaries and of the help of certain officers and others, I make no apology for noting in detail the action of two battles in which I myself participated. On the contrary, these possess the unique value of authentic eye-witness accounts : moreover, they have already been mentioned in the Official History of the War.

The important part which machine guns played in the Great War, and the amazing developments in fire tactics resulting therefrom, justify an attempt to bring together into one volume all that is known of their history and use. In so far as I am aware, no work exists which reviews the tactical handling of machine guns, illustrated both from the lessons of history and by recent changes in military organization brought about by an age of mechanization, with all its possibilities for greater speed in the transportation of men and arms, and for greater power of manœuvre.

Finally, no history of the Machine Gun Corps, disbanded in 1922, has been written. As the War years recede, I feel it becomes more improbable that any such history will be written. I am aware that, as a history of the Machine Gun Corps, this volume, for the reasons given, is incomplete. Nevertheless, since a history of Machine Gun Corps relates of a part of the military history of the British Empire, a part whose importance during the crisis of the Great War in 1918 cannot be over-estimated in its value and interest, I am grateful that I have been able to essay the task of its chronicle.

Machine gun units are now being formed. I may hope that this book will prove of value in suggesting how the supreme weapon of defence can best be organized and ordered. I can claim for this volume that it is written from long study and as the result of four years in command of machine guns on the battlefield.

I desire to express my gratitude to Colonel N. K. Charteris, C.M.G., D.S.O., for his valuable notes; to Lieutenant-Colonel R. Bingham, D.S.O., for his diary of the Guards Machine Gun Battalion; and to Colonel H. J. Davis, C.M.G., D.S.O., for records relating to the higher organization of machine guns. Others whose notes have assisted me are : Mr. Archibald J. McLean, F.R.I.B.A. ; Major-General J. F. C. Fuller, C.B., C.B.E., D.S.O. ; Lieutenant-Colonel T. Buchanan-Dunlop, D.S.O., M.C. ; Major R. B. Wharrie, M.C. The sources of information from other authorities quoted have been added as footnotes.

To Mr. John North I am especially indebted. With meticulous care, based upon a wide study of Military History, he has examined the proof sheets, contributing also a number of valuable suggestions.

I feel confident that this volume will commend itself to those of the disbanded Machine Gun Corps who saw the weapon of which it is the subject rise to an unchallengeable position on the battlefield. Bismarck once remarked that, " Fools say they learn by experience ; I prefer to learn by other people's experience." I trust that so wise a comment may prove an incentive to younger machine gunners to invest themselves with the experience of those who brought modern machine gunnery to its present perfection.

GRAHAM SETON HUTCHISON

ICKFORD
December 1937

CONTENTS

CHAPTER I

PAGE

ORIGINS (430 B.C.—A.D. 1870) 1

CHAPTER II

OPPOSITION (1871–1885) 25

CHAPTER III

MAXIM (1881–1899) 48

CHAPTER IV

THE TACTICAL CONCEPT (1888–1906) 71

CHAPTER V

MANY INVENTIONS (1908–1914) 95

CHAPTER VI

CHARACTERISTICS (1914–1915) 119

CHAPTER VII

MACHINE GUNS IN ATTACK (1916) 147

CHAPTER VIII

DEVELOPMENT OF BARRAGE FIRE (1917) 179

CHAPTER IX

LESSONS FROM YPRES (1917) 201

CONTENTS

CHAPTER X

" David slew his Ten Thousands " (1918) . . . 234

CHAPTER XI

Machine Gun Battalions in Action—The Defensive Battle (March–April 1918) 261

CHAPTER XII

Machine Gun Battalions in Attack (August–November 1918) 306

Award of the Victoria Cross to the Machine Gun Corps 339

Index 343

Index to Formations and Units 349

ILLUSTRATIONS

" THE DEVIL'S WATERING-POT "   .   .   . *Frontispiece*
Depicting the ·303-inch Vickers Machine Gun, under Battalion
organization, in action, from a prepared position, France,
1918
    From the painting by Lt.-Colonel G. S. Hutchison, D.S.O., M.C.

FACING PAGE

TRAINING MACHINE GUNNERS. B.E.F., FRANCE, 1914   .   48
Men of 2nd Battn. Argyll and Sutherland Highlanders,
transformed into a machine gun unit, 1936
    Photograph by the Author

BELGIAN MACHINE GUN SECTION : THE WHEELED CARRIERS
DRAWN BY DOGS, 1914   48
    Imperial War Museum

SOLDIERS OF THE INDIAN ARMY ARMED WITH THE HOTCHKISS
GUN, IN FRANCE, 1915   100
    Imperial War Museum

RUSSIAN MACHINE GUNNERS, CAPTURED BY GERMAN TROOPS,
HAULING THEIR MACHINE GUNS   100
    Imperial War Museum

IN A SHELL-HOLE POSITION   .   .   .   144
    Imperial War Museum

A DEFENSIVE POSITION IN THE EAST .   .   .   144
    Imperial War Museum

BULGARIAN MACHINE GUNNERS IN ACTION NEAR MONASTIR   158
    Imperial War Museum

FACING PAGE

ITALIAN MACHINE GUNNERS IN ACTION . . . 158
Imperial War Museum

MACHINE GUNS OF THE CANADIAN CORPS IN BARRAGE POSI-
TIONS, VIMY, APRIL 1917 196
Imperial War Museum

OBSERVATIONS WITH CLINOMETER AND BARR & STROUD
RANGE-FINDING INSTRUMENT, WHEN SITING A BATTERY OF
MACHINE GUNS, YPRES SALIENT, SEPTEMBER 1917 . . 196
Photograph by the Author

·303-INCH VICKERS GUN MOUNTED ON POST FOR ANTI-AIRCRAFT
WORK—IN ACTION. TYNE COTT, YPRES SALIENT, DECEMBER
1917 214
Photograph by the Author

GERMAN 'HEAVY' MACHINE GUN IN ACTION, 1918 . 214
Imperial War Museum

" WITH BACKS TO THE WALL " 248
The 33rd Battalion Machine Gun Corps at Meteren, Battle
of the Lys, 13th April 1918
From the painting by Lt.-Colonel G. S. Hutchison, D.S.O., M.C.

CHAPTER I

ORIGINS

430 B.C.—A.D. 1870

The role of machine guns—Origin—Dionysius the Tyrant—The Polybolos—*Orgues* and *ribaudequins*—Battle of Ravenna—" The First Rapid-fire Gun "—Gatlings—The Montigny *mitrailleuse* —Important significance of the French disasters in 1870–71— Battles of Gravelotte, 1870, and Nanshan, 1904, compared— Failure of machine guns due to tactical handling—Successful incidents described—Of generalship.

PARAMOUNT among weapons, the Machine Gun is possessed of its own peculiar technique, its own science, a mathematics which differentiates it from other arms, and a tactical organization and handling distinct from those of infantry, cavalry, and artillery. That the machine gun possesses its own spirit none who have served the gun in battle can doubt. The demands on its teams are of a very high order. Unusual strength of body and suppleness of muscles ; the keen eye and cunning hand ; speed of foot, steel nerves, a stout heart—these are the physical requirements. The machine gunner must be possessed, also, of intelligence above the average : his mind must be swift as a bullet in flight : he must be resourceful, audacious, possessed of initiative, capable of endurance to the uttermost. The greatest war of all history demonstrated that in the largest army, that of the British Empire, fighting in nearly every part of the world, machine gunnery could only fulfil its supreme task, and attain to its highest form of technique, both in attack and defence, organized as a separate corps. The spirit of the gun demanded no less; those who joined or were posted to its companies and battalions gained the title of the " Suicide Corps." Something more was needed beyond both bodies and brains of exceptional equipment, namely, invincible courage. The machine gun is the backbone of defence, the deadly scythe which sweeps aside resistance in the attack.

The age of mechanization gives to this weapon, itself a triumph in mechanics, heightened importance. Mechanized transport adds to power, enhances the opportunity for man and his weapon. Their peculiarities and technique properly understood, their capacity to overcome resistance and to search out an enemy in rare circumstance, their overwhelming moral effect fully appreciated, machine guns, manned by picked men, directed by resolute and intelligent generalship, remain the masters of the battlefield.

While infantry, cavalry, and artillery can fulfil only their own specialized role under any conditions, the machine gun performs that of the three other arms. At certain phases in both attack and defence machine gun units function either as infantry or cavalry, or conform to a role analogous to batteries of artillery. Indeed, one unit may often be so disposed that under the direction of one commander it performs the joint role of infantry and artillery, employing for the two tasks a scientific technique vastly different one from the other. Machine gunnery reached a stage of development late in 1917 when the formations responsible for such elasticity in the production of fire-power could only be regarded as a separate arm of the Service, with weapons which, scientifically organized, can rule the fields of war.

The origin of the machine gun is buried deep in history. So remote, indeed, is the earliest record of its technical principle that research brings us to the very edge of legend. The whole panorama of ancient Greece, Carthage, the Kingdom of Minos opens before us. The mythical personages of the vanished past are summoned to herald the most grim reality of modern warfare. It is now known that much that had passed for legend, from about 2000 B.C.,[1] is in fact the amazing truth of a civilization excelling in the arts, skilled in warfare ; and, as the myth of Daedalus and his son, Icarus, suggests, familiar with the phenomena of air currents and of their mastery by gliding. Twentieth-century aeronautics may indeed be but a repetition of history. Certainly the Polybolos foreshadowed the modern machine gun.

Many ancient writers have depicted the character of Dionysius of Syracuse in the blackest colours. Born in 430 B.C., he was both talented and ambitious; and at the age of twenty-five years was appointed sole general of Syracuse. Possessed of full powers, Dionysius first increased the army and converted the island of Ortygia into a fortified residence and base for his military plans. His ambitions embraced the subjugation of all Sicily, the humiliation of Carthage, and the annexation of part of southern Italy to his dominions. In all his projects he succeeded. On account of his acts and personal character the conqueror acquired for himself the title of Dionysius the Tyrant, by which he is known in

[1] Excavations by Sir Arthur Evans at Knossos

history. Yet, unlike some other tyrants of later ages, this builder of the terrible prison of Lautumiae, cut from the solid rock in Syracuse, was devoted to literature and to the arts and was himself a poet, who repeatedly contended for the prize of tragedy at Athens. Could Dionysius but have forecast the culmination more than 2000 years later of the invention he contrived, who can doubt that his name might have stood beside that of Archimedes?

The earliest record of the machine gun principle is that of the Polybolos, contrived by Dionysius the Tyrant. The weapon was a " repeater-thrower," as the name suggests, projecting a succession of arrows supplied by a magazine or hopper.[1] Every warlike race at some period attempted to invent a weapon whereby the fire-power of one man might be increased in excess of the capacity of his ordinary arm. At the battle of Hastings, some of the English archers used a bow designed to fire more than one arrow at a time.

A long interval took place before any further development of the idea occurred: and it was not until gunpowder, already used by the Chinese, came to be introduced into Europe that the imagination of man seized again upon mechanical means for producing an ever-increasing volume of fire. In 1248 Roger Bacon recorded the composition of gunpowder. It seems to have been first used for the propulsion of missiles by Bernard Schwarz, a German monk. He contrived to supersede the bow with iron tubes into which were fitted arrows, padded out in order to provide the necessary resistance to the explosive charge.

The first types of machine guns were known as

[1] Thévenot, " Veteres Mathematici " (Paris, 1643), pp. 73-74.

orgues or *ribaudequins*, that is to say " organs," which in appearance they resembled, or " little bits of laughter," which may sometimes have come near the mark. The *orgue* consisted of six to ten musket barrels mounted side by side on a frame. The composite weapon was usually fired by a single lock firing a quick-match, which ignited the charges of all the barrels in rapid succession. There are only two instances of the use of the mediaeval organ gun in the field, though examples can be found in many military museums, and they were used also in the siege warfare of the fifteenth and sixteenth centuries. The first instance is that of the battle of Piccardina, in 1467. The Venetian General, Coleoni, brought *orgues* into action with the cavalry of his advance guard.[1]

In the year 1512 there is a clear record of a machine gun fight, when history provides the vivid picture of the battle of Ravenna. The battle is of high interest, for it provides a brilliant example of resourceful generalship and of the recognition that surprise is the first element of success in war. In this age cavalry was the battle-winning arm, both mobility and weight of the charge proving overwhelming once the lines of infantry had been broken or shaken by archers and by cannon. The introduction of the long pike in the hands of resolute men, however, proved a formidable obstacle to horsemen armed with the sword, who were often wounded or unseated before able to deliver the thrust and cut of their fighting technique. Pedro Navarro, commanding the Spanish forces, conceived of the ingenious idea of mounting the arquebus, the footman's gun of the period, upon wagons in order

---

[1] ' Machine Guns and their Employment,' by Dittrich, translated by Capt. E. S. May, R.A., in the " Royal Artillery Journal," 1889, p. 75.

to present a large volume of concentrated fire against the ranks of pikemen who threatened to withstand the assault of the Spanish cavalry.

Thirty carts, on each of which several large arquebuses had been mounted, were disposed in front of the infantry. Thus was re-conceived the idea, already fruitfully exploited by Dionysius, of one man, with assistance, delivering a fire greater in volume than he could otherwise have attained with his individual weapon, and effecting an economy in fire-power.

Since modern machine gunnery demands exceptional qualities of those who form the gun teams, the deeds of brave men, the flower of their race, serve to illumine with rich romanticism a tale often as terrible as any upon the pages of world history.

Repeating weapons had become well known throughout Europe towards the close of the sixteenth century, though the expense of manufacture, together with the crudeness of the gunpowder, proved a stumbling-block to their use. The most notable contribution came a little later from a Mr. Palmer, who, in 1663, introduced the principle of a repeating fire-arm, where the action of reloading was governed by taking up the expending force of recoil. His invention was contributed to the " Transactions of the Royal Society." Palmer's idea was " to make a pistol shoot-" ing as fast as it could be and yet to be stopped at " pleasure, and wherein the motion of the fire and " bullet within was made to charge the piece with " powder and bullet, to prime it and to open the cock." Despite this historic invention, foreshadowing the Maxim, upon which all modern contributions have been based, the automatic guns which immediately followed continued the principle of the organ guns.

Nevertheless, there were sound reasons why the Palmer principle, rapidly exploited by armourers of the later seventeenth century in the manufacture of revolvers, could not be extended to that of guns. With revolvers it was found that it was impossible to contrive weapons in which the chambers would all be truly bored, and this enabled an escape of gas between the revolving butt and the end of the barrel, which quickly wore away the metal, and proved such weapons dangerous to use.

Two decisive factors militated against the manufacture of machine guns. Until machine tools had been invented there was no sure method by which metal could be evenly cut and bored. A second problem, only finally overcome during the past half-century, lay in the ammunition. Until cartridges with a solid-drawn brass or copper case had been introduced there was no means of preventing the dangerous escape of explosive gases, nor of being sure that the barrel had been cleared of the empty cartridge case prior to the automatic action of reloading.

A variety of attempts were made to improve upon the mediaeval organ guns. The Artillery Museum at Woolwich possesses a specimen manufactured in 1830. The most notable contribution came, however, from America on the eve of the Civil War. " The First Rapid-fire Gun " is the description given to an organ of twenty-five barrels mounted flat upon a platform, carried on wheels, the invention of Dr. Josephus Requa. It is recorded that only one of these guns was used during the American Civil War and was mounted on one of the forts of Charleston, South Carolina. It may be noted that the highly efficient Machine Gun Battalion of the 30th American Division,

commanded by the late Major W. Pierce, was recruited
largely from the Charleston district ; it was trained
in accordance with British principles in the Ypres
Sector during May and June 1918, during the Great
War.

The most notable contribution, however, was that
of Dr. Gatling of Chicago, in 1862. The gun followed
the organ principle, but the rifle barrels were fixed in
circular form at equal distances around a central axis,
and mounted upon a two-wheeled vehicle. The gun
consisted of six barrels behind which the reloading
mechanism was placed. The cartridges were fed into
a trough above the gun, falling by their own weight
one by one into the gun as each shot was fired, and
entering each barrel at its highest position. The
barrels were revolved by a crank-handle at this side,
each barrel being fired as it reached the lowest position
in respect of the axis, extraction of the empty cartridge
case taking place on the left side, while the barrels on
the right took up the new rounds and carried them into
position for firing. The gun was cooled by a water-
jacket. Several of the Gatling guns were used during
the Civil War, chiefly with the Northern armies.
Considerable enterprise was shown by the Gatling
Gun Company, for, although the guns were never
officially recognized by the War Department at
Washington, the management took advantage of the
fighting to demonstrate, an employee of the company
operating the gun in action.

The military Staffs of European armies paid little
attention to the details of a war so remote from their
familiar battle-grounds and it was not until some years
later that any record was published east of the Atlantic.
Though the Franco-German War of 1870–71 first

awakened military consciousness to the reality of the
machine gun, a Belgian had, however, been elaborating
an invention, the result of which was destined both to
mar and ultimately to make machine gun history. Yet,
the event itself is in fact of less importance than the
name given to it. In 1851, some twenty years before
the outbreak of the Franco-German War, Captain
Fafschamps, a Belgian officer, offered drawings of an
invention to a fellow countryman, Monsieur Montigny,
an engineer and arms manufacturer, with works at the
Fontaine l'Évêque and at Brussels. Montigny improved the Fafschamps model, and constructed some
guns to supplement the permanent defences of the
Belgian fortresses.[1]   In 1869 he was successful in per-
suading the Emperor Napoleon III to adopt them for
extensive use in the French army.

   The French gave to the new gun the name of
" *mitrailleuse.*" Translated, the word *mitraille* means
" grape-shot," and, since *mitrailler* is " to fire grape-
shot," the word *mitrailleuse* could properly be translated as " grape-shooter." Such a description may have
been suitable for what came to be known as the
Montigny *mitrailleuse* ; but the name yet persists in
the French army for the machine gun as we know it,
and is entirely inappropriate as a description of the
gun's action. Psychologists are familiar with the
results proceeding from the association of ideas. It is
not improbable that the misuse of machine guns and
the failure over a long period of years to appreciate
their true role proceeded from the false association of
a name with a weapon whose structural identity and
mechanical capacity suggested tactical employment

   [1] Captain C. J. Tackels, " Armes de Guerre " (Bruxelles, 1868),
p. 180.

wholly different from that to which almost immediately following their adoption on a large scale they were committed in a European war of the first magnitude.

The Montigny *mitrailleuse* was intended as the surprise weapon of 1870 with which France would achieve a devastating victory over the massed formations of the German enemy. At the arsenal at Meudon, 1869, the guns were manufactured in an atmosphere of planned perjury, not unlike that which accompanied the formation of the Armoured Car Section of the Motor Machine Gun Service—" Tanks "—on Lord Iveagh's estate at Thetford in June 1916. Whereas the secret of the Tanks was preserved almost to the moment of their being successfully launched in action against the formidable Flers Line and High Wood position on 15th September 1916, the details of the French *mitrailleuses* had been an open secret long before the mobilization of July 1870. Major G. V. Fosbery, V.C., incidentally one of the first recipients of the supreme award " For Valour," [1] had during 1869 been employed by the Indian Government, reporting upon the *mitrailleuse*, and had attended the Montigny works at Brussels. Though Major Fosbery specifically " disclaims all share in the invention itself," he made important inventive contributions to it. This was, in fact, a period rich in armament inventions, some of which, notably the breech-loading rifle and the metal cartridge case, served to revolutionize tactical principles and even at this date began to limit the potentiality of cavalry.

Major Fosbery recorded: " I consider that in urging " on M. Montigny the adoption of Mr. Metford's " rifling, and the hardened expanding projectile,

[1] The Victoria Cross, instituted 29th January 1856.

" instead of the ill-contrived, cannelured bullet for-
" merly used with a rifling, but ill-adapted to its
" object ; in devising a system by which the cartridges
" are securely carried on service ; and in changing
" the system of cartridge itself, I have been able to
" render the invention more suitable for the purposes
" for which it is intended." [1] Major Fosbery contributed a very full description of the gun itself, noting
that : " It has been found possible to fire this weapon
" twelve times per minute, throwing therefore 444
" rifle shots in that time." Staff officers from several
European armies had inspected the gun at Brussels,
and the Prussians were quite familiar with it. The
mitrailleuse presented no surprise to the Prussians in
1870 ; and because the French so entirely misconceived
the tactical potentiality of the new weapon, the
mitrailleuse of the Franco-German War might suitably
have reverted to the name of *ribaudequin*.

Nevertheless, during 1869 and the early months of
1870, with elaborate secrecy the Montigny *mitrailleuse*
was manufactured at the Meudon arsenal. Only those
officers and men who were to manipulate the weapons
in the field were permitted even to see them. The
French Press, dutifully responding to political expedi-
ency, depicted the secret weapon as one which would
mow down the Prussian battalions and thus secure an
easy victory to France. Even on mobilization in July
1870, the new guns were despatched to the front
wrapped in tarpaulins, and were placed in the concentration camps under armed guards.

The Montigny *mitrailleuse*, made more efficient by

[1] ' Mitrailleuses and their Place in the Wars of the Future,' Major
G. V. Fosbery, V.C., " Journal of the United Services Institution,"
pp. 539-563.

some minor improvements introduced by Colonel de Reffye, weighed 1800 kilogrammes including the limber loaded with 2100 cartridges. An ammunition limber, *caisson*, carried a further 6000 rounds. The machine guns were organized into batteries consisting of six guns, six caissons, two baggage wagons, and a travelling forge. With no practical experience of the arm, or of the tactical organization in which officers and men now found themselves, the batteries were committed to the battle. This, however, was not the greatest of the fatuities which characterized the use of the wonder weapon upon which France had been so assiduously taught to rely for victory. The crowning folly appeared on mobilization, when a new artillery organization was introduced. Hitherto, the French artillery had been organized in groups of three six-gun batteries. On the outbreak of war in 1870 the artillery was redistributed on the basis of two six-gun batteries, the third being armed with ten Montigny *mitrailleuses*.

Catastrophe followed. Yet the defeat and humiliation of the French armies were but the tragic Nemesis of an imperial administration rotten to the core, always a grim warning to those with empire responsibilities. Men were in high places whose antecedents would have shamed the better kind of brigand. The deficiencies of the army were made worse by the diversion of public funds to private necessities. The looseness, the vulgar splendour, the base standards of judgment of the imperial court infected each branch of the public services of France, and influenced perhaps not least those who were in military command. Leadership implies thought, deliberation, judgment, decision, direction, foresight. Yet, neither French generalship, nor

indeed the minds of many other eminent soldiers, had
at this date grasped the elementary fact that artillery is
by its nature designed to carry out its task at ranges far
beyond those of the rifle. The range of the *mitrailleuse*
was limited to that of the Chassepot rifle, with which
the French infantry were armed, a distance just exceeding one thousand yards. The machine gun batteries
not only presented, therefore, a target as attractive as
the French field gun, without possessing equal power
to reply, but would be outranged by the German
Krupp guns.

The result was inevitable. On 4th August 1870
the Commander of the XIth German Corps at Weissenberg began to bombard the French position on the
heights of Château Geisberg. The French reply was
to throw a battery of *mitrailleuses* into the fight : and
to engage the Krupp guns from a knoll, the more
conspicuous as a landmark because identified by three
poplars. A Prussian shell exploded upon one of the
French ammunition wagons, mortally wounding General
Douay who was in command, and the *mitrailleuses* were
hastily withdrawn from action. Two days later at
Spicheren, after General Valbrègue had been forced to
retire behind Styring, a battery of *mitrailleuses* belonging
to the Vergé Division was called upon to fill the gap on
the Styring road as a counter to the German artillery.
The battery had been in action but a few minutes before
it was forced to retire.

Meanwhile, in Paris, the journalists whipped the
" wonder weapon " propaganda to fever heat. It had
bored deep holes in the on-coming attack : it had mown
down the Prussian infantry as some ghostly scythe
might reap its bloody harvest. Such accounts were
but flights of journalistic imagination serving a disastrous

purpose. Nor was there a shadow of justification for these early reports of optimism. In truth, on 2nd August 1870 the *mitrailleuses* had received their baptism of fire. In a modest action at Saarbrücken, dignified as a battle and hailed as a victory, a French division met a small detachment of Prussian infantry, who, greatly outnumbered, wisely deployed into their skirmishing lines, offering no kind of target for machine gun fire, and retired, making of the engagement a rearguard action of little significance. Yet, upon such evidence, the fiction of a machine gun victory was based, heralding the speedy destruction of the German armies.

It must not be supposed that the *mitrailleuse* was everywhere a failure. Whether by design or by chance there were occasions when the machine gun assumed its true role, and fought with the infantry. Then, though it took long for military critics to perceive the true value of the new weapon, it fulfilled the most sanguine expectations. The Prussian infantry fell in a welter of blood, as witness the German official account of the fighting at Montigny-la-Grange on 18th August 1870: " The position of the 36th Regiment on the " open ground afforded it very little shelter against the " enemy's musketry and *mitrailleuses*, so its losses " gradually reached a very high figure."

It remained for Germany, whose soldiers had first felt the murderous effect of modern machine gun fire in 1870, to be the first, also, to realize, albeit some forty years later, the true character of the weapon. The term " modern " is used, for the system of breechloading and of rifling almost completely changed the role of gun-fire and the tactical handling of such weapons. The general principles for the tactical employment of machine guns up till after the commencement of the Great War were nowhere better stated than in Section 187 of the German Regulations :

" Machine guns enable commanders to develop
" at fixed points the maximum volume of infantry
" fire on the smallest possible front. Machine guns
" can be employed over any country that is practical
" for infantry, and when they are unlimbered they
" must be able to surmount considerable obstacles.
" In action they offer no greater target than riflemen
" fighting under like conditions, and they can, in
" proportion to their fire-value, support far greater
" losses than infantry. They can utilize all cover
" that infantry are able to use. Cover which is
" barely sufficient for a platoon of infantry (60 men)
" can protect an entire machine gun detachment."

With the exception that the wheeled mounting of the *mitrailleuse* did not permit of concealment similar to that described, the same, but then new, principles governing fire - power were already present. The Montigny *mitrailleuse*, moreover, was not automatic : it was operated by hand, possessed twenty-five barrels, while its maximum effective range barely exceeded 500 yards, against the range of 2800 yards of modern weapons. Nevertheless the battle of Gravelotte, of 18th August 1870, may be said to have ushered in the era of the machine gun.

The battle of Gravelotte itself is one of the most striking and interesting in all military history. There are, also, many points of deeply interesting comparison between this battle, where the French army failed before the gates of Paris and opened the way for von Moltke, and the battle of Nanshan, of 26th May 1904, where the Russian General Stessel yielded the key to Port Arthur, and therefore the issue of the war, to the

Japanese Marshal Nogi. The generalship of France and of Russia was not concerned with the leadership of men. The latter were ignored while generals schemed for position.

Colonel G. F. R. Henderson in his classic, " The Science of War," wrote :

" War is pre-eminently the art of the man who
" dares take the risk ; of the man who thinks deeply
" and clearly ; of the man who, when accident
" intervenes, is not thereby cast down but changes
" his plans and his dispositions with the readiness
" of a resolute and reflective mind, which, so far
" as is possible, has foreseen and provided against
" mischance."

How very thoroughly may these attributes be applied to the leaders of the German and Japanese armies, and how contrary was the character of the French and Russian marshals. General Sir Edward Bruce Hamley, a military writer of no less distinction than Colonel Henderson, in his " Operations of War " has written :

" The Commander's character has always weighed
" even more than his skill. Above all things he must
" have energy, perseverance, and determination.
" He must have courage, moral and physical . . .
" knowledge of men, and how to excite their en-
" thusiasm and to call forth their utmost endeavours,
" and a high sense of duty to the State."

Judged from this standpoint, how utterly damned are Bazaine and Stessel, how highly exalted such leaders as von Moltke and Nogi !

Before Metz and Port Arthur, everything demanded a defence to the death, a glorious defence, which, even if culminating in defeat, would have removed all sting of shame ; a defence continued, no matter at what cost.

Opportunities for such a course were never lacking. There was a chance, perhaps a certainty, not only of preventing defeat, but of turning defeat into victory. The opportunity, in both instances, was ignored. France and Russia had to pay the penalty for the political and moral indifference which could acquiesce in the practical surrender at Gravelotte and Nanshan. Such indifference found its Nemesis in a Bazaine and a Stessel.

French generalship, possessed of a weapon which, with understanding, foresight, and rightly handled, might have turned the scales, intrigued for personal aggrandizement, while the *mitrailleuses* remained the wonder of Parisian journalese.

Thirty-four years later, following an interval during which French indifference and the grave tactical misuse of the *mitrailleuse* in 1870 had almost completely discredited the machine gun, while the Japanese forces at the beginning of the Russo-Japanese War were entirely without any kind of machine gun, the Russians, uniquely armed with the highly efficient Maxim gun, failed to exploit such a weapon of opportunity. It is suggested that in 1870 the course of the war might have been changed had the character of the new weapon been studied, had its principles been applied to the tactical conditions, had its potentiality been realized by commanders and their subordinates in the field. The claim can scarcely be too high, when, even before the development of machine gun technique to its zenith during the Great War, the British army, on the first day of July 1916, at the opening of the battle of the Somme, sustained 60,000 casualties, most of which were due to machine gun fire.

The German attacking forces at Gravelotte numbered 150,000 men, of whom more than 20,000 were killed or wounded, in those days considered a remarkably high figure. While we may admire to the full the excellence of the German organization, the soundness of their system of practical training, their magnificent discipline, the selfless devotion of the officers, their superabundant energy and their unshrinking acceptance of responsibility, we cannot but recognize their faults. In truth, the whole structure of the Prussian tactics of 1870 was fundamentally unsound. No targets comparable with the heterogeneous crowd of armed men, pressed literally shoulder to shoulder, have ever presented themselves to machine guns, as did von Moltke's corps, divisions and brigades, inextricably jumbled together, incapable of higher direction, such a target as might have made the chattering *mitrailleuses* raise their ribald laughter to a shrill crescendo, the mockery which precedes the *coup de grâce*.

The notable exceptions of *mitrailleuses* in action on the left at Montigny-la-Grange and in the centre at the Bois de la Cusse before Armanvillers proved the rule of a blind obsession in the minds of the French higher command as to the role of machine guns and their place on the battlefield. There is scarcely any parallel in history with this vital misconception unless it be that of the exploiting of the Tanks to bolster up the faded fortunes of the Somme, but this latter instance carried no tragic consequence in its train.

In 1870, MacMahon, the subordinate French Commander, against his own better judgment, was hustled from point to point at the whim of an Empress utterly ignorant of military strategy, while the moral qualities of the French soldiery, who might once more have been rallied to the magic name of a Napoleon, were dissipated by the ignorance, stupidity, and vacillations of the Higher Command. In 1904 Kuropatkin's strategy was thwarted at every turn by the shifty policy of the most corrupt government in Europe, while his army knew nothing of the war, and was never taken into the confidence either of the government or himself. The effect was to paralyse the combative nerves of the two armies and led to ignominious rout. The French, too, were better armed than their opponents, not only in respect of the *mitrailleuse* batteries, but with the Chassepot rifle, sighted up to 1400 yards, though not effective beyond 1000 yards, against the German rifle, which was only sighted up to 700 yards. The moral quality of the troops was rotted and gangrened by the abortive policies of the home government, and by the nerveless policy of their commander. With the initial advantage of superior weapons the first principles of defensive action were wholly neglected.

The purpose of fire and how to obtain its maximum effect was stated with admirable precision by General Sir Francis Clery in " Minor Tactics," a standard work translated into four foreign languages. In 1888 Clery was Commandant of the Staff College, and concisely summarized the functions of fire-power :

" Fire has become more than ever the soul of the
" defence, and it should be applied towards pre-
" venting the enemy from reaching the position, and
" not, as of old, reserved for defeating him when he
" gets there. . . . His progress should be made to
" depend on the effect of his own fire, so that it
" becomes further incumbent on the defence to seek
" to cripple that from the outset."

Human nature in battle remains a constant factor, and its powers of endurance are limited. Had the

French generals troubled to study the *mitrailleuse*, the Prussians might well have sustained along the whole front the same kind of bloody rebuff with which they were met at Montigny-la-Grange on the left, at Bois de la Cusse in the centre, and at St. Hubert Farm on the right.

At Montigny the French, instead of placing the *mitrailleuses* in line with their field guns and thus, while limiting their action and masking their fire, exposing them to long-range shell fire, brought them into action, disposed in small groups, in the infantry firing-line. The German official history records :

> " From this point notably (a cluster of trees west " of La Folie), a battery of *mitrailleuses* swept the " border north-west of the cluster of trees, and " another battery from the south angle of this cluster " held under its fire the clearing which separates it " from the Bois des Genivaux. In a short time " General von Blumenthal saw the impossibility of " an attack upon La Folie."

It seems a remarkable coincidence that of the few, and in this instance outstanding, occasions on which the machine gun fulfilled its proper role during the Franco-German War, the action was at a place which bore the same name as the gun itself—Montigny.

In the centre, a battery of *mitrailleuses* behaved to perfection, and in combination with the French infantry the action is thus described in the German official history :

> " At this moment the artillery in position on the " ridge to the south of the Bois de la Cusse was " placed in an extremely critical situation. A battery " of *mitrailleuses* had debouched in front of Arman- " villers, and fired directly and with excellent range

" upon the extreme left of the line of Prussian
" artillery. The point was occupied by the fourth
" heavy battery already seriously injured by musketry.
" In a few minutes the fire of the *mitrailleuses* so
" decimated it that several officers, five chiefs of
" pieces, and forty men were disabled, and nearly all
" the horses killed or wounded. Such was the
" situation when suddenly large detachments of the
" enemy's infantry rose from the ravine in front of
" the ridge, and threw themselves with surprising
" swiftness upon the defenceless battery. Its chiefs,
" already wounded, succeeded with the few horses
" still untouched and after desperate efforts in getting
" two pieces back to the border of the wood, but
" the remainder of the pieces fell into the enemy's
" possession."

This action was the only occasion on which guns
were lost by the Germans during the whole course of
the campaign. In this instance machine guns were
operating in combination with infantry within effective
range on the exposed flank of the Prussian artillery.
Meanwhile on the right, near St. Hubert Farm, several
batteries of *mitrailleuses* had been concealed, and,
reserving their fire until the Prussian infantry were on
the glacis at short range, suddenly opened with wither-
ing effect, repulsing the attack with terrific losses.

The German casualties at the battle of Gravelotte
were exceedingly severe, due not only to cardinal faults
in the infantry tactics but to habitual neglect of artillery
preparation. The assault of the Prussian Guard at St.
Privat was not preceded by an artillery bombardment.
Although 180 guns were in position against the French
right, the centre of the St. Privat position was still
untouched when the 1st Guard Division advanced to

the attack. Neither the Chassepot rifle nor the
Montigny *mitrailleuses* were secrets to the Prussian
Staff : nor could the German generals have assumed
that the French would so entirely miscalculate the
tactical use of the new weapon. History affords the
examples from which at all times men may by analysis
and deduction find solutions for new problems; and,
as has been said in a famous passage, " Biography, that
is life without theory." Napoleon had said with
truth : " It is the man who is wanted and not men."

An able commander, with far inferior numbers,
possessed of weapons whose use he understands need
never despair of success. Great issues hang upon the
quality and character of the High Command. Before
Waterloo, 1815, in protest, Wellington had written to
the Military Secretary :

    " When I reflect upon the character and attain-
" ments of some of the general officers of this army,
" and consider that these are the persons in whom I
" am to rely to lead columns against the French
" generals, and who are to carry my instructions into
" execution, I tremble."

Wellington had been a careful student. Wolfe,
Sir John Moore, Crawford, Napier, Havelock, were
deeply read. Von Clausewitz, the most profound of
all military writers, refers again and again to the need
for study. " In the realm of knowledge," said Commandant Chouteau in a notable address to the Cadets
of St. Cyr in 1935, " the officer's superiority must be
" even more pronounced."

The Franco-German War of 1870–71 occurred at a
time when vital, even revolutionary, new principles
had by the process of invention and experiment radically
changed European armament. The rifled gun was

new, but not so novel that generalship should have failed to study its potentiality and adopt tactics to the needs of the moment. Eleven years previously Napoleon III had first employed rifled guns on the battlefields of northern Italy. " Read and re-read the battles of the great masters " was the exhortation of Field-Marshal Lord Wolseley to the subordinates of his day. Many years later, to serve the Tank Corps, itself the child of the yet youthful Machine Gun Corps, knowledge of history provided the clue to a tactical formation which prescribed the Tank victory at Cambrai on 19th November 1917. Lieutenant-Colonel J. F. C. Fuller, a noted student, had planned the movements and formations of the new weapon of the age based upon a drill described by Xenophon in the " Cyropaedia," and attributed by him to Cyrus of Persia (*circa* 500 B.C.).[1]

France failed at Gravelotte from sheer ineptitude dominating nearly every phase of strategy and tactics. Prussia succeeded, not so much because in the earlier stages of the war she showed any markedly superior military skill, but because, from the highest commander to the meanest camp follower, the army was inspired by energy, determination, and the irresistible will to victory. Had the French or the Russians before Port Arthur been as strict races as were the Spartans at Thermopylae, or as devout as the Tyrolese who perished at Königgratz, given commanders of the character of those of Germany or Japan, it is almost certain that they would have escaped destruction. Gravelotte and Nanshan are grim warnings for all time to governments which fail to respond to the will of the people, to generals who are indifferent to learning.

[1] Williams-Ellis, " The Tank Corps."

Words of Henri de Montherlant provide food for reflexion :

"Whenever I see young officers, before even "thinking that they defend their country, before "even associating them with the idea of victory, I "think of the tragic right of life and death which "they exercise over their men on the battlefield, and "I grieve for the time when it was still open to "question whether the finest military skill did not "lie in saving your men in battle and in achieving "the greatest possible result with the least possible "destruction of that pure and noble element com- "posed of human material, the very substance of the "nation."

Both science and psychology insist that rhythm is necessary to the incarnation of virility. Man must be at the centre of things. No machine guns can give victory without men of ability and character in their direction, and behind the gun.

CHAPTER II

OPPOSITION
1871–1885

Each arm possesses its special characteristics—Three cycles of
machine gun history—The myth of the *mitrailleuse*—Perkins's
invention—War Office Special Committee, 1870—Gatling
success in Russia—" Gorloffs "—Russian battle experience—
Lt.-Col. G. V. Fosbery, V.C.—Mr. Thorsten Nordenfeldt—
Mr. B. B. Hotchkiss—Gardner—Zulu War, 1879—The Royal
Navy as pioneers—Experiment with H.M.S. *Medway*—Naval
Brigade in Egypt and the Sudan—The year 1885.

PERHAPS, since war by its very nature is destructive,
some intangible often arises in the political sphere
which seems to mutilate the intelligence and integrity
of the politician, whose proper business by true definition is not destruction, but the " building of a city."
The battle of Gravelotte is of immense importance to
nearly every consideration of war, political, strategic,
tactical. Certainly, it was a landmark in the history
of machine guns. The battle marked something of a
gladiatorial entry. It was as symbolic of condemna-
tion, also, as was the down-turned thumb of a Caesar.
   Though the *mitrailleuse* had proved a failure except
in isolated instances where its immense services were
either misinterpreted or completely overlooked, the
faith of Colonel de Reffye was undaunted. With

extraordinary zeal he multiplied manufacture of the new guns on the Loire, while other guns were purchased abroad. From America came guns made to the French pattern and the Gatling Company received its first European orders. These latter were employed at the battle of Le Mans in January 1871, and were successful in the defence of the passages of the river Huisne and of the plateau of Anvours. Carefully concealed from the Prussian artillery, and, either beside the French infantry or in isolated groups, Gatlings were used to check the advance of the German infantry by sudden bursts of fire. There were other instances of success.

A first principle of war is that each arm possesses its special characteristics and functions but all must act in close combination. The proper execution of the principles implies a tacit understanding of the arm. Yet, though voices of authority were willing to speak of the doom which, after Sedan, had overtaken a depraved nation, and the Paris Press spasmodically contributed a new anodyne of sensation to the absinthe tipplers of Montmartre, who might then project the sadistic nightmare of a Prussian butchery, no one in authority dreamed of challenging the false deductions which had from the first made of the *mitrailleuses* a heavy liability instead of an asset of incalculable worth.

The organization of the *mitrailleuses* was equivalent to a reduction of the French artillery by one-third, and contributing the doubtful compensation of adding to each group of batteries a bundle of rifles, with the mechanical principles of which only a few were familiar. It is always easy to be wise after an event: but it seems incredible that in an army which only sixty years previously had achieved under Napoleon Bonaparte the incomparable, there should have been found such a paucity of imagination, so gross a dereliction of duty. Although the population of Paris was kept from panic with blood-curdling tales of execution by *mitrailleuses*, yet in spite of a feverish multiplication of manufacture, no one studied the elementary technique, not a soul grasped the fact that an infantry rifle, even if mounted on wheels, in series, cannot perform the task of artillery.

The duty of the soldier is to read the mind of the enemy, to watch for him, to discover his ruses, to take measures to counter his attacks, whatever be their form. It may well be asked how such duties can be performed if the soldier does not even trouble to study the technique and potentiality of the weapon with which he is armed. On the few occasions when the *mitrailleuse* was used successfully, as the result of a chance, or due to the initiative of some junior officer, it was employed to supplement or take the place of infantry fire.

The military opinion of Europe, apprised that it was a cardinal error to replace field guns with machine guns, accepted the facts. The *mitrailleuse* had been proved a failure.

It will be seen how the history of machine guns is broadly divided into three cycles in the intervals between which there was increasing activity by enthusiasts and much solid achievement in every part of the world. The first cycle closed with 1871. The second obtained importance in 1904–5 during the Russo-Japanese War. The third was reached at the battle of the Somme in July 1916, and attained its zenith in February 1918. Yet the immensity of the disaster which overtook both France and Russia completely overshadowed the tactical lessons of the wars in which these great nations were defeated.

The catastrophes of 1871 and of 1905 seemed to those who witnessed them to tell of more than the vileness of an administration : voices of influence spoke of the holocaust that had destroyed the vice of a sunken nation ; of the triumph of simple manliness, of virtue itself, in the victories of the German and Japanese armies. There may have been truth in this ; yet it would require a nice moral discernment to appraise the exact degeneracy of the French of 1870 from the French of 1854 who humbled Russia, or from the French of 1859 who triumphed at Solferino : again, to what degree the Russian morals of 1812, their glorious year, were superior to those of 1904. And it would need a very comprehensive acquaintance with the lower forms of human pleasure to judge in what degree the sinfulness of Paris and St. Petersburg exceeded the sinfulness of Berlin and Tokyo. Whatever may be the truth of this matter, the new Germany, triumphant as first military Power in Europe, King Wilhelm of Prussia exalted as its first Emperor, could rest on its laurels, while the population of Paris, in savage disillusion, committed palaces, museums, the entire public inheritance in its capital, to the flames, and gave itself over to mass execution. Humanity, civilization, seemed to have vanished in the orgies of ghouls, whose only European parallels are those of 1789 and of Madrid in 1936-7.

The Princes and military chiefs of Germany hailed their Emperor in the Hall of Mirrors at Versailles on the 18th January 1871 : while the terrible drama of civil war, accompanied on both sides by atrocious violence and cruelty unspeakable, overwhelmed the very boulevards and cafés where but nine months earlier delirious men had fashioned their day-dreams of the Prussian butchery by *mitrailleuses* which was to make a Parisian holiday.

The myth of the *mitrailleuse* had vanished.

During the latter part of the campaign a number of machine guns, similar to the *mitrailleuse*, known as " Feld," had been used with the Bavarian army under General von der Tann, who had been detached by von Moltke from the siege of Paris to capture Orleans and seize the arsenals at Bourges on the Loire, where Colonel de Reffye yet contrived to continue his feverish activities. A battery of four Feld guns, whose extreme range was 1500 yards, engaged a French battery of artillery at a range of about 1000 yards and speedily put the guns out of action. Three violent French infantry counter-attacks were made against the *Königliche Bayerische Infanterie-Leibregiment*, the *corps d'élite* of the Bavarian army, which repulsed the attacks, signally assisted by the Feld guns, which took up their positions amid the riflemen. The Feld guns were not, however, mechanically satisfactory, owing especially to imperfect ammunition. The German Staff discredited the machine gun as an effective weapon in the field. The generals were intoxicated with victory, conscious of superior leadership ; deeply impressed with the exploits of the cavalry, whose brilliant and successful charges at Mars-la-Tour overshadowed the annihilation of the 38th Prussian Brigade which lost half its numbers and two-thirds of its officers from *mitrailleuse* fire ; blinded by the triumphant achievements of both artillery and infantry, whatever the errors of employment and the gravity of the losses ; and satisfied to consolidate the existing organization of an army which had given them an Empire.

Though enthusiasm for machine guns in the two

foremost military Powers in Europe had evaporated after 1870, in England interest began to stir. In 1869 the British Government, learning that in France and Belgium *mitrailleuses* were being manufactured on a considerable scale, purchased a number of guns both of the Montigny and Gatling type : and a Special Committee was set up to report on them. Under the chairmanship of Major-General F. Eardley-Wilmot, R.A., a lecture was delivered on the " Employment of Mitrailleurs " by Colonel Fletcher of the Scots Fusilier Guards, a member of the Committee, on 22nd January 1872, at the United Service Institution, which began to stir military opinion of the time.

As early as 1830, one Perkins had invented a steam gun, of which Jomini in his " Art of War " wrote : " it vomits forth as many balls as a battalion." [1] It is recorded that the Perkins gun was demonstrated outside the House of Commons where the Members rejected the invention.

In 1870 the Special Committee, under Colonel Wray, undertook a series of experiments with the Montigny *mitrailleuse*, the light Gatling, and 12-pr. B.L. and 9-pr. M.L. guns, shrapnel being used with the field guns. The tests included ranges of 300, 400, 600, 800, and 1000 yards ; and the totals were : Gatling, 2803 hits ; Montigny, 1708 ; 12-pr. B.L., 2286 ; 9-pr. M.L., 2207. These results were convincing, especially when the important factor of comparative road-space for machine and field guns is considered. The 12-pr. Gatling battery occupies 156 yards ; while the road-space taken up by a battery of 6 9-pr. M.L. field guns is 353 yards. The opinion of Colonel Fielding, more-over, was of historic importance, for it was he who

[1] Jomini, " Art of War " (American translation, 1868), p. 48.

appears first to have appreciated the proper role and tactical use of machine guns. Colonel Fielding wrote :
" The proper use of Mitrailleurs to be as re-
" presenting a certain number of infantry, for which
" there is not room on the ground, suddenly placed
" forward at the proper moment, at a decisive point,
" to bring a crushing fire on the enemy." [1]

The recommendation of the Committee was that the Gatling batteries be formed with an establishment of 12 guns, 5 officers, 101 N.C.O.'s and men, 6 small-arm ammunition wagons, 6708 rounds per gun, 34 riding horses, and 56 draught horses. Machine guns were, therefore, introduced for the first time in 1871, both for naval and military use. A heavier type using ·65 cartridge was adopted for use in ships and for coastal defence, a lighter pattern of ·45 calibre for military purposes. The latter was intended primarily for colonial service.

Already the agents of the Gatling Gun Company were busy with characteristic American sales pushful-ness. Guns were sold to both China and Japan, to Egypt, Morocco, and Tunis, and to Turkey, so that if resistance to machine guns had hardened in Europe as the result of the Franco-German War, the Orient, whose potentates have always shown an inclination for the mechanical wonders of the West, became an eager customer. Russia, fishing in the troubled waters of Balkan politics, was actively preparing for war with the Ottoman Power almost so soon as France had collapsed. Undeterred by the prejudice of both Frank and Teuton against the machine gun, the Slav was ready to arm with the new weapon on a large scale, a

[1] Captain J. F. Owen, R.A., " Compound Guns, Many-Barrelled Rifle Batteries, Machine Guns or Mitrailleurs," p. 10.

surprising matter since, historically, the Russian people
have little mechanical bent, a fact emphasized again in
1936 by the reports of the Soviet Dictator, Stalin, upon
the mechanized objectives of the Five-Year Plans.
The Czar's Government, however, despatched General
Gorloff to the Gatling works at Hartford in America,
entrusted with the mission of commissioning a considerable number of guns adapted to use the Berdan
cartridge of the Russian infantry rifle. The guns were
stamped with the name of " Gorloff," and for several
years the machine guns of the Russian army came to
be known as " Gorloffs." Four hundred guns were
speedily delivered, being distributed among the garri-
sons of Russia in Europe : forty-eight guns were
consigned to the Caucasus and twenty-four to Central
Asia. One battery was attached to cavalry in the field
for trial purposes.

There is no record as to how the " Gorloffs " were
employed, if at all, in the Russo-Turkish War of 1877.
The three battles of Plevna, 20th and again 30th July
and 11th-12th September, were prodigious in their
losses on the Russian side. During the second battle,
Osman Pasha exacted of the Czar's troops one-fifth of
their total number, while the losses on the Turkish
side, where the Commander was prodigal of the lives
of his men, were stupendous. Plevna fell on
December, after further thousands had fallen in
less conflict, the Turkish army hemmed in by ?
fire as were the French at Sedan.

In the campaigns in Central Asia machine
well served their purpose in breaking up the f.
charges of the Turcoman cavalry. As an illust:
of the overwhelming power of such weapons, em·
at the right moment against a suitable target, ther·

brilliant example from the Khiva Campaign. Under cover of early morning mist a huge force of Turkish cavalry attacked a thin Russian line supported by a section of two machine guns. Although the on-coming waves of Turcoman cavalry, destined to break upon the Russian defences, were scarcely visible in the dim light, the " Gorloffs " opened a terrible fire upon the phantom hosts. Streams of bullets bored great holes through the dense masses of horses and men. The carnage was hideous and those who remained, seized with panic, turned their horses and fled in rout.

From the earliest times, due rather perhaps to the Cossack tradition of the Russian Imperial Court than to any kind of good generalship, for which quality the forces of the Czar had little title to esteem, the Russian army favoured the machine guns as a cavalry arm. It was subsequently long held that " the machine gun is a weapon of opportunity " : and, in an age of mechaniza-tion, the extraordinary importance of the " mobility " of the gun cannot be exaggerated. After 1870 Russia led the way in machine-gun armament, but with amaz-ing lack of foresight the Russian cavalry, during the Russo-Japanese War, had forsaken machine guns for the rifle and the bayonet !

For European warfare it is now generally agreed that the cavalry arm can no longer serve a useful purpose, ηg, in a petrol age, been displaced by the armoured car and the light " Tank " ; but horsemen will probably yet be of value on the deserts of the Orient, thoug.. even here the troop-carrying aeroplane may finally succeed cavalry. Writing concerning the use of cavalry by the Russians, "The Times" Special Correspondent with the Japanese in Manchuria clearly demonstrated

D

the necessity for the arming of cavalry with machine guns. He wrote :

" The prime value of cavalry lies in its mobility.
" As an actual fighting unit in battle a body of cavalry
" is much inferior to an equal body of infantry.
" The discrepancy is less marked if the cavalry man
" carries a rifle, but there is always the encumbrance
" of the horses, which require the attention of one
" man in every four when the rifle is employed. It
" being postulated that tactics evolve themselves
" into an effort to obtain a superiority of rifle fire,
" it is evident that the necessity of dispensing with
" one quarter of a body of mounted riflemen before
" their weapons can be brought to bear greatly lessens
" the value of that body. On the other hand, the
" mobility of the mounted rifleman compensates for
" his comparative ineffectiveness. . . . Granted the
" value of mounted and mobile men as an auxiliary
" to infantry, the question arises, What is the weapon
" with which they shall be armed, and what the
" nature of the training to which they shall be sub-
" jected ? These things depend upon whether the
" mobility of a mounted man is regarded as secondary
" to his function as a rifleman, or whether his weapon
" is merely adapted to his mobility. In other words,
" are mounted men wanted for their riding or their
" shooting ? " [1]

The same question in various forms has arisen over and over again. " The Times " continues :

" The Russian cavalry, armed as it is with rifle
" and—shade of Seydlitz !—bayonet, is trained to
" fight on foot, thereby throwing away its most
" valuable weapon, mobility, that it has proved no

[1] " The Times," 23rd August 1905.

" more effective in the field than a flock of sheep.
" . . . They failed as cavalry and they failed aϛ
" riflemen, and the reason of the failure was that they
" are neither fish, flesh, fowl, nor good red herring."
    Later military opinion confirmed the deductions of
" The Times " : and, though the solution was by no
means generally recognized at the time, it appeared
that the machine gun was the very weapon needed to
equip cavalry with the fire-power of infantry, while
retaining their mobility and role in battle. Writing
later of the lessons of the Russo-Japanese War, Colonel
Zaleski emphasized :
    " The addition of machine guns to squadrons
" cannot be carried out too rapidly, and this weapon
" would now appear to be indispensable to cavalry."
    Ten years later the proper role of machine guns
had been realized in the leading armies of the continent
of Europe. In October 1914 the Chief of the 2nd
Bureau (Intelligence), French General Staff, wrote :
    " The Germans have resolutely adopted the plan
" of attaching machine guns to cavalry, and they
" seem thus to understand the modern combination
" of fire and shock tactics. To the machine gun
" the fire action, to the horseman the moral action—
" so much the more easy and productive of results
" as the machine gun is the more powerful."
    So long as the false views governing the failure of
the French machine guns in 1870 dominated military
opinion, no accurate estimate of the potentialities of
the weapon could be formed. During the following
decade, especially in Britain, a military Power of no
comparative importance, the whole question of their
tactical employment was explored. Captain J. F.
Owen had already issued an exhaustive book dealing

with technique in 1874. The following year Captain
E. Rogers lectured the United Service Institution on
" The Gatling Gun : its Place in Tactics." He urged
that the Gatling should not be confounded with
artillery. In 1880 Captain W. H. James, R.E., in a
lecture of almost prophetic vision, covered a wide field
under the title of " Modern Fire : its Influence in
Armament, Training, and Tactics." His views may
be summarized : Effectiveness of fire can be increased
by increasing the flatness of the trajectory and by
increasing the number of bullets poured on a certain
spot. The number of bullets fired at a given object
may be increased by firing at longer ranges and by
firing more often, the latter by the use of repeating
rifles or other means of increasing rapidity of fire.

In 1882 Lieutenant-Colonel G. V. Fosbery, V.C.,
returned with added experience and conviction to
lecture at the United Service Institution on 12th May
1882, under the chairmanship of Colonel Lord Elcho,
whose name will always be associated with marksmanship. In the course of his address Colonel Fosbery said :

" A most ably conducted and exhaustive set of
" trials has already determined that we have a
" system of machine guns by which one or two men
" can do as much destruction as, say, forty ordinary
" soldiers, and that without the chance of deranged
" mechanism or the complications which formerly
" militated against their use : and yet, though it is
" certain that an enemy will always do the un-
" expected thing, and if an European one, use
" machine guns against us, we neglect to acquire
" them for the Army because the exact tactical place
" for the weapon is as yet undiscovered."

While military thought was being gradually awakened, the inventors and commercial interests were not idle. Under Class 92, Ordnance and Machine Guns, British Patent Office Records, the patent registered is No. 790 of 1863. The year 1873 witnessed the arrival of a new-comer in the field, Mr. Thorsten Nordenfeldt, of St. Swithin's Lane, London. Nordenfeldt was in fact a Swedish banker, who financed and managed affairs on behalf of an engineer of Stockholm, H. Palmcrantz, who was associated with J. T. Winborg and E. Unge, Swedish manufacturers. Two patents were registered, No. 1739 in 1873 and No. 3678 in 1878, in the name of Nordenfeldt : and in the following year a further rival, Mr. B. B. Hotchkiss, an American resident in Paris, arrived upon the scene, registering patent No. 4454. Both the Nordenfeldt and Hotchkiss were to make history, their names becoming as familiar as the word " *mitrailleuse.*"

The Palmcrantz, or Nordenfeldt, gun resembled the organ guns of the mediaeval ages, and an improvement upon the loading action produced a further type of weapon known as the Gardner. The Hotchkiss followed the principle of the Gatling : but, influenced perhaps by the military view of the time that machine guns were an adjunct to the artillery arm, for his earlier models Hotchkiss utilized barrels of large calibre, so that explosive shells could be fired instead of bullets ; and the weapon was registered as " Revolving Cannon." Although unsuccessful in interesting the French army in his inventions, Mr. Hotchkiss, whose factory was at St. Denis, secured important orders from the French marine. Hitherto all machine guns had been hand-operated. Mr. Hotchkiss had yet to devise a gun of rifle-calibre pattern which would revolutionize the principles of small-arms design and manufacture.

In England, after Perkins had been summarily turned down by the House of Commons, no one seems to have had the temerity to submit a machine gun invention to the test of authority until 1860, when Colonel Martin deposited designs with the War Office. He was followed two years later by a Mr. Palmer and General Vandenburgh, both of the United States of America, the latter having the distinction of being the first to expound machine gun principles before the United Service Institution, London, in 1862. The Americans were followed by Captain Warlow and Mr. Dupuis, who jointly submitted further designs for consideration to the War Office. All were rejected. The Ordnance Select Committee had first considered the Gatling gun in 1867, in which year the British Military Attaché in Paris submitted another weapon, the design of Monsieur Mouceux. This latter was a monstrous affair, a veritable *ribaudequin*, consisting of twenty-one barrels arranged in three tiers of seven each. In 1868 Colonel Claxton produced his " Rifle Battery " for trial ; but no gun up till 1885 had proved so satis-factory as the Gatling. During the Ashanti War of 1874, Gatling guns were despatched to West Africa, but, due to the form of mounting, were found to be too cumbersome and unwieldy upon the narrow roads of the bush. All kinds of devices have been used for transporting machine guns, bamboo poles in India having often been the custom. Ingenuity appears to have been lacking in Ashanti, where pack transport, or coolies with bearer poles, and some kind of tripod mounting, would have supplied a deficiency which would have proved of the utmost service against the tribesmen's rushes at the action of Amoaful.

Although not a part of the equipment of the British

Regular Army, Gatling guns had been already successfully employed in 1879 during the Zulu War. Lord
Chelmsford, who as the result of his experiences became
a strong machine gun advocate, thus wrote of their
behaviour in the Zululand campaign :

" On the advance to the relief of Ekowe, two Gatling
" guns accompanied the column, and at the battle of
" Ginginhlovo did considerable execution among the
" Zulus *at the opening of their attack*, which commenced
" on the north side of our position. The Zulus very
" soon, however, worked round to the west and south
" side of our laager, and the Gatlings were not in
" action therefore for any length of time.

" At Ulundi we also had two Gatlings in the centre
" of the front face of our square. They jammed
" several times in the action, but when in work proved
" a very valuable addition to the strength of our
" defence on that flank. Machine guns are, I consider,
" most valuable weapons for expeditions such as that
" which we had to undertake in Zululand, where the
" odds against us must necessarily be great, and where
" it is necessary to leave small detachments in charge
" of posts along the line of communications. . . . They
" should, however, in my opinion, not be attached to
" artillery, but should be considered as essentially an
" infantry weapon, and should be worked by infantry
" soldiers. So utilized, they might, I feel sure, be
" used most effectively not only in defence, but *in*
" *covering* the last stage of an infantry attack upon a
" position, where the troops have at last to cease
" firing and endeavour to get home with the bayonet."

From practical experience, it is plain that Lord
Chelmsford had properly appreciated the tactical employment of machine guns, which, where their technique

is understood and their capacity is recognized, form the most powerful addition to fire-power.

There is evidence here of imagination and foresight, of understanding, of conviction, and of a practical sagacity which might well have served French generalship in 1870.

Gatling guns were successfully employed by the forces of Peru against Chili in the war of 1879.

While the Army hesitated to adopt machine guns, owing chiefly to the prejudice of Woolwich, the Mecca of Artillery, the Royal Navy was engaged in the conduct of exhaustive experiments at Portsmouth, its peculiar " holy of holies." The officers primarily responsible were Admirals Arthur, Boys, Fremantle, Selwyn; Captains Colomb, Johnstone; Lieutenant Tupper; and especially the pertinacious Captain Lord Charles Beresford.

During the decade 1870–80, the first trials were being made with the torpedo-boat. The engineering firm of Thornycroft, with works at Chiswick, had specialized in the building of rapid steam launches, chiefly for river navigation and for pleasure purposes. Inventive genius was turned to torpedo-boats, carrying first a spar torpedo and later a torpedo-tube on deck. The first torpedo-boat for the Royal Navy was launched at Chiswick-on-Thames in 1876.

Already the enigmatic personality of Basil Zaharoff had appeared upon the horizon of European armaments, a man who, reaching the zenith of his power during the Great War, acquired the name of the " Mystery Man of Europe," from a reference to him with this title in the House of Commons by Mr. Lloyd George, the British Prime Minister. Zaharoff, beginning life as a vagrant in the purlieus of Constantinople, in his early days passed through various vicissitudes in the less reputable walks of commerce, until opportunity came his way by an invitation from M. Venizelos of Greece suggesting Zaharoff's name as the agent of Nordenfeldt in the Near East. Zaharoff quickly became the first salesman of arms, and for many years, though most often in the background, he dominated the activities of European armament firms, and carried through prodigious international transactions. Zaharoff's first engagement was in the sale of torpedo-boats ; and so successful was he that before 1880 their adoption had become general by the European navies.

With the introduction of every new weapon in history, the problem has always arisen as to how to meet the new form of attack. For the purpose of discovering the designs, plans, and ruses of the potential enemy, the elaborate systems of espionage and counter-espionage have become universal, providing the world with a rich variety of thrilling tales of daring and of treachery, of romance and hair-raising adventure. The torpedo-boat provided a new problem for inventive brains, the *desideratum* being how best to counter an attack of this character. In order to economize weight and be able to put as much power as possible into the engines, the torpedo-boat was constructed of the thinnest steel plating ; rendering the engines themselves vulnerable to projectiles, if a suitable form of delivery and range attainment could be found. It was, therefore, suggested that machine guns provided such a counter-weapon, projecting small shells, or ordinary bullets. The tactics of the torpedo-boat generally were to steal at great speed close to its target under cover of darkness and discharge the dreaded emissary of destruction. The period between the moment when the torpedo-boat was discovered and that at which it was sufficiently close to fire a torpedo would necessarily be very brief, and though a shell from a battleship or cruiser might register a direct hit at a vulnerable point, the chances of such a hit upon a small rapidly moving target appeared exceedingly remote. The machine gun with its technical capacity of discharging a stream of small projectiles appeared obviously to be a more certain defence than reliance upon the ordinary gun-power of the battleship.

In order to test the efficiency of machine guns in action against a torpedo-boat, elaborate experiments were therefore carried out at Portsmouth. The *Medway*, a gunboat, was furnished with two machine guns, of the Hotchkiss revolving gun and Nordenfeldt pattern, mounted on the forecastle. During the trials the *Medway*, between the ranges of 1500 and 600 yards, was kept at full speed. Full-size models of torpedo-boats, built of steel plating, with dummy machinery inside, were used as the targets. The targets were placed sometimes broadside and at others bows-on to the gunboat. The result of the experiment demonstrated that the Hotchkiss, firing shells of one pound weight, with a bursting charge of a little under one ounce of gunpowder, had made excellent practice. Numbers of shells burst inside the target-boat, and in several instances portions of the shell had penetrated the steel plating on the farther side. The Nordenfeldt, firing steel bullets, succeeded even better. The target was riddled : five bullets struck the piston-rods of the dummy engine ; and it was judged that in actual warfare the torpedo-boats would have been effectively disabled and put out of action.

The Admiralty thereupon purchased a considerable

number of guns in variety, for varying tasks. These included ten-barrelled Gatlings of ·45 and ·65 inch calibre : one-, two-, and five-barrelled Gardners of ·45 calibre : and the ·45 inch five-barrelled Nordenfeldt. A new gun by Nordenfeldt with two or four barrels, firing steel bullets, of one-inch calibre, known as the anti-torpedo-boat gun, was also designed and purchased.[1]

In the summer of 1882 naval machine gun equipment received its first test in warfare. Machine guns were mounted in the fighting-tops of battleships for the purpose of bringing a plunging fire upon the Egyptian batteries at Alexandria. Probably the disappointing results obtained were due to the dense fog of powder smoke both from the heavy guns on the main decks and from the smoke of the machine guns themselves, a drawback which Major Fosbery had foreseen in 1869. The results at Alexandria proved that smokeless powder is a deciding factor in the efficiency of all qui k-firing weapons. Nevertheless, not only was considerable use made of machine guns, chiefly of the Gardner pattern, during the expeditions on the Upper Nile in 1884-5, but as the result of war experience such improvements and modifications were made in the mounting and carriage that the guns no longer had the appearance of artillery weapons. At Suakin and on the Upper Nile, naval brigades were landed to co-operate with the military forces. Commander Rolfe, in charge of the Gardners under Lord Charles Beresford, after Suakin, pointed out the necessity for a screw for the purpose of securing a traverse to right and to left, in place of the clumsy method of dragging the trail from one side to the other.

[1] " Naval Annual," 1886.

In the Royal Navy, so completely dependent upon its engineers, there appeared to be a readier co-operation between the fighting men and the technical services than has sometimes been apparent in the Army. The chief engineer of one of the battleships quickly improvised a new mounting from carriages designed for the seven-pounder field gun, whereon the Gardner guns were mounted above the wheel level and could thus be swung through a traverse of 180 degrees without moving the gun-carriage. Certainly, by raising the gun to the level of a man's shoulder, the device made the gun more conspicuous, but this was no disadvantage in warfare against tribesmen armed with primitive weapons. Within a few years after this date, the tripod mounting, or a seat on the trail of the wheeled mounting, had been adopted. After the Matabele War of 1893, there is something more than a legend which records that the Central African native fled at the mere rumour of the approach of a man who, taking up the common native posture for the relief of nature, could, in place of fluid, eject a death-dealing stream of metal.

In respect of the mounting, Lord Charles Beresford was emphatic, remarking that the necessity for limbering and unlimbering " does away with much of its utility " as a machine gun. The limber adds to its weight, " and it is not ready for instant action." After the new naval device had been adopted, Lord Beresford, commanding the Naval Brigade in the Nile Expedition, wrote of an action in the Sudan :

" I was much impressed with the ease with which " the fire of these guns could be directed or controlled " by the officer in command, in comparison with the " rifle fire of both soldiers and blue jackets. The " men were at the time very excited, the noise and

" general confusion preventing orders from being
" heard. Mounted officers rode furiously up and
" down the line with little effect, while the bugles
" almost continually sounding ' Cease firing ! ' seemed
" only to add to the noise. But the machine guns
" were under perfect control, orders quietly given
" to ' Search out that clump of bush ! '—' Keep your
" gun bearing on that corner of the wall ! '—or,
" ' Cease firing till they show again ! ' were carried
" out with the greatest regularity."

The Navy had so thoroughly tested and proved the
efficacy of machine guns in colonial warfare that in the
campaign in Burma after the occupation of Mandalay
against bands of Dacoities,[1] the frenzied gangs of co-
operative murderers acting under the cultivated im-
pulses of sadism, a four-gun Gardner machine gun
battery was handed over by the Navy for use in jungle
fighting, under the command of Captain W. N. Lloyd,
R.A. Wheeled transport being impossible in the
jungle, Captain Lloyd organized pack transport ; and
it was learned that the guns could be released from the
pack-saddles, mounted upon tripods, and brought into
action in half a minute.

The War Office continued its opposition to machine
guns until 1886 ; but in the Royal Navy, guns of the
Gatling, Gardner, or Nordenfeldt type were not only
adopted for service but were used with considerable
effect with naval landing detachments in Egypt and
the Sudan. Captain, afterwards Admiral, Lord Charles
Beresford, a sailor of remarkable perception and always

[1] Dacoity (Hindi Dakaiti), formerly rife in southern India and
Burma, except for rare outbreaks, has been exterminated in India,
where the practice was exclusively confined. Europeans were never
its victims. According to the Indian Penal Code " Dacoity," armed
robbery with murder, must consist of a gang of not less than five men.

full of fight, was an early enthusiast. Speaking on
" Machine Guns in the Field " before the United
Service Institution in 1885, Lord Beresford said :

> " It must be remembered that the Navy had had
> " more actual experience in the working of machine
> " guns in the field than any other branch of Her
> " Majesty's Service ; and guns for this purpose are
> " supplied to the Naval Service, but not to the
> " Army."

He continued :

> " As a seaman I will not venture to give my own
> " opinion on a question so essentially a military one,
> " but will give a few opinions I have received from
> " officers attached to the arm they represent, but all
> " of whom admit its utility under certain conditions.
> " . . . The point I want to bring forward is the
> " question of Mounting. The guns are allowed to
> " be useful under certain circumstances, and the main
> " point is the best way of mounting them."

During the course of the debate which followed, Lord
Chelmsford expressed himself as follows :

> " Because whilst it has been shown that machine
> " guns are capable of very great development, it is
> " clear that that development has not at the present
> " moment received much encouragement from the
> " military authorities."

Lord Beresford had with clarity brought into sharp
relief not only the weakness in the gun for field purposes, but the reason why the opposition of the military
authorities was continued. The War Office chiefs
continued to think in terms of 1870, and, severely
departmentalized, the prejudice of the artillery prevailed. Woolwich still regarded machine guns as a
weak and inefficient substitute for light artillery ; and,

on these grounds, hindered their adoption by the Army. On 13th November 1885, however, there was a notable debate at the United Service Institution, following a paper read by Major M. R. West, R.A.[1] General the Right Honourable Viscount Wolseley, G.C.B., G.C.M.G., Adjutant-General of the Forces, took the Chair, and, in his concluding remarks, he spoke as follows :

" It is a subject I think especially for discussion, " because the English army has now most certainly " arrived at the conclusion that we must have " machine guns, and I am very glad to say the " authorities have at last decided upon their being " introduced into the Army. . . . But there cer- " tainly is a very common impression in the minds " of a great number, that opposition from Woolwich " has prevented our having . . . machine guns for " many years past. . . . But I feel convinced the " fire of this small arm, an infantry arm—it is not an " artillery arm—I think the fire of this small arm, " firing from a fixed carriage at ascertained ranges " of 2000 up to 3000 yards and beyond, will be most " effective."

From this date, at the close of 1885, the idea of utilizing the machine gun as a weapon in the Army can be said to have been born. The same year was momentous, also, in the field of invention, for designs had been matured which completely revolutionized the technique.

[1] ' Suggestions for the Adoption and Adaptation of the Single Barrel Machine Gun for the Various Branches of Land Service,' " Journal of the United Service Institution," 1886, No. cxxxiii. pp. 21-36.

CHAPTER III

MAXIM
1881–1899

Mr. Hiram Maxim—Early patents—A revolution in mechanical
principles—Volunteers as pioneers—Official interest in Maxim's
inventions—The German Kaiser takes note—Li Hung Chang's
strange opposition—Four chief characteristics of the Maxim
gun discussed—Experience of Rhodesians in Matabele War,
1893—The Chitral Campaign, 1895—With Kitchener to Khartoum, 1895.

A NEW chapter in the history of machine guns opened
with the advent of Mr. Hiram Maxim in the field of
invention, one which culminated in the most stupendous
drama in the whole story of mankind.   Maxim was
born inventor, a man of ingenious and searching min·
already successful as a pioneer inventor in the ea
days of electric lighting.   He has given an account
how his mind was first captivated with the idea
automatic rifle and gun manufacture :
    " In 1881 I visited the Electrical Exhibit'
    " Paris, and was made a Chevalier of the Legion
    " Honour on account of some electrical and chemic
    " work that I had done ; and about a year later
    " was in Vienna, where I met an American Jew who
    " I had known in the States.   He said : ' Hang yo
    " chemistry and electricity !   If you wish to mak·

Photograph by the Author

TRAINING MACHINE GUNNERS. B.E.F., FRANCE, 1914

*Men of 2nd Battn. Argyll and Sutherland Highlanders,
transformed into a machine gun unit, 1936*

Imperial War Museum

BELGIAN MACHINE GUN SECTION: THE WHEELED
CARRIERS DRAWN BY DOGS, 1914

" pile of money, invent something that will enable
" these Europeans to cut each other's throats with
" greater facility.'

    " This made me think of the time when I was
" only about fourteen years of age, and was making
" drawings for my father of a hand-worked machine
" gun. I also thought of the powerful kick I got
" the first time I fired a U.S. military rifle. On my
" return to Paris I made a very highly finished
" drawing of an automatic rifle. Happening to meet
" a Scotchman in Paris whom I had known in the
" States, I showed him my drawings. He invited
" me to come to London. I did so, and shortly after
" I started an experimental shop at 57D Hatton
" Garden." [1]

    Maxim's first thought in Paris had been of a repeat-
ing rifle to be fired from the shoulder : but, so soon as
he settled to the drawing-office and workshop in
Hatton Garden, he evolved the machine gun to fire
from a tripod. He worked with prodigious energy
and remarkable speed.

    The first of the Maxim patents, No. 3493, was
registered on 16th July 1883 : an auspicious day the
16th July, for the action fought on this date before
High Wood, Battle of the Somme, 1916, by the 100th
Machine Gun Company, served as a classic at the
Machine Gun Training Centre, Grantham, during the
Great War. The initial patent was for " an invention
of improvements in machine or battery guns, and in
cartridges for the same and other firearms." In this
patent the feed-block was at the bottom of the body.
On 3rd January, 23rd February, 23rd May, and 2nd
October, 1884, followed other patents of improvements :

    [1] Letter to the Editor, " The Star," London, 23rd July 1915.

Nos. 606, 3844, 9407, and 13,113, the last two respectively being for a cartridge feed, and for lubrication.
Further patents followed, 29th January (No. 1307) and
on 8th July (No. 8281) 1885, the last being the firs'
model upon which all those which followed have bı
fashioned.

Hitherto all machine guns had been loaded eith
by a mechanical feed worked by the operator with a
handle device, or by the weight of the cartridges falling
one by one into position from a hopper above the gun :
and without exception all possessed from two to twenty-
four barrels. Maxim's invention revolutionized the
system, producing a self-loading and ejecting single-
barrelled gun. The principle adopted was that the
gun-barrel, after firing, recoiled in its mounting,
through a short distance, elongating a spring which
returned the barrel to the firing position at the end of
the recoil. The movement backwards and forwards
at the same time operated the mechanism which, having
fired the bullet, ejected the empty cartridge and loaded
another in its place in the chamber. A further device
produced a new method of feeding in place of the
hopper. The cartridges were held in clips in a belt
which the action of the gun moved through the feed-
block from right to left, in order to bring a cartridge
up to the loading position, after each shot had been
fired. In all its principal features this is the machine
gun familiar to nearly all the armies of the world since
the Great War, 1914–18.

Hiram Maxim was favoured throughout with the
good fortune which both his genius and tenacity of
purpose deserved. The first trial gave perfect satisfaction, six cartridges being successfully fired in an
estimated time of half a second. " I was delighted,"

wrote Maxim. " I saw certain success ahead, so I
" worked day and night on my drawings until they
" were finished, and went into the shop and worked
" myself until I had made the gun. It was finished
" ·ı due time, and on trying it with a belt of cartridges
found that it fired rather more than ten a second." [1]
Although the War Office had hitherto shown its
hostility to the introduction of machine guns for use
in the Army, in the volunteer infantry both experimentation had been conducted and formal adoption
achieved. Much adverse criticism notwithstanding,
Colonel Alt of the Central London Rangers (Volunteers),
22nd Middlesex Regiment, having designed a magazine
carriage on which was mounted, above wheel-level, a
Nordenfeldt rifle-calibre machine gun, in 1884, brought
the battalion machine gun section of two guns into the
field on manœuvres. The gun had five barrels, and
the caisson held 5000 rounds of ·45 inch ammunition.
It is of interest to note that the Volunteer Movement
of 1859 owed much of the vitality which carried it
through the early years of discouragement to the interest
awakened by the rapid improvement in arms of precision. There were few in the early years, after the
volunteers had been formed as a somewhat dubious
auxiliary to scare the possibility of a French invasion,
who suspected that the citizen army would not only
become a permanent and highly effective reserve, but
after 1919 would be officially regarded as the second
line of defence. The wits of the day had their cheap
fling at the volunteers : Crimean and Indian veterans
looked on superciliously, and not always good-
humouredly, as the new force evolved. Conservative
politicians, reminiscent of the Reform and Corn Law

[1] Sir Hiram S. Maxim, " My Life," 1915, p. 170.

riots, wagged warning heads at the rashness of putting arms into the hands of the people at large. Better such an army—thought the political diehards of the day—as the Iron Duke had described in his *obiter dictum* as " the scum of the earth," or one over which General Sir Charles Napier, great leader and reformer, could exult that Parliament had at last prescribed two hundred lashes as the maximum which could be inflicted even by a general court-martial ! Few, very few indeed, among whom Lord Elcho, afterwards the Earl of Wemyss, was a notable example, perceived the genuine spirit of the movement and the intensity of the martial spirit underlying the thin commercial crust. While the continent of Europe suffered, if not altogether gladly, its conscript armies, the greatest Empire the world had ever known by 1902 possessed a voluntary citizen force of 250,000 men, with its voluntary regular forces recruited chiefly for colonial service. Yet between 1914 and 1917 it raised millions of additional volunteers, without including the volunteers in the Dominions and Colonies, who were the equal of, if not superior to, any marksmen in the world, and superior also in discipline and martial bearing to the regular troops of many other nations. The Great War proved the efficiency of volunteers ; they were, as units of the Territorial Force, already in the field in 1914.

The volunteers, and later their counterpart the Territorial Force, have always been in the forefront at Bisley : no troops have shown greater skill and excellence in musketry ; it is not surprising, therefore, that the volunteers, at their own expense, adopted machine guns while the heads of the Army yet vacillated at the War Office. Following the Central London Rangers, the 4th Volunteer Battalion of the Royal

Fusiliers equipped a machine gun section ; while the Cyclist Battalion of the 26th Middlesex Regiment invented a light carriage for the Maxim, drawn as a trailer by two cyclists, which could be man-handled wherever the battalion manœuvred and went into action. Similarly, machine guns were adopted by several volunteer battalions throughout the country. The experience gained by these unauthorized, and perhaps unorthodox, machine gun sections proved of the utmost value when finally the Regular Army was furnished with these weapons as part of the equipment of infantry and cavalry.

Lecturing before a sympathetic audience at the United Service Institution in 1885, with Lord Charles Beresford as chairman, Captain Armit of the Central London Rangers emphasized the need for a highly trained body of men as machine gunners ; and for this purpose advocated the creation of a Machine Gun Corps, with its own depot for training and an establishment of 250 officers and 400 machine gunners, available for 200 guns, with one captain to each 4-gun battery and one lieutenant and twenty men for each gun.

The volunteers had pioneered the way. The time was ripe for Hiram Maxim.

Until perfected, the Maxim gun was shown to none outside the immediate group of assistants and those who liberally provided the money for the experiments. So soon as he had achieved success, Maxim made several guns and then courted publicity. The English newspapers wrote of the automatic self-loading machine gun which would emit a stream of more than 600 bullets in a minute from a single barrel, deriving its energy from its own recoil. Distinguished personages began to come for demonstrations at Hatton Garden :

and, among the first, were Sir Donald Currie and the Duke of Cambridge, the Commander-in-Chief, accompanied by the Prince of Wales, afterwards King Edward VII.

Soon Lord Wolseley, with a group of War Office officials, visited the works ; and the gun was exhibited at the Inventions Exhibition at South Kensington in 1885. War Office trials were then arranged ; and contracts were placed for the manufacture of the Maxim gun at the works of Vickers at Crayford, in Kent. Lord Wolseley exhibited the most lively interest in the gun and its inventor : and, thinking of the practical purposes to which the gun might be put, especially in colonial warfare, made several suggestions to Mr. Maxim. One of these led to the design of a large-calibre gun firing a shell weighing just over one pound, the lightest weight permitted for explosive projectiles under the terms of the Geneva Convention being half one kilogramme, an even weight. This type of gun was used later in the South African War, 1899–1902, being popularly known as the " pom-pom " ; but it possessed none of the character nor far-reaching possibilities, realized during the Great War, of the original Maxim gun.

The paramount invention was the automatic gun of rifle calibre. Nor was Mr. Maxim, like so many other inventors, obliged to wait in suspense, his hopes alternately raised and dashed to the ground, before the sinister prophecy of his acquaintance in Vienna—" If you wish to make a pile of money, invent some-" thing that will enable these Europeans to cut each " other's throats "—became fulfilled to gratify Maxim's highest financial expectations. He travelled widely in Europe demonstrating the gun to Government officials :

and was most favourably received by the German Emperor, Wilhelm I.

On the occasion of Queen Victoria's Golden Jubilee in 1887, the future Emperor, then Prince Wilhelm of Prussia, had attended the festivities in London. During the visit, accompanied by a suite of German cavalry officers, the Prince visited the 10th Royal Hussars in Hounslow Barracks, Middlesex. He was considerably impressed by the machine gun equipment, which at that time consisted of a Nordenfeldt gun mounted on a two-horsed light carriage. The Prince lost no time in commanding a gun of similar pattern to be sent to Potsdam, and Brevet Lieutenant-Colonel J. P. Brabazon, then commanding, who had seen something of the success of machine guns in 1884 at Suakin, despatched a trained machine gunner to Germany to instruct German troopers in the handling of the gun. Maxim found in the Emperor Wilhelm already an enthusiastic disciple, but, when the Emperor had witnessed a demonstration, he uttered his impressive imprimatur : " This is the only machine gun."

Nevertheless, not even the All-Highest the Kaiser could prevail upon the German General Staff, rooted in the prejudice of 1870–71, to adopt the gun, though a number were despatched to Africa for the use of the German colonial troops against characteristic native charges. The German General Staff persisted in its attitude for nearly twenty years, unwilling to reconsider the tactical use of an infantry and cavalry weapon whose entire technique and tactical potentiality was wholly different from the arm which had failed so disastrously as artillery during the Franco-German War.

For very different reasons, the famous Chinese envoy, Li Hung Chang, the astute Oriental who brought in his personality something of the glittering treasures of the Palace of Peking to dazzle the Court of St. James, rejected the Maxim gun for the use of his Government. At a demonstration, where, with expansive profligacy to impress a personage whose country was noted both for its teeming population and the sweeping despatch of its curious system of justice, a number of belts of cartridges were fired, Li Hung Chang enquired the cost of the rounds discharged in one minute. He was informed that it would approximate to thirty pounds sterling. " That won't do for China," remarked the Envoy. " It is much too expensive in ammunition ! "

Lecturing at the United Service Institute in 1882, Mr. W. Gardner, formerly a captain in the United States army, whose adaptations had been incorporated in the Gardner gun, successfully used with the Naval Brigade, had already provided the answer to the Chinese statesman. In reply to the question, " How fast can " you shoot ? " he said, " I make a distinction between " a cartridge-destroying machine and a machine gun. " It is the number of hits on the enemy, not the number " of shots fired, that we care to score. . . . I should " place the qualities of a machine gun in order of merit " as follows : (a) reliability ; (b) strength ; (c) weight ; " (d) simplicity ; (e) durability ; (f) ease of manipula- " tion ; (g) rapidity of fire." There is no doubt that the persuasive powers of Hiram Maxim were taxed to their uttermost resources in an attempt to captivate the inscrutable mind of the Emperor of China's most illustrious envoy ; but he failed.

Although the leading military Powers of Europe continued their cold regard for the machine gun, by 1887 in England a strong opinion had been formed in its favour, and the years thereafter demonstrate an increasing interest and desire to place the new weapon in its correct tactical perspective.

Machine guns present certain outstanding characteristics which almost from the first were recognized by the leading exponents. The chief factors for consideration are first, Fire-effect; second, Mobility; third, Visibility ; fourth, Invulnerability. The first remains constant, and its importance can only decrease if the vulnerability of favourable targets diminishes with increased armour which does not detract from mobility. The second, after preliminary difficulties in discovering the most suitable form of carriage, has leaped into prominence as the result of the introduction of oil-driven transport, capable of traversing almost all obstacles, and of travelling over almost all conditions of ground at considerable speed. The third remains constant, though, it may be added, the importance of visibility diminishes with increased mobility. The fourth remains constant under the conditions existing prior to 1919 : but vulnerability, taking into account greater immunity from fire due to increased mobility, tends to increase as gun crews are confined within a small and highly dangerous space if hit.

From the foregoing, an estimate of the potentialities of the machine gun and its tactical value as compared with infantry can be formed. The fire-effect of a machine gun can be said to equal that of at least 50 rifles. German opinion considers the fire value to equal that of 120 rifles. There are other advantages in the nature of direction, control, accuracy, concentration, elimination of the human factor, which contribute immeasurably to the fire-effect of machine guns as compared with infantry, especially under the stress of modern conditions of warfare.

" Fire is everything—the rest is of small account," was one of Napoleon's precepts, an aphorism of great importance in considering how to secure the maximum effect from machine gun fire. It will be understood that although it might be imagined in theory that, given constancy of range and target, every bullet fired from a machine gun barrel will hit identically the same spot, in fact this is not so. A variety of causes, atmospheric, fractional inequality in charge and bullet, vibration of gun, produce a very different result, which adds to the peculiar effectiveness of the weapon. Especially at the longer ranges, the automatically secured dispersion of fire implies that a target is not hit several times before falling. Although the rate of fire is very fast and the stream of fire highly concentrated, there is, therefore, no waste of ammunition in direct fire unless gross inefficiency is shown in handling the weapon. Mere volume of fire, direct or indirect, is useless without direction, control, accuracy, and concentration. Used with infantry, from the first the machine gun was shown to be an infinitely superior weapon to the rifle. Infantry under the most favourable conditions can fire fifteen rounds " rapid fire " a minute, but this can only be maintained for a period of four minutes, and then only when the firer is fresh. After subjection to hours of marching and fighting, " rapid," indeed all rifle, fire tends to become wild and therefore ineffective, while except after years of training fire-control is most difficult to secure on the battlefield, and this has always been so. The Maxim gun presented the soldier with a weapon held for him by the mounting, loading and firing itself, while direction and elevation could be obtained with the least effort on his part by manipulating the traversing and elevating gears.

The mobility of infantry is limited to the rate of marching, less than three and a half miles an hour. Running is out of the question, for even among men of the highest physical condition it reduces fire efficiency to a minimum. An experiment conducted in the Austrian army many years ago demonstrated that the percentage of hits, proved at 76·5 per cent after an advance at walking pace, fell to 51 per cent after doubling : and this was under peace conditions.[1] The mobility of the machine gun depends entirely upon the way in which it is carried. Horse-drawn wheeled carriages, pack-saddles, cycles and trailers, sledges, mechanically propelled wheeled vehicles and tractors, must all be considered under various conditions of service requirements, and each method produces its own inseparable problems of visibility and vulnerability.

All the characteristics of the weapon suggest that, for successful tactical employment, machine guns must be as inconspicuous as possible in action. One gun itself, possessed of such immense fire-power, exposes a front of but two men. Its visibility depends, then, on the nature of the mounting, the proximity to its ground, and the cunning displayed by machine gunners in the use of natural or artificial means of concealment. The tripod was the only solution. Yet, since artillery thought still governed the War Office before 1890, and was to be superseded by that of the cavalry, which held its domination until the close of the Great War, 1914–1918, machine gun mountings, with a few departures, continued to be on wheels, as the fixed platform to give the desired mobility to the weapon. In fact, this tendency still to regard the machine gun as a kind of

[1] Balck, " Modern European Tactics."

artillery, or by over-emphasizing the phrase " a weapon of opportunity " and thereby limiting the use of the gun, held up the scientific development of machine gunnery for many years. Indeed, although experts understanding how cones of fire, beaten zones, the trajectory of the bullet, all provided with a mathematical precision under every kind of condition by the fixed platform, the nature of fire, and the traversing and elevating gears, could demonstrate the machine gun as fulfilling a role neither artillery nor infantry. But as a unique arm with its own special contributions to the tactical order of battle, little progress was made in the British army until 1916.

In the consideration of vulnerability, therefore, two factors present themselves. First, the narrow front of two men close to the ground, and probably concealed, offers a very poor target to the enemy ; and, secondly, the efficiency of the gun is not affected in action by severe casualties. With a body of infantry of the equivalent fire-power, at a minimum fifty men, the loss of the officer commanding may destroy, will certainly militate severely against effective fire-control. The loss of each rifleman reduces by so much the fire-power of the unit. Factors of recent introduction such as gas and smoke render good marksmanship impracticable ; while darkness has always prevented the rifleman from anything but haphazard fire. The machine gun, by its nature, is affected by none of these things, and, by the use of various devices, can be made as effective in darkness as in light. While one man of a gun team survives even the most exacting of casualties, the gun is capable of remaining in action to the maximum of its fire-power. No other weapon is possessed of such power and facilities for battle action.

Such were the considerations which occupied the most adventurous minds in the Army in 1887. While the military literature of Europe appears to be bankrupt of any contribution to machine gunnery until the opening of the twentieth century, a continual stream of commentary is recorded in the British army, perhaps because of the persistence of minor operations on the Indian Frontier and in Africa while Europe remained quiescent. Theory, supported by practical lessons from war, stimulated thought in the small British professional army. Two notable lectures were delivered at the United Service Institution in 1887, the first by Major A. D. Anderson, R.H.A., under the distinguished chairmanship of Lieutenant-General Sir E. B. Hamley, K.C.B., K.C.M.G., R.A.,[1] who remarked : " We must " remember that the machine gun, after all, is only " taking the place of the infantry arm—that is, merely " so many rifle barrels discharging rifle ammunition, " and, therefore, the control of them properly, I think, " be entrusted to an infantry commander." The second lecture, by Lieutenant G. E. Benson, R.A., produced a most animated and fruitful discussion, to which Mr. Maxim himself, Lord Charles Beresford, Captain (later Lieutenant-General Lord) R. S. Baden-Powell, Lord Chelmsford, Lieutenant-Colonel J. P. Brabazon, Captain F. G. Stone, R.A., Major-General Arbuthnot, and Mr. Nordenfeldt contributed.

" The machine gun ought to act with the brigade " of infantry," suggested Major W. W. M. Smith, R.A. " I estimate for a 9-gun battery with seventy-five to " eighty horses and 130 men, mounted on trail and " limber." He further urged that a school for " the arm " should be formed at Aldershot, to become the

[1] Author of Hamley's " Operations of War."

nucleus of a future " Corps of Machine Guns."
Major-General Arbuthnot, a Crimean veteran, asserting
that all patterns of machine guns had come under his
personal notice, suggested one equipment for cavalry,
another for infantry : that the infantry should have a
tripod pack equipment : and that the gun should not
exceed 100 lb. in weight, so that it could suitably be
transported on a light carriage. He little visualized
" The Vickers Gun, 1914," whose total weight with
water in the casing for cooling purposes does not
exceed 38½ lb., and can readily be man-handled over
considerable distances under the most trying conditions
of modern warfare. Lord C. Beresford, with characteristic emphasis, insisted upon the term " Machine
Rifles," his purpose clearly being to extricate the
machine gun from the doldrums of artillery prejudice.
Nor have machine guns any connection with subsequent inventions of automatic rifles which later led to
fresh confusion of thought as to the relative role of, for
example, Vickers and Lewis " guns," during the Great
War. The former is properly a machine gun by virtue
of its special characteristics and tactical potentiality :
the latter is only an automatic rifle, possessed of no
features which distinguish it from the man-operated
rifle other than its loading mechanism.

Lord C. Beresford continued in the spirit of the
prophecy. " It would be a very serious thing if
" the German, or any other army, were to take up the
" machine gun question, and we, with all our practical
" experience, having found it so useful on so many
" occasions, were not to take it up and thrash it out as
" has been proposed."

Remarkable success was achieved by machine guns
purchased by the British South Africa Company for

the defence of its posts in the Chartered Territory of Rhodesia. The troops of the Chartered Company were the British South African Police, a corps second to none as a fighting force. In 1893 the Matabele tribesmen under a chief, Lobengula, who remains as one of the outstanding personalities of all African history, rose in rebellion. Fierce tribesmen, inflamed with racial fanaticism, armed with assegais, formed their impis, and in 'great force went forth to battle ; while a thousand war-drums, in wild crescendo, beat their primeval tattoo of vengeance amid the scattered kraals. The B.S.A.P., although hurriedly reinforced by volunteer Rhodesians, were from the outset greatly outnumbered. Past-masters in the art of savage warfare, the pioneers of the Hinterland adopted a technique of tactics which African battle had shown to be effective. They stood on the defensive, forming a wagon laager, within which had been concentrated women, children, and provisions, and provoked the Matabele to charge. Maxim guns were placed at the angles of the laager : and it is recorded how again and again hordes of Matabele bit the dust far beyond the thrust of the deadly assegai.

At Fort Victoria, close to historic Zimbabwe, the legendary site of King Solomon's mines, in October 1893, King Lobengula in person at the head of his impis challenged those who sought the treasures of Africa. The small column under Major Forbes, gravely imperilled with the fate of annihilation similar to that of the gallant Major Wilson on the Shangani River near by, met the Matabele charges with machine guns. A contemporary record provides the following account :[1]

[1] " Daily News," London, 3rd November 1893.

" Most of the Matabele had probably never seen a
" machine gun in their lives, and had but a dim idea of
" the effects of concentrated rifle-fire. Their trust was
" in their spears, for in all their rude experience of
" warfare they had never known an enemy able to
" withstand them. Even when they found their mis-
" take, they had the heroism to regard it as only a
" momentary error in their calculations. They retired
" in perfect order, and re-formed for a second rush.
" In how many European armies could the men who
" had survived one shower from modern artillery
" come forward to try their luck again ? These
" savages were equal to the attempt, and equal, too,
" to the deliberate design of bettering their luck by
" looking for a weak place in the laager. Once more the
" Maxims swept them down in the dense masses of
" their concentration, and once more they retired. It
" seems incredible that they should have mustered for
" still another attack, yet this actually happened. But
" by this time they had reached the limits of human
" endurance. They came as men foredoomed to
" failure, and those who were left of them went back
" a mere rabble rout."

The guns employed in this action were four Maxims,
one Nordenfeldt, and one Gardner. The new Maxims
proved the most effective, owing to their superior
rapidity of fire and readier mechanism.

Great Britain continued to add to its machine gun
battle practice from colonial experience, while the
major armies of Europe, experimenting with artillery
and superbly apparelled for the ceremonies of emperors
and kings, gloried in their glittering bayonets, swords,
and lances. The Maxim gun had first been in action
on the North-West Frontier of India. The march to

the relief of Chitral, the most northerly outpost of the Indian Empire, in the spring of 1895, may perhaps be compared with the historic march of Lord Roberts to Kandahar. A column entering unknown and difficult country, among whose hills and valleys an enemy unmatched in agility, scout-craft, and courage, runs always grave hazards both from ambush and from the cutting of the lines of communication, which in days before aircraft and rapid transport were almost always imperilled.

At the Malakand Pass, amid the deafening din of drums, the mullahs, waving flags, inflamed the Faithful to that pitch of desperate recklessness which renders the onslaught of Moslem devotees so fiery a trial to even the best-disciplined troops. Fanatical Ghazis, mounted and on foot, advantageously posted on the steep hillsides, threatened to outflank and swallow up the little army advancing into the throat of this formidable position ; while they continued to pour fire from lower sangars, preparing to fling themselves on the British force as they had done upon the Bengal Lancers at Ahmed Khel in 1880.

The Maxims suddenly opened a murderous fire, a ferocious defiance which in shrill staccato echoed far among the foothills of the Hindu Kush. In the fight at Gumbat, a sudden onslaught by Ghazis was struck to the ground by a single Maxim gun, brought into action to enfilade their flank as they advanced. " I am " glad," wrote a military correspondent, " to find that " the Maxim guns have done so well in the Chitral " Expedition. By a stroke of good luck six ·303 Maxims " reached India a few weeks before the operations " began."

The " London Gazette " of 14th June 1895,

F

publishing the official despatch of the operations, has the following significant reference to the Maxim guns :
" Sangar after sangar was held, each sangar as it was
" rushed coming at once under the fire of the one above
" it, and here I may note the admirable service done
" by the artillery and Maxim guns. Several attempts
" were made by the enemy to concentrate from above
" and hold lower sangars and positions, but all such
" attempts were frustrated by the admirable practice
" of the mountain batteries and Maxim guns over the
" heads of our advancing infantry."

The successful experience of British troops in the Indian expeditions finally settled the question of the general adoption of the Maxim gun in the British army. Mr. Hiram Maxim was busy with improvements, in 1892, 1894, and 1895, registering four further patents. In these activities he was associated with Mr. J. Silverman, who afterwards, in 1898, joined Lieutenant A. T. Dawson, R.N. (retired),[1] in a further invention. Dawson had been Experimental Officer at Woolwich Arsenal in 1892, and in 1896 became Superintendent of Ordnance to Vickers Limited, already entrusted with the manufacture of the Maxim gun.

The most formidable rival to Hiram Maxim was Thorsten Nordenfeldt, the principles of whose inventions were similar in character to those of Maxim: while the mechanical action of the Hotchkiss gun relied upon gas-pressure. The Maxim, too, was belt-loaded, while the Hotchkiss was fed from metal-clip loaders. Operating in the background, Basil Zaharoff, who had risen from the salesman to the position of financier, fishing in many and varied waters, influenced the termination of

[1] Later Sir A. Trevor Dawson, Bart., Chairman of the Artillery and Shipbuilding Management Board, Vickers, Limited.

a rivalry inimical to the interests of the two foremost inventors. The Maxim-Nordenfeldt Guns and Ammunition Company Limited of London was established before the close of the 'eighties : and among its products was a light-pattern Maxim gun weighing 25 lb. and tripod weighing 15 lb., carried together in an infantry back-pack, brought out in 1895.

After leaving the Sudan under the tyranny of Mahdism for over ten years, Her Majesty's Government in 1896 decided upon its reconquest. Major-General, afterwards Field-Marshal Lord Kitchener of Khartoum, was in this year Sirdar of the Egyptian Army. The Sirdar desired to carry through the preliminary operation of the occupation of the Dongola Province with Egyptian troops only. He sent, however, for the machine gun sections of the two British battalions then in Lower Egypt, those of the Staffordshire Regiment and the Connaught Rangers. A battery of four guns was formed from the two sections. As a special precaution to prevent the mechanism of the gun from being jammed by the desert sands, which, in storms locally called the *haboub*, form a dense fog of minute particles, the guns were wrapped in silk covers until required for action. During the first action at Ferkeh on 7th June, the battery, divided in two sections, shattered after a few minutes the only serious attempts made by the Dervishes to rush the Sirdar's position.

In 1897, with a boldness of conception which staggered the military and engineering critics of the day, Kitchener planned to wrest Omdurman, the stronghold of the Mahdi, from the Dervish grasp, and to project a railway across 800 miles of shifting sands to serve as his line of communications. With relentless energy, impatient with inefficiency, and indefatigable zeal, this iron man, whose heart nevertheless yet a little later fashioned the superb Khartoum College, defeated all opposition to his plans, even those of Nature in all its most formidable circumstance. No harder task-master than this " Sapper " ever lived. No man better used the machine guns at his disposal.

In the battle of Atbara, the machine gun section, to which had been added two additional guns, with 5000 rounds for each of the six guns, and 20,000 cartridges carried in reserve on camels and mules, were thrown out on a flank to bring enfilade fire to bear on the enemy. In the final great battle of Omdurman, where the Sirdar met the formidable hosts of the Khalifa as they poured in serried masses from the exits of the straggling city, which stands where the White Nile meets the Blue, the guns did great execution. The Khalifa, who had succeeded the brutal and sensual Mahdi, the slayer of the saintly pioneer General Gordon, in person com-manded the Dervish hordes who first attacked the composite British and Egyptian force at Egeiga. The onslaught repulsed, the Sirdar moved rapidly in pursuit. More than 40,000 tribesmen were mustered at Kerreri, seven miles from the city of Omdurman, while the Sirdar's troops lay behind the improvised zareba of bush thorn, provoking an attack. The Maxim battery was posted on the right front of the zareba between an Egyptian brigade and a brigade formed at Atbara and commanded by El Bimbashi Hector Macdonald.[1] The Dervishes seemed to rise out of the ground, making full use of the concealment offered by the numerous *knors* with which the battlefield abounds.

For a moment it seemed that the Dervish hosts

[1] Later General Sir Hector Macdonald, K.C.B., D.S.O., A.D.C.

might overwhelm the Sirdar's forces. The Khalifa gave orders for the *ombeya* to be sounded, while the dull beats of the great *mansura*, the war-drum, boomed through the city. In dense array the Dervishes moved to consume their feast of flesh : but their ranks were torn by murderous machine gun fire. Major von Tiedemann, the German Military Attaché, explains how he rode out to the right flank to observe the effect of the Maxim battery. So soon as the machine gunners found the range the enemy fell in heaps, and it was evident that to the Maxims went a large measure of credit in repelling the Dervish onslaught. The weapons had the further advantage that they possessed a longer range and flatter trajectory than that of the Martini rifles with which the Egyptian and Sudanese infantry were equipped.

The Khalifa himself escaped and re-formed an army on the White Nile with the object of recapturing Omdurman. The Sirdar despatched Colonel Francis Wingate, head of the Egyptian Intelligence Department, and later Lord Kitchener's successor as Sirdar, to rout out the skulking Baggara leader, Khalifa Abdullahi. Colonel Wingate met the Khalifa's forces at Abu Adil, where the Khalifa was encamped, and attacked. The Maxims opened fire from a hill about 800 yards from the Dervish zareba. With their usual courage, the tribesmen left their camp, and, making straight for the hill, which was bare of scrub for some 100 yards from the base, desperately tried to carry it. The Maxims beat off the assault, the foremost of the enemy falling within ninety-four paces of the gun position. The enemy retreated on their main body of 4000 tribesmen at Omdebreikat. Here the Khalifa, with some twenty of his Emirs in the forefront of the battle, made a last stand. The Maxims opened fire with deadly effect. On 24th November 1899, 600 tribesmen were left dead in the field, while 3000 prisoners, many of them wounded, were also taken. The Khalifa with most of his Emirs perished, the losses among Colonel Wingate's forces amounting to no more than 4 killed and 29 wounded.

To the Maxim primarily belongs the victory which stamped out Dervish rule in the Sudan.

CHAPTER IV

THE TACTICAL CONCEPT
1888–1906

The School of Musketry, Hythe—Lieut. J. H. Parker (U.S.A.)—
His experience at Santiago, 1899—Tactical ideas quoted—More
inventions, Augezd, Bergman, Perino, Madsen—Differentiation
between machine guns and automatic rifles—Col. C. B. Mayne,
R.E.—Russo-Japanese War, 1904–5—Russian use of the weapon
—Reports of British Military Attachés—Japan adopts machine
guns—Speedy development of tactical use—Instances described—Testimony of Foreign Military Attachés—The second
cycle of machine gun history.

WHILE in the campaigns on the Indian Frontier, in
the Sudan, and in Rhodesia, the Maxim gun in the
hands of British troops was proving pre-eminently
successful, progress in the Army at home was very
slow, suggesting that authority was not yet convinced
of the utility of the weapon.

At the School of Musketry at Hythe, instructions
in the use of rifle-calibre machine guns had been given
since their first use in the Services, the report of 1888
mentioning the Nordenfeldt and Gatling. The report
of 1889 records the first experimental work on the range
with the Maxim gun. Various guns were still in use in
the Army, although in 1894 the Maxim became the
standard weapon, the first War Office Manual having
been published in 1893. Although there is no reason

to suppose that there was any difficulty in supplying as many Maxims as might be required, years passed before units were issued with one gun. The Hythe Report for 1897 is significant.

> " Machine gun practice is not satisfactorily con-
> " ducted, and this can hardly be looked for until
> " each regiment and battalion has been supplied
> " with the gun. The present system works badly,
> " and the officers, N.C.O.'s and men of the gun
> " detachments very soon become rusty and forget
> " all they have been taught on account of months—
> " often years—passing without ever handling one
> " of these intricate weapons."

In spite of the outstanding achievements of the Maxim in battles in which the British army was engaged, and notwithstanding the fact that interest was again stirring in both France and Germany, where enthusiasts taught the new creed of the machine gun, the War Office exhibited little interest in the weapon, regarding it as something of a dilemma, impaled on the horns of infantry and artillery, and, though useful in savage warfare, an impossible addition to the complex of the civilized battlefield.

Between 1890 and 1914 only junior officers, captains and subalterns, received instruction in the use of the machine gun at Hythe. It was these, often well under thirty years of age, who were to command the large unit of a Machine Gun Battalion, with its overwhelming fire-power of 64 machine guns, the equal of 3200 riflemen at least, greater than a whole brigade composed of three full battalions.

In the South African War, 1899–1902, machine guns and " pom-poms," a confusing and almost useless innovation, unfortunately gave poor results and the gun, largely due to its ill-considered wheeled mounting, regained its former unpopularity. In America, however, in 1899, most valuable contributions were made both to popularizing the weapon and in defining its tactical uses by Lieutenant J. H. Parker, of 13th U.S. Infantry, who had charge of a battery of Gatling guns in General Shafter's army in the Cuban Campaign in the previous year. He published three books in 1899, based chiefly on his experiences of the fighting before Santiago. Lieutenant Parker was a fighter, and he recognized in the machine gun a unique weapon, amazingly effective in defence, superlative for attack. The name of Parker remains that of one of the pioneers, for until his teaching, military thought, cold indeed as it was, had not considered the machine gun as anything beyond an aid to defence.

Lieutenant Parker foresaw the development of modern artillery as long-range weapons shooting most often against unseen targets by indirect fire. He visualized also a new arm, taking the place of light field guns, which would fight beside the infantry in attack and defence—the machine gun.

" The machine gun man," he wrote, " must be " hot-blooded and dashing. He must have all the " nerve and élan of the best light cavalry, all the resist- " ing power of stolid and immovable infantry. He is " not to reason on abstruse theorems, nor approximate " difficult ranges ; his part is to dash into the hell of " musketry, the storm of battle, and to rule that storm " by the superior rapidity and accuracy of his fire. The " characteristics of the machine gun and its crew are " therefore essentially different from those of the " artillery of the future and, it may be added, from " those of the artillery of the present. The line of

" reasoning that must actuate the conduct of the
" machine gun man is essentially different from the
" artillery motif. The experience of the battlefield has
" demonstrated that a greater degree of independent
" action pertains to the machine guns than is the case
" with artillery."

Lieutenant Parker recognized that the spirit of
machine guns and of artillery differed fundamentally
from one another : and he projected ideas for organization of an original character. He required that guns
should be organized in companies, the equivalent of
batteries, of three guns each : and he suggests the
single gun as the tactical unit. Later experience has
demonstrated that whatever other organization may be
adopted, two guns must always provide such a unit, in
case of accident to one or the other by casualty, or
from temporary mechanical derangement. Parker propounded the idea of the machine gun battalion, with
striking originality. The most arresting idea, however,
which Lieutenant Parker put forward was that machine
guns, invaluable as they are to the defence, are essentially offensive weapons. With this concept in mind he
developed tactical suggestions which, with all the
astonishing changes in the tactical handling of troops
on the battlefield, proved to be the foundation of
positive and successful machine gun actions during
the Great War.

" The offensive uses of the machine guns," he wrote,
" have been as fully demonstrated as those of any other
" arm of the service. They have been used at close
" quarters and against entrenchments ; in the open,
" and under cover ; with and without supporting
" troops ; they have demonstrated their mobility and
" service ability over any and every kind of ground,

" and in all kinds of weather. Therefore, we state that
" on the offensive they are useful in conjunction with
" every other arm, and may be used alone where no
" other arm could be so used. The offensive use will
" be treated with respect to infantry, cavalry, and
" artillery, and as an independent arm ; with ad-
" vanced guards, outposts, the cavalry screen, and in
" battle."

The following paragraph is also pregnant with
truth, as often it was experienced, tactically, in the
Great War :

" Machine guns are expected to develop the fire-
" action of good unshaken infantry, plentifully supplied
" with ammunition, always under perfect control and
" fire discipline, and utterly without nerves. They will
" also be expected to have all the mobility of the best
" cavalry at all stages of the battle. When they get
" into so tight a place that animals cannot live for pack
" or draft, the men will be expected to draw the pieces
" by hand for a sufficient distance to render the use of
" the animals again available. Usually this will not
" be necessary, except in seeking a more effective
" position to enter the fight. If the guns reach so hot
" a place as the one supposed, they will be in an effective
" position. It must be always remembered that if the
" enemy can reach us with his small-arm fire, we can
" reach him with our machine gun fire equally as well.
" We can, therefore, make the machine guns effective
" wherever infantry fire could be used. Artillery fire
" is not to be considered. It is assumed that the
" machine guns will not be pitted against artillery at
" long ranges ; it has been demonstrated that the
" machine gun has nothing to fear from artillery after
" it once gets within effective range. It can bring so

" effective a fire to bear that no men can live long to
" serve the pieces.   But in the general case, the enemy's
" artillery is firing, or at least occupied by the artillery
" of the attacking force."

Lieutenant Parker was writing of field artillery, and
had not then in view the heavy long-range guns of the
present age, nor yet, of course, the bomb-dropping
aeroplane.   His case, however, holds good, for the
amazing mobility of the machine gun, even when
man-handled, and the factor of easy concealment,
clearly suggest the retention of Parker's hypothesis as
it stands.

This far-seeing American further established the
principle of economizing infantry with the use of
machine guns, a rule which the Germans exploited to
such great advantage during the later stages of the
Great War, notably at Passchendaele in the late autumn
of 1917, and in the process of their infiltration tactics
during the battle of the Lys in early April 1918.

It is now recognized that machine guns economize
infantry by increasing the fire-effect at the beginning
of action, both by short-range, direct and indirect,
long-range, overhead fire.   They can and must be
thrust forward in the attack.   In defence, disposed in
depth, the cones of their fire planned to interlace
diagonally across the defensive front, machine guns
can hold the defence, in almost any circumstances
conceivable, unaided except for patrols, especially by
night, thus economizing infantry and other arms, who,
in reserve, can be kept in security and comfort, free
from fatigue and of high morale, until required for the
offensive or for counter-attack.

Other passages from Lieutenant Parker's works are
worthy of quotation, for, in that graphic language which

so well befits the weapon and its service, his pronounce-
ments remain wisdom for all machine gunners :

" It must not be thought that these guns will keep
" up a continuous fire, that they will go on for an in-
" definite time pumping a solid stream of lead at one
" place, as some of the opponents of machine guns
" seem to think in their discussions of the amount of
" ammunition used by the guns. Such targets are but
" rarely presented, though they do show up for a few
" minutes at a time. When a target is presented, the
" machine gun whirls around and cuts in ; as soon as
" its target disappears, it at once takes advantage of its
" superior mobility to catch up with the infantry and
" seek a new place to go in."

" The orders to be given to the machine gun men
" at the beginning of the battle need not be very
" explicit. The commander of the machine guns
" should know where the real point of attack is, and
" should be kept well informed of the progress of the
" action. With this information he should be able to
" get into action in an effective manner on his own
" account, and is likely to do better when not hampered
" by orders than when compelled to try to comply
" with instructions laid down probably by an officer who
" does not understand the true role of the machine gun
" in the battle. A very high grade of talent is demanded
" in order to be thus able to cut in alone, but a high
" grade of talent is demanded for the service of the
" machine gun at any time."

Certainly, up to and during the Great War until
1918, the commanders of armies and lesser formations,
including many brigade and infantry battalion commanders, did not understand the potentialities of the
machine gun, and therefore its tactical uses.

Lieutenant Parker continues : " To ensure the full " development of these ideas it will be necessary to " call the best talent into the service of the new arm. " The pioneers in all fields of human endeavour must " be men specially fitted for what they are to do. " Hundreds are competent to do what has been once " done, but few are competent to originate. The " machine gun man must understand fully all the " tactical uses of all the other arms of the service, and " the exact relation and usefulness of his own in relation " thereto. He must have the keen eye that takes in at " a glance the salient points of a battle, and detects with " unerring certainty the critical time and place. He " must have the finest combination of nerve, patience, " audacity, and determination, and be prepared to fight " always ' to the last breath of horse and man.' No " part of the service demands higher qualities." [1]

Although the Regulations of the American Army, issued in 1908, did not accept Lieutenant Parker's conclusions, some of his precepts were adopted. Another thinker, although without Parker's war experience, was Captain Vuilleumier of the Swiss Army Staff, who contributed a valuable discussion upon the uses of machine guns in 1904.[2] It is interesting that he quotes the French exponent, De Montbrisson, who argued in favour of the machine gun as an attack weapon, and the German Boguslawski, who conceives of it only in defence. The conception of indirect machine gun fire was a far later development.

[1] " Tactical Organization and Uses of Machine Guns in the Field " (Kansas City, U.S.A.); ' Machine Guns in the Spanish-American War,' " United Service Magazine," March 1899 ; Lieut. J. H. Parker, 13th U.S. Infantry, " The Gatling Gun at Santiago." Introduction by Colonel T. Roosevelt, 1st U.S. Volunteer Cavalry, U.S.A.

[2] ' Le Combat entre l'infanterie et les mitrailleuses,' " Revue Militaire Suisse." Lucerne, September and October 1904.

Meanwhile, up till the year 1904, Maxim, Norden-feldt, Hotchkiss, and Gatling no longer held the field of invention. In 1899 Baron A. Odkolek von Augezd, " Imperial and Royal Cavalry instructor of the Austrian Army," produced the Augezd gun, registered at the British Patent Office under No. 23271, followed in 1906 by a further improvement. More important was the invention of Lieutenant O. W. Bergman of the Royal Swedish Artillery, who produced the Bergman gun under two patents (Nos. 483 and 17857) in 1890. In Italy, G. Perino, Chief Technician of the Artillery, Rome, produced several inventions, some of which were registered at the British Patent Office under the name of A. J. Boult, Chartered Patent Agent, the first in 1900, and later in 1907 and 1912 under his own name. The Rexer Arms Company introduced the Madsen gun in 1904 when it competed at Bisley. The Madsen was invented by M. Schouboe, a Danish engineer, and by him named Madsen after the then Danish Minister of War. Its weight was only 17½ lb. Confusion of thought as to the potentiality, characteristics, and tactical uses of machine guns arose from the introduc-tion of this and later other weapons of similar type, the best known of which is the Lewis gun. Neither the Madsen nor the Lewis are " guns," that is to say, neither possess any of the characteristics of the artillery weapon, the most important feature of which, being common to both artillery and machine guns proper, is the fixed platform. The Madsen is an auto-matic rifle : and is liable to all the errors of fire of the infantry soldier. The only points in common between the Madsen and the machine gun are rifle-calibre, self-loading, continuous fire.

It is of the utmost importance to mark the

differentiation between machine guns and automatic rifles.

In the sphere of tactical thought no man contributed more during this period than Captain (afterwards Colonel) C. B. Mayne of the Royal Engineers. His first work on " Infantry Fire Tactics " was published in 1884, revised in 1888 ; and without doubt Captain Mayne's striking reflexions exerted a considerable influence upon the War Office text works of the day. In 1903 Lieutenant-Colonel Mayne published " The Infantry Weapon and its Use in War." The originality of his thought lay in the argument that the reverse slopes of hills or rising ground behind which an enemy might be sheltering his reserves could be swept with rifle-fire, by conforming the trajectory of the bullet at a given range to the ground contour, or by placing riflemen at such a distance from the unseen target that this could be achieved. The idea was simple enough and sound in principle, although indirect rifle-fire, due to the uncertainty of the human element, is likely to be very imperfect in realization. Applied, however, to machine guns, with their peculiar characteristics of the fixed platform and consequent absence of the human error in aim, and of the cones of fire producing a novel and certain effective beaten zone, Colonel Mayne's reasoning opened up a new field of discovery and exploitation in the use of small arms.

Events in the Far East were at this time (1904) destined to bring the machine gun again into prominent consideration. Russia and Japan, as again thirty years later, were seeking for the expansion of their several interests in Manchuria, and the armed strength of the Imperial Czardom was challenged by the ancient fighting tradition of the Samurai vested in a twentieth-century military force. The striking similarity between the events of 1870–71 and those of 1904–5 has already been noted. It may be deemed impertinent to look beyond the actual history of the machine gun battle : yet, the plans of the strategist are determined by diplomacy ; and where strategy ends, tactics begin. Thus statecraft, strategy, and tactics carry equal weight, or nearly equal weight, in determining the results of battle. Forethought, preparation, study, exercise an immense influence upon the issues of a campaign.

The silver thread of continuity of strategic and diplomatic purpose runs throughout a campaign, drawing in its train not only commanders-in-chief, but all subordinate leaders. Statecraft and strategy go hand in hand ; strategy and tactics are absolutely linked together. No campaign can be successful unless the general principles of these three are strictly adhered to. The firm grasp of political, strategic, and tactical situations influences in equal proportion the success, not only of a campaign, but of each battle. Conventional or spineless politics, intriguing and cowardly politicians, may destroy success even more easily than will nerveless and ignorant generalship. Unimaginative leadership is ill-equipped for bringing troops to victory. Japanese generalship in 1904, as will be seen, was of that elasticity of mind, ready to seize upon new inventions, fresh ideas, sometimes those of the enemy, and convert and transpose them even to better uses.

In studying the history of the Russo-Japanese War nothing impresses us so much as the fact that the Japanese—their General Staff trained under the supervision of General Meckel, the author of " Summer Nights' Dream "—had become saturated with the German idea

G

of making war. As in 1870, so with Japan in 1904, the time had come for striking sharp blows which would allow the country to emerge from a doubtful position into one of complete independence.

" The first amongst all causes of victory," wrote von Clausewitz, " is to pursue a great object with energy " and perseverance." Marshal Nogi did not fail his Emperor. In the face of the prejudice of those who had schooled his army for victory, he adopted machine guns with most striking results.

The Russo-Japanese conflict marks the second cycle of the machine gun.

Prior to the War, both Nordenfeldt and Maxim, assisted by the uncommon diplomacy of Zaharoff, whose foresight had brought the two rivals together, had received a favourable reception in St. Petersburg. Whereas most of the European governments still regarded the machine gun with the same disfavour as had resulted from its ill-use by the French in 1870, or at most were prepared to experiment with a dangerous toy of intricate mechanical construction, the army of the Tsar had already a machine gun establishment. The weapons were Russian rifle-calibre Maxims, and both draft and pack methods were employed for transport. The gun itself, mounted on wheels which served also as the fixed platform, and screened by a shield of steel, was drawn by one horse in shafts. Alternatively the gun carriage, as a separate unit, was hooked to a two-horse ammunition limber, thus resembling an artillery weapon. The organization consisted of the Machine Gun Company, one with each division. The method of carrying was not, however, universal, for the Second and Sixth East Siberian Rifle Divisions had their guns carried in packs ; but whatever the method of transport adopted, the scale of ammunition allowance was at the rate of 6600 rounds for each gun, while the tactical unit consisted usually of the section of eight guns.

By providing a special establishment for the machine gun section, the Russian army had indeed pioneered the way of tactical progress ; for, as the result of both Russian and Japanese experience, a school of thought, with its most tenacious and imaginative thinkers within the small British army, seized upon the idea that the machine gun was in fact a distinct weapon, neither automatic rifle nor artillery, with its own peculiar characteristics, its own tactics, and of necessity, therefore, its own establishment, training, and *esprit de corps*. The British army was later described in an Army Order of the Day, captured by the French from the Germans in August 1914, as " contemptible "—a popular sobriquet—and even a Chief of the Imperial General Staff, the late Field-Marshal Sir Henry Wilson, with his flippant tongue, was accustomed to refer to the military forces of the Crown as " our funny little army." It is a remarkable fact that although immediately after the Russo-Japanese War the development of machine guns in the German army made formidable increases, in the " contemptible " little British army the technical and scientific uses of these weapons, leading by experiment to modern machine gunnery, was the work of a few enthusiasts, starved of material and hedged about with opposition.

In submitting their reports to the War Office, the British Military Attachés with both the Russian and Japanese armies did not fail to note the growing importance of machine guns. The General Officer commanding the First East Siberian Rifle Division, after twelve months of the war had elapsed, explained to Major G. H. G. Mockler and Captain H. C. Holman that " he was perfectly satisfied with his machine gun " company, and that he thought machine guns ab- " solutely necessary for infantry." There was ample evidence already on which to base so emphatic a claim. Lieutenant-Colonel A. Haldane, D.S.O., of the Gordon Highlanders, Military Attaché at the headquarters of the Second Japanese Army, reporting on 4th November 1904, wrote : " On several occasions the Japanese left " at the battle of Shou-shan-pu was checked by " machine gun and rifle-fire, and there is no doubt " that a strong feeling exists in the infantry that the " presence of machine guns with the Russian army " confers upon it a distinct advantage."

In the fight at Shokozan Hill, between 7th and 9th August 1904, the 43rd Japanese Regiment lost 540 men from machine gun fire. When the Japanese attacked the Banriusan East Work before Port Arthur on the 22nd August, it is reported by Captain C. A. L. Yate that " the Japanese suffered terribly from the fire of " machine guns skilfully placed behind the outer " parapet as well as from those behind the Chinese " wall. The brigade attacking the Banriusan Works " lost about 50 per cent."

Throughout the Russo-Japanese War, the Russians were acting on the defensive. Foreign observers, impressed with the effectiveness of the new organization, were not prepared, however, to think of machine guns as other than a valuable aid to the defence. During the earlier stages of the war, Lieutenant-General Sir Ian Hamilton, serving as the military representative for India with the Japanese field army in Manchuria, who had been Chief Musketry Officer on the Simla

Staff in 1890 and Commandant of the School of Musketry at Hythe in 1898, fails to note the existence of machine guns at all in any of his reports in the earlier stages of the war, a fact which may appear remarkable having regard to the impression which their annihilating effect had had upon the Japanese attack. Later, however, Sir Ian Hamilton paid a striking tribute to the Japanese Hotchkiss guns at the battle of Sha-Ko. He wrote : " Prince Kanin is not the sort of " man who would miss good chances, and certainly on " this occasion he seems to have unhesitatingly seized " the ripe gift offered him by fortune. Stealthily " manœuvring his six machine guns into position on a " high and broken spur which ran down to the water's " edge, he suddenly opened a hellish rain of bullets " upon two Russian battalions who, at half-past eleven " o'clock, were comfortably eating their dinners. In " less than one minute hundreds of these poor fellows " were killed, and the rest flying eastwards in wild " disorder."

There were very few, however, who had begun to consider what might be achieved by a weapon possessed of such unique features. Even the Russians themselves, though using machine guns in batteries, were so organized rather for reasons of ammunition supply, the training of personnel, and as a means of securing sustenance of fire during stoppages due to mechanical defects, than on account of considerations such as target density, the formation of interlacing cones of fire, the varying trajectory of the bullet at different ranges, and the use of ground. The consideration was technical rather than tactical, although the technique itself was scarcely understood.

The Russian army was also furnished with auto-

matic rifle detachments (Konnaya Pulemetnaya Ko-
manda Polka). These mounted automatic gun detachments were armed with the Rexer rifle, adapted to the
Russian cartridge.[1] The weapon, resting upon biped
supports, had no appreciable recoil. Even as during
the Great War, 1914–18, there remained much un-
instructed thought concerning the nature of Vickers
and Lewis " guns," followed often by an amazing confusion of use, so during 1904–5 the peculiar nature of
the machine gun, with its fixed platform and capacity
for sustained accurate fire at long ranges, was confused
with that of the automatic rifle, capable only of short
bursts of fire, accurate only at close range. The
Littoral Dragoon regiment at Tao-lu kept their six
automatic rifles together, and in that organization the
intention on the part of the Russians was to use the
weapons in batteries, just as they had with their
Maxims. The Danish Attaché in Manchuria was cited
as an authority by Captain Jardine in his report ; and
is said to have " concluded the battery organization to
" be a mistake," though no reason is given for such an
opinion. No reports are available as to the use of
automatic rifles, nor was the issue on a large scale.
The Maxim gun alone began to dominate the imagination of the questing military mind. Described by
Captain Jardine as " clumsy, heavy, and conspicuous,"
with a total weight of 15 cwt., the Russians were
forced as the result of exceptionally heavy losses among
the machine gun batteries and teams to substitute a
low tripod for the wheeled platform.

The state of affairs within the Japanese army was
very different from that of the European enemy. With

---

[1] For description see Streffleur's " Oesterreichische Militärische
Zeitschrift," July 1905.

the exception of the cavalry, up to November 1904, the Japanese had not been armed with machine guns. To each cavalry brigade one battery of six guns with six ammunition wagons was allotted. The gun was of the Hotchkiss pattern. The impression made upon the Japanese General Staff by the Russian use of machine guns in defence inclined the Japanese generals to the view that their role need not necessarily be limited to defence ; and that the use of this form of fire-power might be made to serve the attack. On 4th November Lieutenant - Colonel Haldane reported that " the " opinion of the Japanese Staff is very strongly in " favour of machine guns for infantry, and that cavalry " brigades ought to be accompanied by horse artillery, " either in addition to or in place of the machine " gun battery at present attached to them." Colonel Haldane had the opportunity to discuss the subject with Lieutenant-Colonel Yamata, of the General Staff, Second Army, who had for four years been attached to the German army ; and who was, in addition to his other duties, military instructor to Prince Hashimoto. Colonel Yamata informed Haldane that " he had just " submitted a report to the army commander in which " he pointed out the urgent necessity of arming the " infantry with machine guns."

Having drawn attention to the conspicuous nature of the Russian machine gun mounting, Colonel Yamata advised that "it was most important that the guns should " be as inconspicuous as possible, and that they should " be capable of being drawn by men." Following this report, the Japanese Government appears to have taken immediate action. The proximity of Colonel Yamata to the Emperor's person perhaps accounted for such speedy action on the part of a Government in response to urgent representations by the fighting forces in the field. The army in Japan has always enjoyed the right to nominate the War Secretary in the Cabinet ; and such a system without doubt seemed to produce that efficiency and sympathy between the soldier and politician so necessary to the successful prosecution of war.

The Japanese had already suffered heavily from the Russian machine guns, as the following illustrations fully demonstrate :

M. W. Norregaard in " The Great Siege " writes of Port Arthur : " On the attack on 203 Metre Hill, " machine guns on Akasa Kayama flanked the positions " and enfiladed the attackers. Four hundred Japanese " were sheltered together in a parallel, where they were " completely screened from fire from any part of 203 " Metre Hill. Suddenly two machine guns, which had " been concealed on Akasa Kayama, where they could " fire directly into the parallel, opened fire. Within a " few seconds it was turned into a veritable pan- " demonium, a seething mass of humanity, where men " were wildly fighting to get away, trampling on the " wounded, climbing over piles of corpses, which " blocked the entrance, and trying to escape down the " coverless hillside. But the Maxims did their work " as only Maxims can, and within a few moments " practically the whole force was wiped out ; a few " men were shot dead as they ran down the hillside, " but nearly all the others were killed in the narrow " trench. It took the Japanese days to extricate and " carry away the fearfully intermingled corpses."

" At the third general attack on November 26th, " at 2.0 P.M.," continues M. Norregaard in another report, " a large force of Japanese assaulted Sing-shu

" fort, and having crossed the moat through a bomb-
" proof passage, they gained the parapet of the rampart
" and swarmed over it.   Into this seething mass of
" humanity the machine guns of the forts and batteries
" on An-tzu-Shan poured such a tremendous fire that
" the attackers were mowed down, crushed, dispersed,
" and sent head over heels to the moat again in less
" than half a minute, before a single man had reached
" the interior of the fort.   The same fate befell a
" fresh attempt undertaken at five o'clock."

There were not more than 38[1] machine guns available
for the Russian defence of Port Arthur, 28 being allotted
to the bastions and works, 10 to the outer harbour defences.[2]   Those within the inner fortifications were
trained upon the parapets by day, so as to be correctly
sighted to meet a surprise attack by night.   At the
storming of the Erh-lung fort at midnight on 26th
November 1904, the Japanese, writes Norregaard,
" made a desperate attempt to storm the upper battery,
" but the assailants were mown down by machine guns,
" as soon as they appeared on the parapet."   Mr.
Frederick Villiers, the well-known war correspondent,
in his book " Three Months with the Besiegers,"
contributes the following in respect of the Japanese
assault on the West Panlung redoubt : " The death-
" dealing machine guns of the Russians in the casemates
" of the fort are playing ghastly havoc—such havoc
" that only a score or more of Ouchi's battalions
" reached the first ditch of the fence, where they threw
" themselves panting into the grateful cover of the pits
" their own artillery had torn."

Until the production of heavy artillery and air

[1] United States Official Report.
[2] Nojine, " The Truth about Port Arthur."

bombs, siege or fortress warfare had remained, since the earliest ages, a feature of warfare with its own special characteristics and tactical means. The Western Front in France and Flanders during the period of trench warfare presented many similarities to siege warfare, the use of machine guns being generally identical in both. The siege of Port Arthur fully demonstrated the value of machine guns in defence, as, much later—in 1936— did the illustrious defence of the Alcazar at Toledo in the Spanish Civil War by General Franco's forces.

Writing generally of the use of machine guns for the defence of Port Arthur, Norregaard says : " As an " active means of defence the searchlight and *machine* " *guns* undoubtedly come in the first rank. The " Japanese acknowledge the immense value of machine " guns to the defence. The searchlights are stationary, " they say, and the ground round Port Arthur is broken, " so that they can avoid them, but the machine guns " can be moved about anywhere and can easily be " shifted from place to place by a couple of men. It is " nearly impossible to detect them and put them out " of action ; their effect on the Japanese was most " disastrous and time after time enabled the Russians " to beat off their attacks, inflicting severe losses. " Nothing can stand against them, and it is no wonder " that the Japanese fear them, and even the bravest " have a chilly feeling creeping down their backs when " the enemy's machine guns beat their devil's tattoo. " They shoot with amazing precision even at very long " range, and they were splendidly served." The U.S.A. Official Report on the siege of Port Arthur pays no less tribute to the efficacy of the Maxim gun : " Machine " guns played an important part in the siege, being " freely used by both sides. . . . The guns were used

" with telling effect against the Japanese in the numer-
" ous bloody assaults, being trained to cover all the
" approaches with murderous fire." The Russians did
not, however, employ the guns as long-range weapons,
rarely firing at distances exceeding 1200 yards. Most
of the Japanese dead were found within 400 yards of
the assaulted position, an indication that the Russians
held their fire until the most favourable moment and
when the enemy artillery would be largely masked
by infantry from bombarding the hitherto concealed
machine gun positions.

Having realized the potentiality of the machine guns,
the Japanese lost no time in equipping the field army
with such formidable weapons. The Russians, for the
most part, used the ·312 calibre Maxim manufactured
by Vickers, Sons and Maxim in England, while the
Japanese employed the ·253 calibre Hotchkiss, having
purchased the patent rights from France and manu-
facturing at the arsenal at Tokyo.

The Japanese furnished their troops before Port
Arthur with 72 Hotchkiss guns, allotted on the scale of
24 to each division, each group being under the immediate command of the divisional commander. They
proceeded at once to exploit the gun as an attack
weapon, dragged by hand, and thrown with the utmost
boldness into the fight; and the evolution of the
tactical handling of the new arm was speedily developed,
and the importance of enfilade and overhead fire became
paramount in the Japanese calculations.

Illustrations of the successful tactical employment
of guns by the Japanese are many. Captain von
Beckmann, a German Military Attaché, reported : " At
" Mukden on March 1st all the machine guns of a
" whole Japanese division (12 to 18 guns) were brought

" into action upon a Russian *point d'appui*. The
" Russian fire was silenced, but burst out again when-
" ever the machine gun fire slackened. The Japanese
" infantry used these pauses in the enemy's fire to
" press forward to close range under cover of their
" machine gun fire."

The Japanese did not make the error of pushing
their guns into the infantry firing-line, a mistake which
was largely responsible for the ill-success of the Maxim
in the South African War. At Rietfontein, the machine
gun section of the Gloucester Regiment, positioned in
the firing-line, was annihilated. In the assault on
Cronje's laager at Paardeberg, the machine guns in the
firing-line, after suffering severe losses, could not be
withdrawn and were abandoned. Those of the Scots
Guards at Modder River remained isolated, out of
action all day, the teams in the infantry firing-line having
been annihilated by Boer " pom-pom " fire.[1]

The Japanese wisely employed their guns both for
overhead supporting fire, while the infantry assault
was carried forward, and, thrown to a flank, for enfilading the Russian firing-line.

General Nogi reported : " Our troops trained
" machine guns on the most advanced lines of infantry
" to overwhelm with fire the points at which resistance
" was greatest. They have often enabled the infantry
" to advance with success." Herr Ullrich, correspondent of the " Kölnische Zeitung," wrote: " In
" the offensive the Japanese frequently made successful
" use of machine guns. When the infantry were
" carrying out a decisive attack, they were supported
" by their machine guns, which concentrated their
" fire on points arranged beforehand. . . . When

[1] Recorded in " The Times History of the War in South Africa."

" machine guns have been skilfully employed, their
" action has been infinitely more effective than that of
" field artillery, more especially when they fire at
" infantry ranges."

The Japanese were teaching the armies of Europe
that overhead fire is not only effective, shatters the
enemy's morale, and prevents him from concentrating
and moving his reserves, but that such fire, under
conditions which can be calculated with mathematical
precision, is entirely safe over the heads of one's own
advancing infantry. That safety depends upon the
range, the level of the guns as compared with the infantry at various stages of the advance, and the position of the target.

The history of the Russo-Japanese War has many
instances of assaults brilliantly and successfully executed
as the result of the skilful use of machine guns with overhead fire. On 13th March, during the great battle of
Mukden, the Japanese infantry were able to cross the
river Fan, supported by machine gun fire at 1800 yards
range, which, while the attack climbed from the river-
bed and completed the difficult and arduous uphill
assault, kept up their fire until the infantry were within
40 yards of the Russian trenches. In a lecture on 5th
March 1905, after the Ma-chun-tan action, the officer
commanding the machine guns of the 2nd Japanese
Division said : " I got a good position for the guns
" and, firing over the infantry's heads, covered their
" advance at a range of 1200 yards. The enemy in
" their trenches fired heavily ; but we were soon able
" to make them keep their heads down. Whenever I
" ceased fire up went their heads again. Each machine
" gun expended 1500 rounds during the action, which
" lasted about an hour."

Colonel A. Haldane was much impressed with the tactical handling and exploitation of situations by the Japanese machine gun officers, while Lieutenant-Colonel C. V. Hume, D.S.O., R.A., wrote : " The " guns did excellent service during the battle of Mukden, " and were immensely appreciated by all infantry " commanders. I have spoken to many brigade and " regimental commanders on the subject since the " battle and find them all very keen about their guns. " . . . Several instances occurred in the First Army " where the machine guns produced very decisive " effect."

Machine guns were raised from the ignominy to which they had sunk after 1871 as the result of the war in Manchuria, a period which denotes the second cycle of their history. Throughout the armies of the world a period of great activity between 1905 and 1914 followed. Yet it is remarkable that in Great Britain, except for a few enthusiasts, despite the foresight and originality of much British thinking upon fire problems and tactics, no further advances were made in machine gunnery. Only in the third cycle of machine gun history does the supreme excellence of British theory in practice and organization appear.

CHAPTER V

MANY INVENTIONS
1908–1914

Germany arms with the machine gun—Colonel McMahon's lecture on " Fire Tactics "—Literature—Commandant Lavau—The field of invention—French hesitancy—The Maxim pre- dominates in world armies—German tactical principles— Russia—The Sokolov mounting—Hythe perseveres—Captain R. V. K. Applin as pioneer—British tradition as marksmen militates against introduction of machine guns—Fire discipline —Different arms view ground from various angles—Staff errors from lack of knowledge—Captain J. F. C. Fuller— Machine guns and automatic rifles not to be confused—Captain Nigel Charteris—1914.

THE experience of the Russo-Japanese War was decisive in its effect upon German military opinion. The Emperor Wilhelm himself had never relaxed his early enthusiasm for the Maxim gun ; and when the General Staff, in 1899, decided to allot four-gun Maxim batteries as auxiliary weapons to the Jäger battalions allotted to the cavalry on the Imperial manœuvres, the Kaiser personally provided a Maxim gun for each of the Dragoon regiments of the Guard.

The military critics were not, however, enthusiastic. Captain Fritz Hoening considered that one battery for each army corps would be sufficient, a criticism which, had it been followed, would have strangled the new

idea at birth.   General von Rohne, writing in the
" Jahrbuch " of December 1901, considered machine
guns an embarrassment on manœuvres, but there was
some originality in his thinking, also, for he put forward
the proposal that machine guns could effectively range
and locate a target, as it were spraying a considerable
area with bullets, by slightly traversing the gun from
side to side, at the same time operating the elevating
gear up and down.   This notion was taken up by
Lieutenant-Colonel W. D. Bird,[1] Chief Instructor at the
Hythe School of Musketry, in a lecture before the
Aldershot Military Society in 1904.   The idea was
certainly the forerunner of the methods now employed.
Colonel Bird, however, was not an enthusiast.   In
Germany, arming with the Maxim went ahead.   By
the end of 1902, thirteen batteries had been formed,
one attached to the Guard Corps, and a further battery
to each cavalry brigade stationed near the frontiers,
each battery consisting of six guns.

By the close of 1908 every German regiment (three
battalions of infantry) possessed its own battery of six
guns, under the direct control of the regiment commander.   In effect, therefore, the guns were " brigaded."
In the same year the German Government, in the
Military Estimates, allotted fourteen millions of marks
(£700,000) for machine gun experimental purposes.
As the result, the German Maxim gun was reduced in
weight to $16\frac{1}{2}$ kilos ; prismatic telescopic sights were
provided by Carl Zeiss, of Jena ; and the sled, an
ingenious carriage which can be used as a trailer,
stretcher, or to raise the gun to various elevations, was
reduced in weight to 24 kilos.   At the same time, the

[1] Later Major-General Sir Wilkinson Bird, K.B.E., C.B., C.M.G.,
D.S.O

machine gun armament of the German fortresses had proceeded apace.

While, however, German opinion remained to be convinced as to the correct application of machine gun fire tactics, a lecture of far-reaching consequences was delivered by Lieutenant-Colonel N. R. McMahon, D.S.O., of the Royal Fusiliers, on 18th December 1907, before the Aldershot Military Society. Colonel McMahon's lecture, entitled " Fire Tactics,"[1] contributed a wide survey of the potentialities of the gun, but, of greater significance, laid down the tactical principles in accordance with which it should be manœuvred. His ideas were immediately incorporated in the British Field Service Regulations and Training Manuals. So anxious was the German General Staff to obtain further information on the matter, as it appears, that while the Regulations were yet in draft form they were communicated to the German Military Attaché in London, in exchange for other information. In the earlier stages of machine gun tactical training in Germany, therefore, the system was based upon the experiments and direction of the small band of enthusiasts at Hythe. Colonel McMahon, a great loss, was killed in action at Ypres in 1914.

After 1908, the arming of German forces with machine guns proceeded rapidly, so that by August 1914 the numbers available for the field armies has been estimated to have amounted to some 5000 machine guns of the Maxim pattern.

Both literature and inventive genius, too, received stimulation from the Manchurian War. In the former, German commentators were much to the fore, especially in the momentous year of 1908, the contribution of

[1] " Proceedings of the Aldershot Military Society," 1907.

Captain A. von Fleck being especially valuable.[1] This author not only describes the various guns, Maxim, Hotchkiss, and the new-comers Schwarzlose, Madsen, Bergman, Colt, Skoda, Fitzgerald, but discusses their various uses, including the types best adapted for aircraft. In the following year, no doubt stimulated by German interest, French military writers occupy most of the literary stage, among them Commandant J. C. Lavau, of the 15th Dragoons, being outstanding. In two volumes, published in 1908 and 1910, the work completely surveys machine guns and their tactics. Commandant Lavau, although a cavalry officer, and using the title of " Mitrailleuses de Cavalerie " for his compendium, by no means confines himself to exploring tactical uses with the mounted arm. He visualizes *mitraillerie* as a separate arm, but, no doubt influenced by the Japanese experience combined with his own specialized training, Commandant Lavau insists upon the machine gun as an attack weapon, and urges the development of the " machine gun spirit."

A little later, in 1912, Lieutenant Du Peyré summarized the world machine gun position in a work titled " Nos mitrailleuses, ce qu'elles sont, ce qu'il faut en attendre." Without pretence of originality, the author analyses the tactical ideas extant among the principal world military nations.

In the field of invention the year 1908 is again most remarkable. No less than fourteen inventions were registered at the British Patent Office, including six by Mr. A. T. Dawson (late Lieutenant R.N.), Director and Superintendent of the Ordnance Works of Vickers, Sons and Maxim of Victoria Street, Westminster,

[1] Captain A. von Fleck, " Maschinengewehre : ihre Technik und Taktik."

mostly relating to improvements in the tripod mounting and elevating apparatus (Nos. 14966 and 10312 respectively). Mr. Hiram Maxim, too, on his own account registered three patents in this year " for lessening the sound of discharge of guns." In the following years, up till 1914, both Sir Trevor Dawson and Sir Hiram Maxim, both knighted for their services after 1908, were most active with improvements to the Maxim and Vickers-Maxim gun. Of other guns, the most important new-comers were the Colt, with which the Canadian contingent to the Imperial Forces in 1914 was first armed ; the Schwarzlose, meaning " Smokeless," of Germany ; and the Browning from the United States of America.

While both critical thought and inventive genius were active, as are pioneers in every field of human activity, even without any sign of official encouragement, the War Departments of Europe were stirring from the lethargy into which they had fallen after 1871. Great Britain alone seemed to remain oblivious to what was transpiring in the German army, especially after 1905 ; concerned alone, as it seemed, not with the possibility of any test of arms upon a European battlefield, but with the minor affrays of the Indian Frontier and Africa.

In France, Mr. B. B. Hotchkiss continued his work at St. Denis with unabated zeal. After some success with breech-loading apparatus, he turned his attention to the rifle-calibred machine gun, and, improving upon the invention of the Austrian Captain von Odkolek, produced the Hotchkiss machine gun. The principle was very different from that of Maxim and Nordenfeldt. A portion of the gas produced by the explosion of the charge escapes through a hole under the barrel before the bullet leaves the muzzle. This gas operates a piston which itself causes the breech action to eject the empty cartridge-case and reload. The ammunition, contained in a metal belt, is fed from left to right, and the gun is air-cooled by means of flanges on the barrel.

The Hotchkiss guns were somewhat timidly introduced into the French army in 1899 : and the Government, led by General de Gallifet, the War Minister, decided to undertake future manufacture in the State arsenal at Puteaux. At once the whole question was thrown into the political arena ; and while, in characteristic fashion, the French politicians stormed and argued, the manufacture of the gun itself fell into abeyance.

In 1907 the French had, however, ample opportunity to test machine guns in practical fashion against the turbulent tribesmen of their extending colonial possessions in Morocco. Hotchkiss guns, both of the St. Denis and Puteaux pattern, were used with admirable effect against the Moors, who, adopting the same tactics as did the Khalifa's forces at Omdurman in 1897, met with the same fate. The reports from Morocco, stimulated by the knowledge gained from Manchuria, stirred some of the French deputies to a frenzy of agitation : nor was this lessened by the fact that in 1905 the amazing Kaid McLean had introduced Maxim guns purchased in England into the Moorish army.

M. Charles Humbert, a brisk and well-informed commentator upon military matters, in October 1907 issued his challenge in the French Chamber to the vacillations and indecision of the French Government by the publication of a book, " Sommes-nous dé-

Imperial War Museum

SOLDIERS OF THE INDIAN ARMY ARMED WITH THE
HOTCHKISS GUN, IN FRANCE, 1915

Imperial War Museum

RUSSIAN MACHINE GUNNERS, CAPTURED BY GERMAN
TROOPS, HAULING THEIR MACHINE GUNS

fendus ? " which rushed through twelve editions within a few weeks. In the Chamber of Deputies the Government spokesmen, threatened with a vote of " No Confidence," appealed to its party supporters, as is usual, not to produce a Government crisis upon a trivial matter, and won the day with the stereotyped promise that it would push forward manufacture and distribution without delay. The Government, on this occasion, was as good as its word, and at the French manœuvres of 1908 each regiment possessed a battery of six machine guns.

Throughout the world generally, the various armed forces were equipped with machine guns following the Russo-Japanese War. Sweden, Holland, Turkey, Greece, Rumania, Spain and Portugal, the United States of America, and most of the armies of the South American States, were furnished with the Maxim gun. Austria and Bulgaria were supplied with Schwarzlose guns ; France with the Hotchkiss. In various armies, wherein understanding of the functions of the machine gun proper had not attained to clarity of principle, both Maxim and Madsen guns were distributed, without any specification as to their different tactical uses : while the lesser nations were sometimes armed with both the Maxim and the Hotchkiss, a suggestion that interest in a contract may have preceded the needs of efficiency, as was exampled, although in one of the Great Powers, in the Putiloff arms scandal in Russia immediately prior to the Great War in 1914.

In Italy, the Maxim gun had been the standard weapon until 1908. In this year the claims of the Italian engineer, Signor G. Perino of Turin, were pressed before the Royal Commission on armaments, and his invention, a modification of the Maxim gun, was adopted, probably not for any reason of mechanical superiority, which it would be difficult to establish, but on the grounds of Italian *amour propre* and of economy in manufacture. The Perino gun did not, however, entirely supersede the Maxim, for in 1909 and later there were further issues of Maxim guns to the Alpini regiments guarding the northern frontiers of Italy.

In the Central Powers of Germany and Austria, the greatest advances were made both in technique with its ancillary *matériel* and in tactical organization. A new edition of the German " Felddienst Ordnung," corresponding to the British Field Service Regulations, was issued in March 1908, and formed the doctrine up till 1914. A vital passage which clearly establishes the correct view of machine gun tactics ran as follows :

" The fire-effect of machine guns is influenced
" principally by correct sighting, possibility of observa-
" tion, size, and density of the target, and methods of
" fire. It is further affected by the suddenness with
" which the fire is opened, by the number of machine
" guns firing at the same target, and by the enemy's
" fire.

" The high rate of fire concentration of the bullet-
" sheaf, and the possibility of bringing several machine
" guns into action on a narrow front, enable great effect
" to be produced in a short time, even at long ranges.
" When the front of the target is broken and irregular,
" the effect is reduced. A wrong sighting elevation, or
" imperfect observation of fire, may render the fire
" completely ineffective.

" Dense lines of skirmishers standing suffer severe
" losses at ranges of 1550 metres (1700 yards) and under.
" At lines of skirmishers lying, good effect is to be ex-

" pected at 1000 metres (1100 yards) and under, pro-
" vided that the observation of fire is good.

   " Against artillery in action the fire-effect is similar
" to that of infantry. Owing to the mobility of the
" machine gun batteries, they are especially adapted for
" securing the increased fire-effect due to oblique fire.

   " At short ranges under hostile fire, machine guns
" can only be brought up and withdrawn under cover."[1]

With a thoroughness characteristic of the race, once
having convinced themselves of the value of machine
guns, the Germans omitted nothing in their equipment.
Machine gun organization consisted of the machine
gun company (Maschinengewehr-Kompagnie) and the
machine gun detachment (Abteilung). Companies were
allotted to each regiment of three battalions, each
company consisting of six guns. The machine gun
detachments, similarly armed, were organized upon a
non-regimental basis to be at the disposal of Army
Corps commanders. After 1914 the number of these
detachments was greatly increased. The organization
itself, in its elasticity, and for the reason that machine
guns were not confined in their use to areas or sectors
held by individual battalions, as was so with the British
system in the earlier stages of the Great War, permitted
the fullest exploitation of the varied characteristics of
the gun from the outset. Machine gun competitions,
upon an inter-regimental basis, were devised and
followed with great enthusiasm, contributing to efficiency in handling the weapon and to knowledge of its
use. In the British army, it was not finally until
January 1937 that the Army Rifle Association decided
to separate competitions involving machine gun and
rifle units.

[1] " Felddienst Ordnung," 1908, paras. 581-584.

In Austria, probably for the same reasons as in
Italy, the Skoda gun, an adaptation as was the Perino
of the Maxim principle, invented by the Archduke
Charles Salvator in collaboration with Major von
Dormus, was adopted, while Maxims were exploited
with the cavalry. In 1906, however, both were discarded for the Schwarzlose, manufactured at Steyr.
The Schwarzlose was claimed to be a definite advance
upon the Maxim and, mechanically, the gun certainly
possessed the advantage that it had but one spring
against fourteen in its rival. In mechanical handling,
the school of machine gunnery at Bruck on the Leitha,
established in 1906, developed Schwarzlose fire to a
fine art. The school issued six reports annually, based
often upon fire-observation experiments conducted
upon snow surfaces in the mountains.

Russia, ignominiously defeated at Port Arthur, did
not forsake her early love for the machine gun ; and,
after hostilities had ceased, proceeded to arm cavalry
and infantry on a liberal scale with Maxim guns. The
only innovation was a special mounting designed by
Colonel Sokolov, adaptable either for wheels or as a
sled, and possessed of a trail and two folding legs,
making it possible for the gunner to fire either seated
or lying. Another ingenious novelty was the method
by which ammunition was packed for use, after it
became necessary to abandon limbers in the face of an
enemy. Each machine gun wagon carried two metal
cylinders, each containing four belts of 250 rounds
each. When unlimbered the cylinders were able to be
rolled along the ground by prone men, virtually in
complete concealment, to the gun position. No records
exist as to the success or failure of this device, and
useful as it might appear upon hard, unbroken soil,

the weight of the cylinder would seem to prevent its use upon battlefields much broken by shell-fire.

The British army, which had pioneered the way of machine guns in its colonial wars after the ill-success of 1870, and, moreover, which had up till 1908 contributed almost everything of value to the literature of the weapon, was forced by a niggardly Treasury until the outbreak of the Great War, 1914, to remain, dissatisfied, with an armament of two Maxims with each battalion of infantry and regiment of cavalry, under the command of a subaltern officer, who often alone among the officers of his battalion possessed the requisite knowledge even of how to fire the gun.

At the School of Musketry at Hythe in England and at Pachmari in India, a small band of enthusiasts were exploring the possibilities of the Maxim gun under every kind of condition. An over-insistence upon the delicacy of the mechanism and the utility of the gun as " a weapon of opportunity " was, even so, responsible for delaying the more general adoption of machine guns in the British army. Commanders on manœuvres, into whose minds the text-books had drilled these slogans, were inclined in the first instance to place no reliance upon a weapon liable to so many imaginary hazards ; while almost invariably, also, battalion machine gun sections were kept in reserve for an opportunity which never presented itself, or were galloped as horse artillery to a flank in full view of the enemy in order to fulfil the assigned task of protecting a flank. At the best, or maybe the worst, the two guns were placed in the firing-line in repetition of the disastrous experiences of South Africa, in the hope, on manœuvres, no doubt, that no umpire of imagination would put the guns " out of action," as in more realistic fashion had been British experience against the Boers.

Among those who realized the true role and potentiality of the machine gun was Captain R. V. K. Applin, D.S.O.,[1] of the 14th King's Hussars, who in 1910 delivered a striking lecture at the United Service Institution and in the same year published his " Machine-Gun Tactics." Captain Applin, who had served in the Syed and Mat Salleh rebellions in North Borneo (1895–7) and throughout the South African War (1899–1901), possessed unusual experience, which undoubtedly enriched a forceful personality. Captain Applin was not, moreover, of the type of the " strong, silent men." He was always vigorous and lucid in speech, frequently sparkling with wit and humorous yet homely illustration. His lecture, under the chairmanship of Colonel W. N. Congreve, V.C., M.V.O.,[2] Commandant of the Hythe School of Musketry, was remarkable as the most intensive study of machine gun tactics yet delivered in Great Britain. Among those present was Captain F. V. Longstaff, who later, with Captain A. Hilliard Atteridge, contributed the most complete history of machine guns up to that date (1917) published in any country.[3] It is notable that even as in 1886 the old volunteers had pioneered machine guns on manœuvres, both these authors were members of the Territorial Force.

Captain Applin put forward a thesis as to personnel which is best summarized in his own words : " We " can scarcely expect to obtain a high standard of

[1] Lieutenant-Colonel R. V. K. Applin, D.S.O., M.P. Enfield Division, 1924–9, 1931–5.
[2] Later Lieutenant-General Sir Walter Congreve, V.C.
[3] " The Book of the Machine Gun," by Major A. V. Longstaff and A. Hilliard Atteridge.

" tactical training or organizing bodies capable of
" manœuvring under fire and combined effort from
" the regimental subaltern and his two guns left
" absolutely to his own resources. The best, and
" nothing but the best, is essential to the successful
" employment of machine guns in war, and the
" necessity for obtaining the very best officers as section
" commanders is so great that I am inclined to doubt
" the utility of having machine guns at all if they are
" not commanded and handled by those who are in
" every way expert in their use." Of tactics, he said :
" The beaten zone is perhaps the most important
" factor in obtaining effective fire. Machine gun fire
" is always collective and concentrated, unless de-
" liberately dispersed by the firer, while rifle-fire is
" always individual and dispersed, unless specially
" controlled by fire-discipline under a leader." [1]

The tradition as marksmen had been sustained for
centuries. In Froissart's " Chronicles " there is a fine
detailed description of the battle of Crécy, 20th August
1346, which in some passages recalls the bitter fighting
of 1914 at Mons, the Marne, and Ypres: " There is no
" man, unless he had been present, that can imagine, or
" describe, truly, the confusion of that day. . . . The
" English rose undauntedly and fell into their ranks. . . .
" The English continued to take aim forcibly and
" vigorously. The battle was very murderous and
" cruel, and many gallant deeds of arms were performed
" which have never been known." The riflemen of
the British regular army in the years prior to the
Great War were the finest in the world. It may be,
therefore, that the force of Captain Applin's appeal

for the greater consideration of the machine gun failed adequately to impress an audience accustomed to a very high standard of training in marksmanship, and, therefore, of fire-discipline. Indeed, it is apparent that although the staff at the School of Musketry at Hythe was largely responsible for the foundations of machine gun organization and tactics, Great Britain was the last among the great European Powers seriously to develop this arm of the Service. The reason appears to be plain, namely, that British troops did, in fact as well as in theory, almost miraculously as it might seem, achieve so high a standard of fire-discipline that the effect was often, as the early actions against German troops in 1914 proved, almost equivalent to the collective and concentrated fire of machine guns.

Such fire-discipline was without doubt only attainable in a small long-service force with such ample opportunities for field-firing exercises as are provided by the wide expanses of India and Africa : whereas the short-service conscript armies of Britain's European neighbours possessed neither time nor opportunity for such intensive devotion to the rifle, and applied their energies to machine gun training. Such excellence in individual and collective marksmanship may well have blinded British military opinion to the outstanding and peculiar merits of the machine gun, as advocated by Captain Applin and those others who thought with him. The deficiency was in no way revealed until heavy casualties among the original Expeditionary Force and subsequent reinforcements by ill-trained men on an ever-increasing scale laid bare the bankruptcy of fire-discipline ; while in the circumstance of trench warfare, for obvious reasons, effective control was seldom possible. It was only then that the advantage of the

German machine gun organization and training on a large scale became apparent.

A further point, also, requires emphasis. Armed forces, organized upon a national scale, as are conscript armies, draw upon those industries and civilian occupations most likely to supply men trained to the use of the various arms. Men accustomed to the use of mechanical or horse transport, for example, are required as a general principle to perform analogous tasks upon military mobilization, while the permanent General Staff, concerned at all times with war, or in more popular phraseology, with defence plans, is not severely departmentalized. In a small professional army, sufficiently large to provide avenues of promotion within the several arms, the tendency is that the views of both officers and men will become more strictly circumscribed by the needs and tactics of the arm in which they serve, with all the rivalries which arise therefrom, as between "gunners," "sappers," "footsloggers," cavalry. The personnel of each arm frequently comes to view all military problems through the eyes of its own branch of the Service, as was well illustrated by the hostility of the artillery hierarchy at Woolwich to machine guns in their early days. Against the prejudices, therefore, of a combination of the four older arms, the claims of machine guns as an individual arm were not likely to receive much attention. None but the most daring would seek distinction from the herd of his own arm of the Service by championing a novelty so critical, in effect, of that very virtue of fire-discipline which had always been one of the most illustrious distinctions of the British soldier.

The early prophets gained little of honour as they preached the gospel of "the Devil's watering-pots."

Moreover, officers of each arm of the Service are inclined to view ground from the point of view of their own arm. This is inescapable, and results from training. When, therefore, a small professional army, as was the British in 1914, was suddenly expanded to a force consisting of hundreds of thousands of fighting men, with their ancillary services of all kinds, officers of various branches of the Service suddenly found themselves no longer concerned with problems of gunnery, engineering, cavalry, or infantry tactics, but as Staff officers dealing with situations requiring a knowledge of the four arms. In battle they had need, therefore, of a capacity to view and visualize ground from the point of view of artillery, cavalry, machine gunners, and infantry, and later from that of the air and the tank.

The infantry officer, with his weapons of rifle and automatic rifle, views ground from a standpoint vastly different from that of the machine gunner, because of the different nature of the two weapons. This is the point to press. It is, however, far less probable that a machine gun officer, who is likely to have passed through some preliminary training in youth with the rifle and of necessity must also understand the nature of the weapon, will fail to be able to view the tactical possibilities of ground from an infantry standpoint. Moreover, since the development of " barrage fire " by batteries of machine guns, the machine gun officer is well equipped technically to appreciate the viewpoint of artillery officers in the selection of gun positions and in attaining to fire-action. Even up to the last stages of the Great War, infantry commanders were frequently unable to appreciate the reasons which guided machine gun commanders to select gun positions outside the limits of battalion, brigade, and divisional areas. An illustration of this fact is provided by the disposal of the Guards Machine Gun Battalion on 23rd March 1918 at Henin, near Arras, where the Battalion Commander noted : " No. 3 Company, true to the tradition " of the 3rd Guards Brigade, was divided up amongst " the battalions of the Brigade irrespective of whether a " section of Vickers guns could be efficiently disposed " in each battalion front." There were many similar incidents.

An even more remarkable illustration is provided in an article by a commentator in an important British military review.[1] He writes : " I have already hinted " that we have perhaps not got a proper perspective " of our weapons. To show how important such a " view may become let us think back on the Great War. " Was ever a most useful weapon so mishandled, and " on some occasions even forgotten, as was the machine " gun ? When one considers the use made by the " enemy of his machine guns as an attacking weapon, " then we can realize what sheer waste of organization " we indulged in. When one remembers coming across " earnest machine gun teams in the back area studiously " firing into the night, one is still apt to feel very sad. " I never knew what became of their bullets, but I " never read that the enemy suffered."

The history of machine gun development during the Great War demonstrates the divergence of view between those whose knowledge of fire-tactics was limited to the rifle, and those whose use of ground was dictated by the nature and peculiar characteristics of the machine gun. In later passages this critic seems to

[1] ' Weapon and Target,' by Lieutenant-Colonel N. L. Macky, M.C., A.D.C., New Zealand Military Forces, " Army Quarterly," vol. xxxiii. No. 2, January 1937.

think of machine guns only as front-line weapons, necessarily therefore of short range, concerned with frontal fire. He confuses automatic rifles with machine guns, and in other matters appears to share the thoughts of Li Hung Chang and the early critics of 1887.

Very many Intelligence Reports, Histories of German Regiments, in addition to the Official History of the Great War, contribute irrefutable evidence of the havoc wrought among the enemy, both in attack and defence, by machine guns, disposed in what are described as " back areas," " studiously firing into the " night." The infantry officer, if he lacks machine gun knowledge and is unable to discern the difference between machine guns and automatic rifles, is likely to fall into the same errors of thought as did the leading military authorities in Britain for the very different reasons noted.

At the same time as Captain Applin produced his work, books upon the mechanical technique and tactical use of machine guns were being contributed from Germany in considerable numbers and importance. The most important contributions were those of Captain A. von Fleck, Lieutenant-General G. von Haslingen, Captain H. von Kiesling, Lieutenant Kretschmer, Major Schulz, and Colonel Balck, the first and last named being considerable writers with creative ideas.

Through the School of Musketry at Hythe, the thought stimulated by Captain Applin's work began to make itself more generally felt in infantry battalions, though progress was slow. On the 11th March 1911 an important lecture was delivered before the Aldershot Military Society by Lieutenant-Colonel J. Campbell, D.S.O.,[1] of the Cameron Highlanders, upon " Fire

[1] Later Major-General John Campbell, C.B., C.M.G., D.S.O.

Action." The lecturer noted that foreign countries were " paying great attention to the question of over- " head fire by machine guns in support of advancing " infantry." A report by a Japanese officer from the Manchurian War, 1904–5, had already demonstrated that " advancing infantry like to hear the crackle of " supporting machine gun fire overhead," an opinion corroborated many times over during the Great War.

Nevertheless, military thought in Great Britain continued to be enclosed, as it were, within separate walls, each arm of the Service resembling some kind of monastic seminary with its own rituals and doctrines and sometimes a little prejudiced against, even contemp- tuous of, those of other arms. This, undoubtedly, was a fault inherent in a system which segregated the various arms of the Service at an impressionable age in the Military Colleges, and was fostered later by a strong *esprit de corps* well established by tradition, and which perme- ated the rank and file. The system, in a small voluntary, professional army, had its merits. It possessed also its defects, as the sudden expansion of the small regular army, with its auxiliaries the Special Reserve (Militia) and the Territorial Force (Volunteers), to an immense national army of millions, amply demonstrated.

One other thinker became an outstanding per- sonality, not alone as a machine gunner, but in the War and post-War eras of mechanization, involving often entirely fresh conceptions about the tactical dispositions and uses of both men and material. In November 1914 —the article had in fact been written before the out- break of hostilities—Captain J. F. C. Fuller,[1] of the

[1] Later Major-General J. F. C. Fuller, C.B., C.B.E., D.S.O., Chief Staff Officer, Machine Gun Corps (Heavy Section), 1916, and of the Tank Corps, author of many works and essays of military criticism.

I

Oxford and Bucks Light Infantry, who had been machine gun officer of his battalion, contributed an article upon machine gun tactics to the " Journal of the United Service Institution." Captain Fuller was the very antithesis of Captain Applin in both personality and appearance. Among a wide circle he came to be known as " Bonaparte ": [1] a man of surprising mental agility, penetration, and foresight. He referred to the gun as " a nerveless weapon," and having so aptly summarized its chief characteristic, he proceeded :
" There is as much difference between machine gun
" and infantry fire to-day as there was between light-
" infantry and heavy-infantry fire a hundred years ago.
" So great is this difference that we might almost say
" that the light infantry of the future will be evolved
" from the machine gunners of the present. That is
" to say, that the assaulting column of the future will
" be flanked by these terror-spreading weapons, and
" that these new light-infantry men, like the old, will
" not only precede the assaulting column by working
" up close to the line of the holding attack, but will
" flank it on both sides, producing a somewhat similar
" effect on the hostile line as grape, canister, and case-
" shot did during the first fifty years of the last century."
In effect this is precisely the role which the evolution of the machine gun during the Great War prescribed for it : and no doubt, as mechanization develops, within the limits of its capacity to surpass obstacles, it is the line marked for both machine gun and automatic rifle tactical development of the future. Experience proved over and over again during the Great War that

---

[1] " There was the ' Colonel ' of the Tanks—' Napoleon,' they called him. A great brain he had."—" An Onlooker in France," by Sir William Orpen, K.B.E., R.A., p. 62.

machine guns are the greatest impediment to infantry advance ; and it appears that whatever mechanized aids may be added, by air or land, the principle that ground can actually be gained and held by infantry alone will remain true. Automatic rifles, sometimes also confusingly described as " light machine guns," are *par excellence* the weapons best adapted for the attack by infiltration, as the great German offensive in March–April 1918 sufficiently demonstrated, while machine guns proper, due to their special character- istics both in attack and defence, have shown their fullest powers in overhead and frequently indirect, un- observed fire, as well as in short-range direct fire.

During the Great War, machine guns, despite their weight and that of the accompanying loads, were shown to be possessed of amazing mobility, almost, if not quite, the equal of that of infantry in modern battle conditions. In an advance, however, the machine gun teams, as groups, no matter what kind of formation was adopted, proved to be conspicuous targets, often those most dangerous later to forming defensive positions. Here, again, is a reason why it is inadvisable, apart from the waste of a weapon better able to do its work at longer ranges, to throw machine guns into the fore- front of the battle line or trench system. Though machine gunners never flinched from the fire battle— and in fact nearly 50 per cent of the personnel of the Machine Gun Corps became casualties during the Great War—and though with a plentiful supply of weapons, the temporary loss or total disablement of a machine gun is not a serious matter, foolhardy exposure of highly trained men and weapons, where another arm can more effectively carry through the task to success, is the folly born of ignorance.

Both Captain Applin and Captain Fuller, the latter one of the three trained brigade machine gun officers who had been appointed shortly before the outbreak of hostilities in August 1914, were responsible for most important contributions to the tactical literature mechanization. To these must be added the name of Sergeant-Major Bostock of the Instructional Staff at the School of Musketry, Hythe, whose book[1] became the *vade-mecum* of nearly every officer and N.C.O. who passed through the school courses.

At Hythe, despite all kinds of restrictions, the mathematics of machine guns began to be evolved, both by theory and practice. In 1913 instruction was being given in the ·45 converted to ·303 Maxim, the ·303 Maxim, and in the new ·303 Vickers light gun.

In addition to " Mechanism," a most thorough course, instruction was also given in " Night-firing," including " traversing " and " searching " ; " indirect firing by graticules " ; and drill on rough ground. " Overhead fire " was demonstrated only. Up to the outbreak of the Great War, the War Office forbade " overhead fire " to be taught to students, but the demonstrations by the School of Musketry staff opened their eyes to its possibilities.

" Immediate action "—that is to say, the almost subconscious manipulation of the mechanism of the gun in the rectification of stoppages due to temporary mechanical faults—was introduced by Captain R. G. Clarke, of the Queen's Royal West Surrey Regiment. This officer was also responsible for the evolution of the mathematics for overhead fire by taking the 100 per cent vertical cone dispersion and converting it to

[1] " The Machine Gunner's Handbook, including the Vickers Light Gun," by Sergeant-Major Bostock.

angles. Captain Nigel Charteris produced the first instrument for reckoning angles of fire, immediately prior to the War, known as the " Card and String " method. The original was made from the lid of a cigar-box. After 1914, both the handbook[1] by Captain Charteris and his invention, manufactured in copper, achieved enormous sales.

In order to test the theories, hundreds of thousands of rounds of ammunition were fired from the " Roughs " at Hythe over the Hythe–Dymchurch road on to the foreshore.

Upon mobilization in August 1914, the School of Musketry was at once closed. All the instructors, both officers and N.C.O.'s, were despatched to various military stations in England, Scotland, and Ireland to assist in the training of reservists in musketry and machine guns. Captain Charteris himself was sent to Queenstown, Ireland, and thence to Carlisle Fort at the entrance to Cork Harbour, where were two machine guns on fixed mountings in the fort, but not one of the reservists in charge had the remotest notion what to do with them.

As the war clouds gathered the War Office returned to think more in terms of the familiar branches of the Service with their customary weapons, cavalry, and sabres, and lances ; artillery with field-pieces and howitzers ; infantry armed with the rifle of which it was the past-master. In Germany and Austria, machine gunnery developed to a high art, though confined to direct fire, but at Hythe a small band persevered. It was due to their dogged persistence, supported by the knowledge which only a pioneer, never dismayed by

[1] " Some Lectures and Notes on Machine Guns," by Captain N. K. Charteris, Instructor, School of Musketry, Hythe.

failure and learning eternally from experiment, ever so fully possesses, that the amazing advances in the technique of machine gunnery was able to be realized during the later stages of the War when opposition had perished and a plentiful supply of able men and weapons became available.

Of the pioneers the most notable were Captain George Lindsay of the Rifle Brigade, Captain N. K. Charteris of the Royal Scots, Captain C. C. Hewitt of the Royal Inniskilling Fusiliers, Captain R. G. Clarke of the Queen's Royal West Surrey Regiment, all of whom later held high appointments in the Machine Gun Corps, for whose formation they were largely responsible.

As the bonds of diplomacy weakened and war seemed to become inevitable, the year 1914 found the Army in a transitional stage in its equipment. A few battalions and cavalry sections had been issued with the ·303 Vickers, R.C.A.M. guns on Mark IV tripods, the gun which later came into universal use, while most regiments were armed with the heavy pattern of Maxim gun, whose mechanism also required a different performance of the hands due to the reversal of the lock and trigger positions.

The hour of war struck. While the Expeditionary Force mobilized and Lord Kitchener issued his dramatic appeal for a manhood to fight for Britain in the battles of the nations, machine guns were forgotten.

CHAPTER VI

CHARACTERISTICS
1914–1915

Rifle versus machine gun—Effect of casualties in the British regular army—Decline of marksmanship and fire-discipline—Fire-power discussed—The six characteristics of the machine gun considered—Development of mechanized means—The tank—Superiority of German machine gunnery—Machine Gun School, St. Omer — Captain Baker-Carr — Hyperscopes — Web and metal belts — Mr. Lloyd George on machine guns — The "weapon of opportunity"—Conflicting views as to tactical control—Brigade Machine Gun Officer—Formation of the Machine Gun Corps—Introduction of the Lewis "gun"—Machine Gun Training Centre, Grantham.

SUNDAY, the 23rd August 1914, came with its mist, suggesting heat. The British army was in the field, advancing, patrols of Chetwode's[1] cavalry brigade thrown out as a screen. The people were returning from mass, when suddenly a curtain of fire rolled down upon them as the prelude to the clash of steel. By 1 P.M. the German troops had entered Mons, and the British Guards met the full fury of the attack; and soon cavalry and infantry were engaged in a death grapple.

The most remarkable feature of the battle of Mons

[1] Brigadier, afterwards Field-Marshal Sir Philip Chetwode, Commander-in-Chief, India.

119

was its test between two fundamentally different methods of training infantry. The British relied on the rifle, the Germans upon the mass attack.

As at Crécy and Agincourt, each British foot-soldier was trained to be a marksman ; and, whatever havoc the German machine guns in defence later made of British attacks, the German methods of employing infantry in these first stages of the War proved immensely costly against an army of marksmen. 130,000 Germans attacked 80,000 British soldiers. They attacked almost shoulder to shoulder, each battalion in three double ranks, the rear double rank possessed of its machine guns, carried upon their sleds in stretcher fashion by two men. The German training was intended to accomplish victory by sheer weight of numbers, the machine guns to hold the positions after attack. This was before the era in which was developed, with such amazing precision, indirect fire by machine guns mounted upon a fixed platform.

By the close of the first day vast armies of Germans with hundreds of machine guns and 920 pieces of artillery were opposed to the front of the British army with its 80,000 men and 300 guns, and not more than 100 machine guns, over a front of some twenty miles. On the British right, half a million Germans with thousands of machine guns and 920 weapons of artillery were in pursuit of the French, leaving the British army as a tiny fortress fighting at Mons. Despite a crusade by Commandant Lavau[1] no less strenuous than that of Colonel de Reffye in 1870–71, the French, although sufficiently supplied with Hotchkiss machine guns, made comparatively poor use of

[1] Later in the War, Director of the French Machine Gun School at Vincennes.

their weapons ; and, except in rare instances, failed to dispose them in depth, the cardinal principle in the tactical disposition of machine guns in defence.

The glare of burning villages and houses mounted to the skies, pigmenting the darkening gloom with all the fierce red of which the Flemish Rembrandt was the master. General von Kluck, the German Commander, blundered on, victory within his grasp. At Landrecies, Maroilles, and Le Cateau, the British army, well-nigh exhausted with tramping, greatly reduced in numbers, its men famished with hunger and thirst, stood firm. The British lacerated the German attacks with lead, stretching thousands dead on the fields. The assistance of the French saved this Army from complete annihilation, though the rapidity of the Retreat and the strength of the final stand when men could move no farther, testify to the fact that the first Expeditionary Force was a self-contained force, fighting its own battles in its own way against a gigantic German attack.

Thursday, 27th August, presented battalions reduced from a thousand rifles to not more than two hundred. The superb riflemen so assiduously trained and nurtured had begun to disappear. With the Mons Retreat the tradition of British marksmanship, carried upon a world's battlefields since the days of Crécy, entered its decline. Individual marksmen could not again be trained. There remained few instructors beyond the permanent musketry staffs and Territorial marksmen with whom to instruct a civilian population entirely unused to arms. The factor of time, which of necessity must weigh heavily with generalship, rendered the task quite impracticable. The superb fire-discipline and control exercised by the old regular army had perished with the men who, before they had died or were hopelessly outnumbered, had mown down the storm troops and met machine guns almost on equal terms.

It is always interesting to speculate upon what results might have been achieved had different measures been adopted. The loss of each man from the Expeditionary Force of 1914 implied the loss of a fire-unit absolutely irreplaceable during the whole course of the War. The reduction of the fire-strength by 60 per cent after the first few weeks of war meant that no fire-power of the same consistency and value could again be supplied to replace the casualties. As the men weakened through several weeks of fierce fighting and endless marching, enduring every privation of thirst and hunger, what remained of fire direction and control almost evaporated. The physical capacity to shoot straight was almost extinct.

The characteristics of the machine gun, this " nerveless weapon," clamour for recognition. Its hunger can be assuaged so long as one round of ammunition remains in the belt or limber. Thirst can be slaked from any foul pool, even, as improvised by a battery of the 100th Machine Gun Company which fired one million rounds in the assault upon High Wood on 24th August 1916, from urine. Neither casualties nor utter weariness among the gun teams alter the precision of the weapon. So long as one man remains alive, the Vickers gun will spout its terrible death-dealing stream, as was illustrated many times later by both friend and enemy. Had far more machine guns been available to the British troops and had far more personnel been trained to a standard of excellence equivalent to that of the marksmanship among infantry, the fire-strength of

Sir John French's army would have been enhanced immeasurably.

Fire-power is the factor which wins victories. The characteristics of the machine gun were ideal for the purpose of the British defence, especially against infantry assaults trained to the German system. Machine guns at Mons might have proved almost as effective as they had at Omdurman in 1897. Nevertheless the Maxim gun wrought fearful execution upon the massed ranks of Germans.

Once again during the course of the War, in March and April 1918, the British army, suffering almost unbelievable losses, was forced to retreat before the hammer-blows and newly evolved skilful infiltration tactics of the German armies. It is recorded that one machine gun battalion, the Thirty-Third, holding a front of nearly three miles during the battle of the Lys, almost unaided and then only by a comparatively weak brigade, for five days withstood the repeated assaults of several German divisions.

The characteristics of the machine gun may well be re-emphasized. The first is that of the fixed platform, producing " the nerveless weapon." The factor of human error and of human temperament is almost eliminated. As the result the shots fired are closely grouped. This highly concentrated fire is pre-eminently adapted for surprise effect, while in the crisis of battle, when even the best disciplined troops are inclined to fire wildly, the accuracy of the machine gun remains a constant. Observation of closely grouped shots from one source is very frequently practicable. The dimensions of the effective beaten zones for various ranges have been obtained as the result of careful experimentation and are laid down in the Range Tables

for various types of machine guns. The most satisfactory targets are those which are deep and solid.
Effective fire can be obtained against almost any kind
of target capable of being penetrated by the rifle bullet,
up to a range of between 2500 and 3000 yards, by the
employment of combined sights for depth, and different
aiming-marks for width, or by means of manipulating
the elevating gear for searching in depth and by traversing for width. The fixed platform, too, renders night
firing possible. Guns can be laid by day upon various
points, or, for example, to produce a continuous band
of fire across the front of a position held ; or, alternatively, the guns can be used, both in direct and indirect
fire, with aiming lamps, when in either case the same
results are obtained as in firing by day.

The second characteristic is that of a capacity to
produce with extraordinary rapidity a large volume of
accurate fire. The rate of fire attainable is 500 rounds
per minute, though each burst of fire is ordinarily
limited to about 20 rounds, in order to enable aim to
be checked. This characteristic also enables men to
have more rest, while one man can command any
required target or area for any length of time with far
greater effect than even fifty riflemen.

The third characteristic arises from consideration of
this latter fact. It is that of a narrow front and shallow
depth from which a large volume of fire can be produced.
Six square feet are alone required for the gun and two
operators, Nos. 1 and 2. Two riflemen would occupy
the same space. From this narrow front, reducible to
that of two feet, the machine gun produces a volume of
fire twenty-five to fifty times greater than that of infantry
on the same front. The immense value of machine
guns in enclosed country, to enfilade hedges and roads,

in street fighting, but especially, concealed, to be thrust forward prior to an attack, or to cover a retirement, is sufficiently obvious.

The fourth feature is the all-round traverse provided by the mounting. With the ·303 Vickers Mark IV tripod, the gun can be swung through 180 degrees. A sudden attack from a flank can be met immediately, without movement of the gun position, though concealment may sometimes have to be sacrificed to field of fire. It would be necessary to move infantry over ground, with all the risks involved by casualties and the loss of time involved, in order to obtain the same effect of fire.

The fifth characteristic again is considered in the light of those preceding. It is that of invulnerability. The machine gun in action presents a very small target. The gun and teams are easily concealed and, therefore, difficult to locate. Even if located they are difficult to hit. Moreover, if the gun operators should be hit, they can immediately be replaced by other members of the gun team.

The sixth point is of always increasing importance —mobility. Machine guns with the tripod or sled mounting can move at the same pace as infantry over country of any character. Machine guns are mobile both upon and off the battlefield. Whatever the form of transport, machine guns are more mobile than infantry. The transport is so organized, and so has been since the date that machine guns were first allotted to infantry battalions as part of the establishment, that it is self-contained. The whole of the equipment and a reserve of ammunition is carried in the wagons which form an integral part of the machine gun unit, whether section (platoon), company, or battalion. Machine guns are also as mobile as cavalry. Pack transport can travel wherever cavalry can go.

So soon as machine guns are removed from transport, whether pack, limbered wagons, or mechanized means, they may become less mobile than infantry. Though infantry, rarely cavalry, and in certain circumstances tanks and armoured cars, must be relied upon ultimately to take ground, machine guns, carried into the battle as far as transport will permit, can at once proceed to contribute supporting fire of great volume and intensity over the heads of advancing infantry, reasserting the gun's powers of mobility once the infantry, with rifle, bomb, and automatic rifle, have gained an objective. In battle therefore, whether advancing or retiring, the machine gun's mobility consists of bounds.

The introduction of mechanized means of transport for weapons in battle, a feature which first made its appearance on 15th September 1916 against the Flers Ridge, produced a new kind of mobility for machine guns, twofold in nature. Firstly, guns could be carried in tanks, originally known as the Motor Machine Gun Corps, and later as the Machine Gun Corps (Heavy Section), at a greater speed than that of advancing infantry and across obstacles, such as wire, impassable by them. It must be clearly understood, however, that the *raison d'être* for the conception of the Tank was to provide a weapon capable of destroying German machine guns : in the phrase of the inventor—a "machine gun destroyer." But tank tactics achieved more than this. Secondly, the machine guns carried in tanks were enabled to fight from their means of transport, even on the move. This feature is admirably illustrated from the same battle in which tanks made their first appearance. One tank entered Guedecourt, where it attacked a German field battery, destroying one of the guns. Another rendered great assistance to attacking infantry held up by machine guns and wire. The tank commander placed his machine astride the enemy's trench and enfiladed it with fire. The tank then proceeded along the trench and 300 Germans surrendered and were taken prisoners.

Armoured mechanized transport, therefore, had produced the moving fortress. The idea was born in the mind of Colonel E. D. Swinton.[1] Major T. G. Tulloch, R.A., an original thinker, also, joined the "Sapper." Major Hetherington and Mr. Diplock contributed special features. But the idea was a re-incarnation. In 1482 Leonardo da Vinci, the famous Italian master, so far divorced himself from art to invent a kind of tank. " I am building," he wrote, " secure " and covered chariots which are invulnerable, and " when they advance with their guns into the midst of " the foe even the largest enemy masses must retreat, " and behind them the infantry can follow in safety " and without opposition."

The often repeated assertion that " there is nothing new under the sun " appears to possess its truth. From the very edge of legend it is known that Dionysius of Syracuse produced his Polybolos, the machine gun of the age, though the first trace of the tank is so late as 1482. The speculator might be led to wonder if Daedalus, the " cunning craftsman " of Minos, did not pass on the mysteries of air currents to his son Icarus, who, having learned the art of gliding, finally " crashed " at Cumae in Italy after flying the Ionian Sea !

A wooden " war cart," drawn by horses enclosed

[1] Major-General Sir Ernest Swinton, K.B.E., C.B., D.S.O., Chichele Professor of Military History, Oxford University.

with the wooden armour, was also used by the Scots in the fifteenth century; and a tank was designed for the Crimea, but such a project was abandoned as a barbarity. The history of the Crimean War might perhaps have been very different. If, too, the 93rd Highlanders (the 2nd Bn. Argyll and Sutherland Highlanders), converted into a machine gun unit in 1936, had been armed with machine guns at Balaclava, the famous picture of " The Thin Red Line," by Robert Gibb, would have presented a very different spectacle. The swinging traverse of the machine gun would immediately have despatched the Russian cavalry, against whose flank Captain Ross with such adroit, though difficult, manœuvre, turned victoriously.

Historical speculation must always prove of value. An old idea reincarnated is the fruit of knowledge and re-flexion. History demonstrates that each new invention and tactical manœuvre is promptly met by appropriate counter-measures. The tank produced the anti-tank gun and armour-piercing projectiles. So long as the tank is mobile it will remain a fleeting and difficult target, but once stationary it becomes the objective of every counter-measure until disabled.

Mechanized transport well serves to convey machine guns, personnel, and ammunition, sometimes to enable guns to be brought into action from a moving platform: but it is nevertheless probable that man will be forced to fight upon his feet. Such characteristics as the narrow front, capacity for concealment, and the extra-ordinary invulnerability of the machine gun with its crew, make of them, assisted by mechanized means, a fighting instrument of ever-increasing value.

In 1914 results probably very different from those which would have been attained by a defence with machine guns produced a situation of the utmost gravity for both the Allied cause and especially the British army. The comparatively few trained machine gunners were mostly casualties. The weapons which subsequent events proved could achieve the greatest results at the minimum cost of men and material, for all practical purposes, had become almost non-existent. Practically no records of machine gun achievement during 1914 can be traced. For the most part, the machine gun sections were commanded by junior officers with little experience even of manœuvres. The rare machine gun, taken with great gallantry to the front of the fight, became a conspicuous target and the casualties both among personnel and guns were very high. An illustration of this is provided by the action at Le Maisnil on 21st October 1914. 2nd Lieutenant Liddell [1] (2nd Bn. Argyll and Sutherland Highlanders) brought his guns into action in the corner of a meadow, placing the ammunition wagon behind a house in the village in rear. " At 11.30 A.M.," states the battalion War Diary, " the house behind which the M.G. wagon was " sheltering was struck by shell-fire during a severe " German attack, the horses bolting and the wagon " upset, smashing the rear portion. At 4.0 P.M. the " guns were withdrawn, ammunition failing owing to " the bolting wagon."

In Great Britain, the enormous task of recruiting hundreds of thousands of civilians and of training them in the first elements of the soldier's craft thrust all such considerations as machine guns far into the background. It was taken for granted that the need was

[1] 2nd Lieutenant Aidan Liddell, 3rd (R.) Bn. Argyll and Sutherland Highlanders, transferred to the Royal Flying Corps in 1914. He was the first airman to be awarded the Victoria Cross, and died of wounds.

K

always for man-power. Expert marksmanship had disappeared. In the overwhelming task of organizing whole army corps, no one appears to have suggested that the production of fire-power was the first requisite and that there might be a short cut to it. The recent conflicts on the continent of Europe, especially in Spain, have shown of what high value in war is a trained machine gunner. Well posted, with a fine field of fire, he needs little more than the first requisites of courage, intelligence, strength, and a knowledge of mechanism; and the least possible drill. The fine art of machine gunnery can follow after.

Nevertheless, in France, the overwhelming superiority of German machine gunnery was at once apparent, while, as the high standard of British rifle marksmanship declined, the deficiency in machine gunners became the more apparent. Arising from an after-dinner conversation between one of the owner motor drivers of the volunteer corps hastily improvised to serve the General Staff, and some Staff officers, at the Vincent Restaurant, St. Omer, the headquarters of Sir John French, machine guns were discussed. The driver, C. D'A. Baker-Carr,[1] formerly Captain, the Rifle Brigade, who had served as an Assistant Instructor at the School of Musketry, Hythe, was asked if he would undertake the work of training machine gunners to replace casualties at a school to be established at G.H.Q.

On 2nd December 1914 the school opened at the Caserne d'Abret in St. Omer, and the first students selected as potential instructors after training were sixteen men from the Artists' Rifles (28th Bn. County of London Regiment), already being utilized as an Officers' Training Corps in France. Captain Baker-

---

[1] Afterwards Brigadier C. D'A. Baker-Carr, C.M.G., D.S.O.

Carr, with Quartermaster-Sergeant Instructors Ward and Bloomfield, formed the first staff, the instruments at their disposal being two Maxim guns with four dummy cartridges, borrowed from the 2nd Battalion Royal Irish Regiment. From this germ, within three years, was created a Corps, a new arm of the Service, which by 1917 numbered 159,000 officers and men.

No time was lost in making good the deficiency of trained machine gunners with the Expeditionary Force. On 14th December the first course assembled, consisting of 8 officers and 120 other ranks. By April 1915 the classes had increased for 470 officers and 170 other ranks, and the school was moved to the Benedictine Convent at Wisques, four miles from St. Omer. During May and June, the school was visited by the Prime Minister, Mr. H. H. Asquith, and several of the Senior Commanders of the B.E.F. The 6th July was a memorable day, for Mr. Asquith returned accompanied by Lord Kitchener. One of the early enthusiasts for machine guns had been Captain George Lindsay, Rifle Brigade, who joined the instructional staff at Wisques on 22nd March 1915. On this day a hint was given to him that the War Office contemplated the formation of a Machine Gun Training Corps, an advantage, if not a necessity, which those familiar with machine gunnery had advocated since 1887.

Meanwhile, on the battlefield machine gunners were learning their lessons painfully, though the stationary character of trench warfare during the harsh winter of 1914–15 enabled a reserve of trained machine gunners to be built within each battalion and the Army to be equipped with the ·303 Vickers gun, one which remained as the standard weapon for both infantry and cavalry throughout the whole period of the War upon every front.

Well-trained machine gunners quickly discovered that there was afforded ample opportunity for improving their technique, especially in the matters of night, over-head, and indirect firing, provided by the fixed-position character which the war had assumed. The enemy was unceasingly active, especially at night, sweeping the British parapets with storms of steel, directing bracketing fire upon roads and communications ; and, as it came to be called, " strafing " the assembly points behind the front lines. It was not long before machine gun officers, previously denied the opportunity at Hythe, were engaged upon similar tactical annoyances, a performance known as harassing fire.

In battle, too, the machine gunner who knew his weapon and its tactics was able to cause the German enemy to begin to fear the training which Hythe had first inspired in their own ranks, as is instanced by the following quotation from the " London Gazette " in respect of Captain Ludwick, who was awarded the Distinguished Service Order—" For conspicuous ability " and gallantry as brigade machine gun officer, from " March 10–13, 1915, at Neuve Chapelle. He re- " connoitred the captured positions from end to end " and brought twenty machine guns into position, " which caused an immense number of casualties to " the enemy when they attacked on March 12." The biter bit ! Captain Ludwick had been an Assistant Instructor at the Central School of Musketry in India when the War broke out.

The winter of 1914–15, one of stagnation in water-logged trenches, showed no tactical interest ; and machine gunners were preoccupied in the line with keeping guns clean, out of the line in training reserve men in simple mechanism. Behind the British lines, however, there was considerable activity : while the principal Allies, France and Russia, were also developing their machine gun resources. In February 1915 G.H.Q. had requested that the establishment for the machine gun section should be increased by a further officer, the establishment then being one officer, two sergeants, and 32 other ranks. The War Office, it is said, replied that there was an insufficiency of officers for the purpose.

The number of casualties among machine gun teams in trench warfare was high. The guns, for the most part, were positioned in the front line, often at prominent corners to cover a salient, or in sapheads to cover the line with enfilade fire. When in action, the gun numbers were much exposed behind the gun, assuming the normal position of sighting and firing, and made conspicuous targets. In order to overcome this danger a number of devices were produced, some by those who had actual experience of the gun in action. These inventions were termed hyperscopes and, obviously, corresponded with the periscope, an innovation of trench warfare. Among the hyperscopes tested were the Meissner and Youlton. A cumbersome wooden box with mirrors was produced by the Royal Engineers in the field in some quantities, but was found to be too heavy.

A more original and practical invention was that of Lieutenant G. S. Hutchison, machine gun officer of the 2nd Bn. Argyll and Sutherland Highlanders, who received the " thanks of the Army Council " for his invention. It consisted of a gun-metal prismatic hyperscope, fitted to the tangent sight, enabling a view across the sights, while the head of the firer was held well below the level of the gun. A firing-lever formed part of the arrangement, in order that the gun could be held steady and fired from the same concealed position. The firing-lever could be fixed to the handles and the thumb-piece operating the trigger mechanism, and could be depressed by the action of one hand gripping the lever handle ten inches below the base of the gun. The device was manufactured by private enterprise in Edinburgh, and tested by this officer in the Pentland Hills with machine gunners from the 3rd (Reserve) Battalion of the regiment. It was claimed that the invention, besides contributing cover, also gave a better control of the gun in action, with a clearer punctuation of bursts of fire. It was further urged that for open warfare the device would enable far greater concealment. The specimen hyperscopes made were subsequently used with considerable success in the Somme operations: but the use of other hyperscopes was shortly discontinued, and there was no general adoption of the principle.

A technical difficulty of some importance was that of firing-faults due to stoppages from wet ammunition belts. On 15th May 1915 the Commandant of the Machine Gun School, after the experience of the winter, wrote : " More than 75 per cent of the failures of " machine guns in the trenches during the winter were " ascribed to faults-in-feed owing to wet or damaged " belts. . . . The metal belt should be entirely free " from these defects." Experiments with steel belts had already " proved satisfactory." An order for 3600 belts of 250 rounds had, therefore, been placed on 22nd April, that is, at the rate of 4 belts per gun for the 900 machine guns at this date in France. Very few

seem to have reached the battalions in the line, and, on
22nd June 1916, G.H.Q. ordered the discontinuation
of the issue : and that the establishment of web belts
be raised to 16 per gun, notwithstanding the fact,
incidentally, that Sir Herbert Plumer, commanding
the 2nd Army, had, on 12th April, specifically recom-
mended that the number should be raised to 40 per
gun, the scale allowed by the Germans.

The authority of Mr. Lloyd George, both as
Minister of Munitions and Prime Minister, cannot be
denied, though there have been many who dissent
from the manner of his impeachment of the military
High Command. In his " War Memoirs," Mr. Lloyd
George has much to say on the subject of machine guns,
which he very properly describes as " the most lethal
weapon of the war." He writes : [1]

" How completely the military direction failed to
" appreciate the important part this arm would play
" in the War is shown by the fact that between August
" 1914 and June 1915 four contracts only were placed
" by them with Messrs. Vickers for a total of 1792
" machine guns. This would work out at two machine
" guns per battalion, with none left for training at
" home as provision for machine gun companies and
" no margin for losses or breakages. The first order
" was dated 11th August 1914, and was for 192 guns.
" The second, on 10th September, was for 100. The
" third, dated 19th September, was for 1000, and the
" fourth, a few days later, for another 500. A pro-
" vision in the third contract laid it down that the rate
" of delivery should be 50 guns per week. Only 10 to
" 12 had been the rate specified under the first order.
" The whole 1792 guns were to be delivered by June

[1] " War Memoirs of David Lloyd George," vol. ii. p. 599 *et seq.*

" 1915. In fact, however, only 1022 had been received
" by that date.

" An explanation of the failure of the military
" authorities to realize the importance of this weapon is
" to be sought in the fact that, as one distinguished
" officer wrote : ' The machine gun was regarded by
" the British authorities as a weapon of opportunity
" rather than an essential munition of war.'

" It took our General Staff many months of terrible
" loss to realize the worth of the machine gun."

Mr. Lloyd George quotes from the book by Brigadier-
General C. D'A. Baker-Carr in order to press home the
attack.

Brigadier-General Baker-Carr, the first Commandant of the Machine Gun School established at
St. Omer in 1914, should also be regarded as an authority
with knowledge of facts. He writes : " At that time
" [pre-War] the sole mention of machine guns was
" confined to a dozen lines in the ' Infantry Training
" Manual.' Nobody in authority concerned himself
" with this weapon of enormous potential importance,
" and battalion commanders before the War frankly
" and cordially disliked it.

" ' What shall I do with the machine guns to-day, sir ? '
" would be a question frequently asked by the officer
" in charge on a field day. ' Take the damned things
" to a flank and hide 'em ! ' was the usual reply." [1]
This is, of course, an exaggeration.

After the Machine Gun School had been set up,
Brigadier Baker-Carr records : " Not one single member
" of the Staff of G.H.Q. ever took the trouble to pay
" a visit to the School during the six months that it was

[1] " Notes on the Tactical Employment of Machine Guns and
Lewis Guns," SS. 106, 1916.

" quartered in the Artillery Barracks, a quarter of a
" mile distant from the General Staff Office." Since
Mr. Lloyd George appeared to make a point of this
statement in criticizing the General Staff, it should be
stated that the impeachment is not true. Many officers
of the General Staff did in fact visit the School.

General Baker-Carr makes it plain that, except for
twelve lines of print, there was no other general or
detailed instruction in regard to the tactical uses of
weapons rightly described by Lloyd George as " an
essential munition of war." In March 1916 the General
Staff at G.H.Q. issued its conclusions in a pamphlet
titled " Notes on the Tactical Employment of Machine
Guns and Lewis Guns," the " Introduction " to which
opens with the following paragraph : " The experience
" of the present war has shown that the general prin-
" ciples as regards the employment of machine guns
" laid down in Infantry Training 158-163 are perfectly
" sound, and remain unaltered by the introduction
" of the machine gun company organization. . . . In
" view of the increase in the number of machine guns
" with infantry units, it is most important that all
" commanders should understand thoroughly the main
" principles of their use. These are therefore briefly
" recapitulated in this pamphlet."[1]

The principle upon which there is insistence was
that " The machine gun, to a great extent, is a weapon
" of opportunity," a meaningless definition, which was
not entirely removed even by the Armistice. The
point of absurdity is fully appreciated when it is realized
that success in a fight of any kind is only attained as the
result of making the most of opportunity. The dog

[1] Brigadier-General C. D'A. Baker-Carr, C.M.G., D.S.O., " From
Chauffeur to Brigadier."

seeks for the opening which gives access to the engagement of his rival's throat with the teeth. The boxer feints, parries, side-steps in order to elude his opponent's guard for the knock-out blow : in other words, creates an opportunity. Bayonet, bomb, bludgeon, rifle, field-piece, the heavy gun, are all " weapons of opportunity," to be used when the appropriate opportunity is present. The rifleman engages the sniper, or takes aim at a leader directing an operation. The automatic rifle may engage as its target the density of an infantry group, an excellent opportunity. But the mere fact that an essential characteristic of the machine gun is its capacity for sustained and accurate fire suggests that the description " weapon of opportunity " is misapplied. The word " opportunity " itself suggests a period of time which is fleeting. True, the period when many targets are engaged by machine guns will be of a fleeting character, certainly moving, a circumstance which the fixed platform of the gun is purposely designed to meet. But this usually applies to the use of machine guns with direct fire at the shorter ranges only. In the light of such considerations the description of the machine gun as a weapon of opportunity is almost fantastic, for it implies a suggestion that the machine gun is a weapon which will not be used in the fight unless specially exhorted to action. Thus, in the end, because of the circumstances of battle which had caused guns to drift into a company organization, it was decided that a natural co-ordination and direction should be arbitrarily overruled.

The document further demanded that " The " machine guns that go forward with the attacking " infantry will be under the control of the infantry " commander to whom they are attached. The re-

" maining guns will be under the control of the Machine
" Gun Company Commander who acts under instruc-
" tions from the Brigade Commander. Machine gun
" officers must be acquainted with this principle in
" order to avoid dual control and consequent mis-
" understanding."

It may be suggested that such a "principle"
immediately invited " dual control." The fact that the
machine gun unit consisted both of the gun and its
" transport " was overlooked. The fact, also, that the
infantry commander and the machine gun officer
regarded ground with different eyes was not apparent.
The military arguments for the formation of machine
gun companies had been severely logical. The Notes
issued by the General Staff at this same date were not
only illogical, but were calculated to upset the tactical
organization, control, and direction which the formation
of machine gun companies was specifically designed
to initiate.

The machine gun sections of infantry battalions
had already been joined together during the summer
of 1915, for they had often been in the trenches with
battalions other than their own, under a brigade
machine gun officer. In August 1915, when the
Guards Division was formed, the machine gun sections
of each brigade were joined together into companies,
units with their own commanders and headquarters,
acting under the direct orders of their brigadiers. Such
a system was usual throughout the Expeditionary
Force in France but had little immediate bearing upon
the tactical handling of the guns. The change sim-
plified the administrative problems of supply and
training, but the new problems concerning seniority,
promotion, and reinforcements immediately arose.

A practice of some standing in the Army had been that of what was termed " attached men," that is to say, soldiers lent to specialist groups within the battalion organization, such as pioneers, band, machine gun section, in excess of establishment. Trench warfare imposed duties of so arduous a character upon machine gunners, both in the matter of long periods without relief in the line and in that of carrying heavy loads over great distances of difficult ground, that often from eight to sixteen men per battalion were " attached " to machine gun sections above the War Office establishment of thirty-two men. The men so attached were often those whom infantry company commanders had found to be the least tractable, below the average in physique and intellect, and when machine gun companies were formed these "attached " men presented a difficult problem, for they were not usually of the standard which would make an efficient machine gunner.

The military formations of all countries have always made much of local *esprit de corps*. The British army was never an exception. The Territorial foundation of the Army was a factor of considerable importance to its morale. Both officers and men had the strongest attachments for their own regiments and battalions. A machine gun company organization deprived the personnel of their regimental attachments, while nothing appeared immediately in their place. Though the new organization appealed to their reason, there was no appeal to sentiment: and with the majority of regimental officers and men sentiment weighs more than reason, a factor which has always proved obstructive, unless carefully provided for, to every scheme of Army reform or reorganization.

The Machine Gun Company organization had appeared some months before the Royal Warrant, Army Order No. 416, of 22nd October 1915, had brought the Machine Gun Corps into being as a separate arm of the Service.

Despite the difficulties under which, as "nobody's child," they laboured, however, machine gun companies rendered a good account of themselves. Prior to the battle of Loos in September 1915, the Guards machine gun companies had had but ten days' preliminary training. Their equipment and establishment were yet incomplete. Nevertheless, one brigade machine gun company was successful in action as a unit, in support of the attack of its brigade on Hill 70, with direct overhead fire, using "combined sights." Though such action was in no sense a new development in tactics, it would have been difficult, if not impossible, to arrange under the old system where each infantry battalion controlled one machine gun section. The action was praised both by the Brigadier and the leading Battalion Commander. Beyond this, however, there was no attempt in the co-ordination of machine guns for overhead fire supporting the attacking infantry.

The assault by the 9th (Scottish) Division at Loos included the feature of the greatest tactical importance on the front of the British attack, "Fosse 8." The objectives included such formidable and famous strongholds, also, as the Hohenzollern Redoubt, with its communicating arms, the trenches appropriately named by the British "Big Willie" and "Little Willie." For the attack each of the infantry battalions had four machine guns, while fourteen were "brigaded" in rear of the front line to co-operate with the artillery. This organization was a definite advance in tactical handling, and served as the preface to the more elaborate organized barrages which were a development of 1917. More important, however, was the realization by the Divisional Commander, Major-General G. H. Thesiger, C.B., C.M.G., that to secure the utmost from the potential fire-power of his machine guns, the weapons themselves must be disposed and used in such a manner as to secure this result. He did not make the so frequently repeated error of flinging an unalterable percentage of guns into the forefront of the attack, to keep pace with infantry as best they might, and at once to become the target of the most intense hostile fire; while retaining a further unalterable percentage, the remainder of the guns, in his own hand, inactive, a reserve waiting an " opportunity " which would never present itself.

For the attack by the 9th Division the fourteen machine guns were so organized that, in five minutes following the commencement of the artillery bombardment, the guns were to open intensive fire on hostile communications for thirty minutes. During the night they were to play on the enemy communicating trenches, and on the wire, in order to prevent the Germans from repairing the gaps cut by the artillery fire. On the day of the attack they were to open intensive fire, five minutes after the beginning of the bombardment, for fifteen minutes : they were then to fire deliberately for ten minutes, thereafter resuming intensive fire for other ten. The success of this brigading was fully demonstrated during an action which presented most formidable difficulties to the attacking infantry.

A weakness, however, was the deficiency in automatic rifles, two Lewis guns only being available for each battalion in the attack. The automatic rifle is *par excellence* the weapon most suitable for the engagement of hostile machine gun nests.

After Loos, the establishment of Lewis guns was increased to four per battalion. The ill-success of the Loos offensive is outside the scope of this volume ; but such failure, combined with the replacement of Sir John French by Sir Douglas Haig in supreme command, again thrust the question of machine gun organization into the background.

Before Sir John French left, however, the idea of the Machine Gun Corps had taken shape, and on 22nd October was officially consummated. In November the brigaded machine guns were transformed into companies of the Corps, each bearing the number of the brigade to which it was allotted. Twelve Sergeant-Instructors were sent from the Machine Gun School at Wisques, as a nucleus of the newly formed Machine Gun Training Centre at Grantham. Almost at once thousands of men began to pour into the wooden huts which rapidly spread themselves over Lord Brownlow's parklands at Belton Park. Thousands of horses, mules, and vehicles appeared ; and, within two weeks of wintry rain, the park was submerged beneath a sea of mud. The task of sorting and re-equipping all conditions of men, in every kind of uniform, some holding the rank of sergeant and corporal, from the various New (Kitchener) Army battalions from which they had been drafted, others regular and special reserve soldiers from regimental depots with much machine gun experience, would have tried the patience of a Job.

Moreover, the great majority of officers and men were eager to get " to the front." No doubt about this, whatever. They chafed at delays ; and cases of ill-discipline, which were not infrequent, were due for the most part to the slow progress made in equipping companies for service. The forced inactivity was due, however, to the slow delivery of machine guns. The sudden expansion of a small regular army, with its auxiliaries, to that of millions of men in arms necessarily implied the multiplication of arms upon a scale never previously contemplated, which in itself further implied factory reorganization and the building of plant, manufacture of small tools, and the training of thousands of operatives. All this had to precede the manufacture and issue of machine guns.

The supplies of guns to the Expeditionary Forces had been greatly hurried forward, both to complete establishment and to replace losses, following that tardiness due to lack of, factories and machinery of which Mr. Lloyd George has provided the evidence. It may here be suggested that industrial equipment for war is not the function of the soldier, but of the statesman. The demands, moreover, of the Royal Flying Corps, itself being expanded as rapidly as possible, meant also that the supply of available machine guns was being continually diverted from the Army to meet the needs of the air.

Prior to the War, it had been considered that the education of the trained officer or man was a matter of years : the training of a machine gunner, certainly that of two years. At Grantham, trained machine gunners were produced within six weeks, though it cannot be asserted that the degree of training was high. Mechanically, they were proficient. In the use of ground, map-reading, in machine gun mathematics, and in the technical use of instruments essential to all but direct fire at short range, they were, on the other hand, almost

Imperial War Museum

IN A SHELL-HOLE POSITION

Imperial War Museum

A DEFENSIVE POSITION IN THE EAST

entirely deficient, their minds often muddled by a smattering of knowledge from a training curriculum which may have looked well on paper, but which had far too little regard for the practical needs of popular education.

Considering the chaos which prevailed at Grantham during its first weeks of life as the Machine Gun Training Centre, almost a miracle was performed in the production of completely equipped machine gun companies, personnel, guns, transport. On 18th September 1915, Major G. M. Lindsay had left the Machine Gun School at Wisques to assume duty as Senior Staff Officer at the Machine Gun Training Centre at Grantham. A forceful personality, with imagination, George Lindsay succeeded in impressing others with his energy. The administrative officers available at home for the most part were drawn from the ranks or retired officers, past the age of active military service ; popularly known as " dugouts." Devoted and earnest as no doubt were such officers, their habits were most often set in a groove, their ideas of military organization out of date, their notions of discipline not at all suited to the leadership of a civilian in arms. A storm of resentment not unnaturally frequently followed, and it was left to George Lindsay to ride the storm.

Not only were large drafts of trained officers and men sent continuously overseas, but the progress of forming and equipping new companies began to go steadily forward. In March 1916, at the newly formed Machine Gun Corps Base Reinforcement Depot established at Camiers, there were only six men available as reinforcements from which to supply the machine gun companies in the field in replacement of casualties.

L

Within one week drafts at the rate of 500 men began to arrive from Grantham. By June the number of men at the depot had increased to 1800 : while the school had been transferred from Wisques to St. Cecile Plage hard by. Every brigade with the Expeditionary Forces was completed to the establishment of its machine gun company, with ample reserves of men, guns, and transport.

In short, within six months a complete arm of the Service, a new Corps, the Machine Gun Corps, with a strength of some 4000 officers and over 80,000 other ranks, had been created, destined to advance the science of machine gunnery beyond the practice of any other army in the world, and which was to be the model, technically and tactically, upon which every other army was to be fashioned.

The Machine Gun Corps was about to be submitted to the acid test of battle.

CHAPTER VII

MACHINE GUNS IN ATTACK
1916

German tactical dispositions — The Lewis " gun " — Automatic
rifles considered—British and German use of small arms compared—Advent of tanks—Abyssinia and Spain, 1937, instanced
—Important French G.Q.G. memorandum—Sir Henry Rawlinson's memorandum, May 1916—Battle of the Somme—Experience of the Guards in the Somme offensive—Co-ordination
of arms for the infantry assault—Eye-witness account of the
first attack on High Wood—The experience of Gallipoli—
Officers of Machine Gun Corps not specially selected for
aptitude—The battle of Arras—Surprise illustrated—Canadians
as pioneers—Existence of Canadian organization—Beginning of
barrage fire—Tasks of organization.

DURING the year 1915 there were no notable developments in machine gunnery. The Machine Gun Corps
had been proved in October : and the period was one
of factory organization to meet the demands of the Army
and of intensive training both at home and in the field.
Neuve Chapelle, Ypres, and Loos were battles fought
without any fresh machine gun organization or change
in tactical handling.

Germany had not formed a Machine Gun Corps—
there was no need—but had rapidly increased the
number of her machine gun units, acting independently
from the regimental (brigade) companies which formed

part of the establishment. These units (Maschinen-gewehr Scharfschützen) were numbered as detachments (Abteilungen) in rotation. Prior to the battle of the Somme, 1916, the independent units had been organized in sections (Feldmaschinengewehrzüge), normally with six guns.

The independent companies, as it is simpler to call them, were at the disposal of army group commanders, and served to reinforce the regimental machine gun organization. As a general principle in trench opera-tions, the German attack was divided into three phases. The first wave conducted the assault and pushed on to its final objective. The second was called the " clearing wave," its duties being to protect the flanks of the assault and " to ensure the consolidation and retention " of the captured position. The most essential necessity " to secure the captured position is to install machine " guns as soon as possible. The third wave may be " accompanied or followed by fatigue parties carrying " up material for the consolidation of the captured " position." [1]

So soon as the Germans were aware that the British attack on the Somme was in active preparation, the most careful examination of machine gun dispositions was made. Regimental sectors were divided into three sub-sectors, as with the British infantry brigade. Guns were allotted to, and disposed in, these sub-sectors in positions commanding the wire obstacles and for oblique, flanking fire. It was recognized that the British bombardment would pulverize the front trench system, but after the attack was launched that there

---

[1] " Principles governing the execution of the infantry attack in trench warfare, in combination with other arms," 10th Bavarian Division, 11th May 1916.

would be an interval, no doubt of very short duration, between the moment at which the artillery barrage lifted and the time at which the attacking infantry would reach their objective.[1] Momentary as would be this interval, it was perceived to be vital. An order laid down the principle governing defensive machine gun action and the siting of emplacements, which proved to be the key to the German defence when the British attack developed on 1st July. The order affirmed : " When siting machine guns in the front line, " it must be remembered that it is possible for the " enemy in attack on a large scale to force an entrance " into the front line before the machine guns can come " into action. This can only be avoided by siting the " emplacement not on the parapet but *behind* the parados " of the front line : this method at the same time " affords a much better field of fire. In addition, owing " to the feeling of safety which this position inspires, " the men will work their gun with more coolness and " judgment than if the gun were sited on the parapet. " Underground cover for machine guns so placed may " be afforded by providing an ordinary infantry dugout " with an underground passage having its exit behind " the parados."

In accord with this plan deep dugouts were constructed, with a passage-way leading to emplacements, carefully camouflaged against aerial observation. The scheme worked to perfection. Though the German lines were smashed almost beyond recognition, these fastnesses remained secure. Nor must the watchful heroism of the German machine gunners be forgotten.

[1] It should here be noted that British attack operation orders had always defined the advance as " at a steady pace." The New Armies especially should have been impressed with the idea of " advancing in rushes."

The failure of the British attack along two-thirds of a twenty-mile front, with only partial success elsewhere, was due to the vigilance of the sentries and to the perfect timing of exit from the dugout and to mounting guns in action. In some cases, where the rear exits had been blown in, the machine gunners, with the highest courage, rushed their weapons in advance of the trench and brought a destructive fire to bear upon the advancing waves of British infantry.

It is important to note that, although possessed of great numbers of machine guns, all sufficient for the purpose, no attempt was made by the Germans on 1st July to co-ordinate those disposed in support and reserve positions for indirect overhead fire. The probability is that had such measures been adopted the British casualties would have been even heavier, while reserves, massed as they were, and transport roads, would have been subjected to fire which might well have proved annihilating. It was not until late in 1917 that the Germans seriously organized machine guns for barrage fire. Indeed, such a development within the German army is rather a post-War concept, and at no period during the War did the Germans organize machine gun batteries on the scale or for the objectives of the British technique.

Against the German machine gun positions sited so carefully, so well protected by wire, and held with such intelligent tenacity, ground could only be won by infantry at enormous cost in casualties and of shell-fire. The only alternative, as was proved, was to dig in, sap, and leap forward, here and there, by localized attacks with limited objectives. Such a policy had, from the first, been favoured by Sir Henry Rawlinson, commanding the Fourth Army, upon which fell the brunt of the attack in the Somme operations. Such a method of advance, however, clearly was not calculated to achieve a " break through " to new horizons and to favour the exploitation of the cavalry arm, the idea which seems to have preoccupied the mind of the Commander-in-Chief.

The British machine gun companies, organized as a separate corps for the first time on a large offensive scale, achieved all that was possible and at high cost in casualties. As a corps, a distinct arm, possessed of a weapon with unique characteristics, machine gunners failed to establish their technique and to develop the remarkable attack potentiality of their weapon ; this was postponed until 1917 and often later, owing to misunderstanding and misconceptions as to its use by brigade and higher commanders. On the formation of the Machine Gun Corps, the Chief of the Imperial General Staff had issued a memorandum, dated 6th October 1915, which expressed this misconception. It went further, and seems to imply a doubt as to the wisdom of the new organization. " I suppose it is " realized," he wrote, " that there is a great responsi- " bility in confining the battalions to the use of the " Lewis gun, which is a comparatively new pattern of " gun, only supplied to supplement the provision of " the Vickers gun."

The Lewis gun, so called, was an automatic rifle, with a role of its own, prescribed by its nature. To infantry, such a weapon, if its tactical uses were properly understood, was an asset of priceless value in the hands of scouts and skirmishers. Its " hammer blow " effect would have proved paralysing to the German machine gun posts. At the risk of a few casualties from our own shell-fire, automatic rifles should have been pushed boldly out into No Man's Land in front of the British " jumping off " positions, with orders to bring fire to bear upon the German machine guns as soon as they appeared.   Such is the true and invaluable role of automatic rifles in the attack.   The interval of time between the lifting of the artillery barrage and the moment when German machine guns could be withdrawn from their sanctuary and mounted with safety was of a few fleeting minutes, indeed a period to be calculated in seconds.

Only infantry could gain ground.   To make possible the advance of infantry in such circumstances required that some weapon, dominant in its fire-power, readily mobile, extremely accurate at short range, capable of being handled by one man and easily concealed, should be available to fill in the gap between the lifting of the artillery barrage and the moment at which the *arme blanche* could be used.   The machine gun could not, except in rare circumstances, be used for this purpose, for it possessed insufficient mobility once removed from wheeled, pack, or mechanical transport, required two and more men to its service, and usually could not be easily concealed.   Nevertheless, in many cases, higher commanders were apt to think of the Lewis automatic rifle as a " gun," " to supplement the provision of the Vickers gun," when a closer consideration of the characteristics and functions of the two weapons would have made plain the tasks favourable to two vitally different weapons.

During March and April 1918 the Germans had fully developed the " infiltration tactics."   The infantry advance was preceded by a screen of automatic rifles (light machine guns) thrust forward with the utmost boldness, accompanied by snipers.   It was the first duty of the " storm troops " who formed the personnel to engage and destroy hostile machine gun nests, without which the infantry could not advance, and, in consequence, ground could not be gained. The tactics were eminently successful, and failed only where British machine guns, disposed in depth, were organized both for direct flanking and indirect barrage fire by batteries, a technique of fire application still both novel and devastating to the German infantry advance.

In July 1916 the British had yet to learn how to co-ordinate automatic rifle with machine gun fire. Failure in co-ordination persisted until the Armistice. The automatic rifle should have served as the counter to the machine gun. The latter should have been grouped in the first stage as batteries organized to break the power of enemy resistance, the soul of which is the counter-attack, which requires the capacity to mass. In the second stage, the machine guns would have been advanced, after the objective had been attained, for the purpose of consolidating the position and preventing the ground gained from being re-won.

In war, it may be said that weapons " cancel one another out." There must, however, be clarity of thought. Heavy artillery may destroy field-pieces by counter-battery work: it is more probable, however, that artillery will be forced to abandon their positions by the advance of infantry, these positions becoming either technically useless or untenable due to coming within range of the machine gun barrage or to fear of loss of the field-pieces themselves. The counter to the tank may be a tank, but bombing aircraft, artillery, or the anti-tank weapon designed for the purpose are perhaps better. Similarly, the counter to the machine gun is not usually the machine gun. Sometimes it will be aircraft, sometimes artillery, often tanks, and at closer ranges the automatic rifle. In 1918 the German infiltration tactics, wherein light machine guns (automatic rifles) engaged British machine guns, were successful in disposing of the forward guns not already knocked out by bombardment, and thus enabling the infantry to advance, but they were not successful in breaking down the destructive fire of machine gun batteries, utilizing indirect overhead fire, wherever they were organized with a preconceived and carefully prepared co-ordinated barrage plan. The German advance was facilitated, because they utilized the automatic rifle to its fullest advantage in countering British machine guns. The advancing infantry were not met, except in rare circumstances, with barrage machine gun fire from the greatest number of available weapons, disposed on selected ground and possessed of well-tried defensive plans.

Where the weapons on both sides are evenly matched only the higher technique, boldness, and retention of power to manœuvre will ultimately contribute predominance to one side or to the other.

A superior strategy is the first contribution to victory. Tactical efficiency must add to the favourable chances so produced. Conversely, the inferior tactical use of weapons diminishes the advantage of a superior strategy. It may be claimed that Ludendorff's strategy in the spring of 1918 was ill-devised, aggravated as it was by curious vacillations of mind, yet the superior tactical use of weapons came near to contributing a decisive German victory.

For the most part, notably in the Fifth Army,[1] the

---

[1] Compare 'The development of the German defensive battle in 1917, and its influence on British defence tactics,' by Captain G. C. Wynne, "Army Quarterly," April 1937.

British machine guns were disposed in front-line positions, allocated often to infantry battalions in line : and there they remained until overwhelmed, or ran short of ammunition, while the infantry lines were withdrawn from one position to another. The rear guns were seldom utilized at all : nor were they even planned to function within any defensive scheme. They should have been disposed in depth for the dual purpose of direct and barrage fire, in the first instance arranged as the framework of the defence, invulnerable except to automatic rifles handled with intrepid skill ; and as the second object, arranged in batteries, for the purpose of bringing long-range barrage fire purposed to prevent the enemy from massing for the attack, and gaining ground behind his infiltration screen. In fact, the higher staffs had arranged for a defence in depth certainly in some sectors, but it appears that in the rapidity of the retreat reserve positions were overlooked, or had not been notified to machine gun battalion commanders.

Up till the late summer of 1918, although technically not so efficient as British machine gunnery, the German continued to control the battlefield with his use of small-arm weapons, especially the machine gun. Failure fully to exploit machine guns and automatic rifles is perhaps remarkable in view of a memorandum written by Lieutenant-General Sir William Robertson in August 1915, after the conferences which preceded the formation of the Machine Gun Corps. He wrote : " The experience of the present campaign has proved " that the effect of machine gun fire is greatly enhanced " both in offence and defence by the employment " of a number of guns in co-operation in accordance " with a definite tactical plan." Yet, when such cohesion was a vital necessity to the conditions of attack or defence, as a result of confusion of thought as to the nature, and therefore the tactical handling of two different weapons designed for different tactical duties, all sense of "co-operation in accordance with "a definite tactical plan" was permitted to vanish. For lack of plan, and in order to make use of machine guns, they were therefore "attached" to infantry battalions, with no clear idea as to their purpose or use. This may have resulted from the doubt later expressed by the C.I.G.S. already quoted.

The advent of tanks scarcely changed the situation. The service rendered by tanks, upon favourable ground, in enabling the advance of infantry by breaking through barbed-wire entanglements and holding in check or sometimes obliterating machine gun nests was at the outset of considerable magnitude. The tank weapon came as a surprise; and, as such, until counter-measures were adopted, proved formidable and awe-inspiring. Paucity of numbers unfortunately destroyed a surprise which might have proved overwhelming. Soon, however, the tank provoked its counter-measures, the anti-tank rifle, impassable obstacles, and the use of the field gun in advanced positions. With the rapid growth of the tank, armoured car and tractor in all armies since the War, counter-measures have been provided. The invulnerability and astonishing mobility of the tank remains its chief asset. When, however, battle is joined it seems that infantry, armed with the machine gun, again must dominate the battlefield.

The Italian campaign in Abyssinia, 1936, demonstrates that grand-scale mechanization contributes special problems, not the least being the need for armies of road-makers and large concentrations of fuel

and other supplies. The Spanish War, 1937, notably
the operations before Madrid, similarly is an illustration
of European war conducted for the first time on a
mechanized basis, with comparative equality of weapons
on both sides, aided considerably by the aerial bombing.
It has been shown at Toledo, Oviedo, and Madrid that,
as in the Great War, tanks and other mechanized
weapon devices are an adjunct to the infantry battle,
formidable in leading the attack and counter-attack;
but that the actual capture and retention of ground
depends upon foot soldiers armed with machine guns
and automatic rifles. The human factor remains. The
repeated bombing of the city of Madrid and other
centres has inflicted comparatively few casualties even
if the destruction of property has been great, a result
equally damaging to both sides of the contest. It has
not even succeeded in shaking the morale of the civil
population, nor are Spaniards usually credited with
the stoicism of the peoples of more northerly latitudes.
But the use of one machine gun upon a procession in
Madrid spread widespread alarm and precipitated the
revolution. Machine guns in defence of the Alcazar
defied the attack for long months, and enabled the
siege to be raised. Machine guns held beleaguered
Oviedo for long weeks ; and, even in the hands of mere
novices, often with little zeal for the fight, frustrated
continued attacks upon Madrid city for week after week
by regular Spanish, Moorish, and Italian troops.

In estimating, therefore, the tactical application of
the machine gun to the Somme battlefield, it must be
recognized that the Germans in defence fully exploited
the weapon for direct fire, organizing their defences,
even in the most adverse and exacting circumstances,
so as to permit machine guns to develop their fullest

powers as short-range, direct-fire, nerveless weapons. The secondary and in some circumstances most important role of the machine gun as a barrage weapon, augmenting, and often superseding, artillery, was not developed. The British, generally, had so far failed to diagnose the case for the use of the machine gun in attack, although the configuration of ground, throughout the whole area of the Somme battle, was pre-eminently suitable to machine gun operations. Pre-War manœuvre ideas of "attaching" machine guns to attacking battalions continued to dominate the minds of the General Staff, so that the closer co-operation for which primary purpose the Machine Gun Corps was formed was made non-effective. The machine guns were not exploited in accordance with their real capacity and characteristics. Confusion of thought as between automatic rifles and machine guns placed both at a disadvantage, and largely negatived such fruitful action as would without doubt have ensued from their rightly considered tactical exploitation.

The result of this failure to harmonize the two weapons was illustrated by the mounting casualties among infantry. True though it is that ground can only finally be gained and consolidated by infantry, there can be no advance unaccompanied by immense losses unless the fullest tactical preparations are made to enable that advance. Machine guns are the framework of defence. Unless and until they are either destroyed or held in check, the infantry advance is impossible, of which the complete failure before Gommecourt Park is a tragic illustration. Pre-eminently the weapon designed for this purpose is the automatic rifle : while the weapon which is best adapted to prevent an enemy massing for the counter-attack,

Imperial War Museum

BULGARIAN MACHINE GUNNERS IN ACTION NEAR
MONASTIR

Imperial War Museum

ITALIAN MACHINE GUNNERS IN ACTION

the very soul of defence, is the machine gun. Given freedom of movement upon the battlefield, also, the machine gun can render invaluable services in sustaining the infantry attack and in protecting its flanks. Advanced with boldness, immediately after the infantry have gained ground and occupied a position, machine guns become the framework of the defence against the counter-attack.

In 1915 the French Grand Quartier Général des Armées had published a memorandum which previsaged these conclusions with remarkable clarity. This document ran : " Machine guns, acting solely by " fire, can prepare an attack or repulse an offensive, " but cannot actually gain ground. This role almost " always rests with the infantry, the only arm which is " capable of moving across all obstacles.

" Machine gun fire produces a dense, deep but " narrow cone of fire. By increasing the traverse, the cone " becomes wider, but owing to loss of density, the effect " produced is lessened." The grouping of machine guns in companies " fosters co-operation and *esprit de* " *corps*. Machine gun companies are not only adminis-" trative organizations, but also tactical units." [1]

It is for this last reason that the grouping of machine guns in batteries began to dominate machine gun thought. Such batteries operated a technique of fire based upon plans of mathematical precision, by the expedient of interlacing cones of fire, ensuring that the effect shall not be lessened.

In March 1916, G.H.Q. itself produced a memorandum (SS. 106), showing striking verbal parallelisms with the French document which had preceded it. It was stated that " The experience of the present war

[1] " Emploi tactique des mitrailleuses."

" has shown that the general principles as regards the
" employment of machine guns laid down in Infantry
" Training (158-163) are perfectly sound, and remain
" unaltered by the introduction of the machine gun
" company organization. . . . Machine guns, acting
" solely by fire, can prepare an attack or repulse an
" offensive, but cannot actually gain ground. This
" role always rests with the infantry, the only arm which
" is capable of moving across all obstacles."

While a doubt existed as to the value and correct
use of the machine gun in attack, it was generally agreed
that the machine gun was the supreme weapon in
defence. By January 1918, however, G.H.Q. had
entirely altered its view. " Next to the artillery," ran
the vital memorandum (SS. 192, January 1918), " the
" machine gun is the most effective weapon employed in
" modern war, and against troops in the open at suitable
" ranges it is proportionately even more effective than
" artillery. . . . The distinguishing feature of modern
" machine gunnery is its offensive power. . . . Modern
" machine gunnery has reversed this passive tendency."

The " Official History of the War," " 1916," vol. i.,
lays down that " The main features of the theory of
" assault, the co-operation of infantry and artillery, was
" well understood by Corps and Divisional Staffs." It is
clear that in the theory of assault the role of machine guns
and automatic rifles had received insufficient attention.

Sir Henry Rawlinson's monumental memorandum of
35 pages, published in May 1916, under the sub-section
dealing with the " Equipment of Machine and Lewis
Guns," opens with the paragraph :

" The different characteristics of the two types of auto-
" matic firing weapons must be thoroughly appreciated
" before the tactical handling can be rightly determined.

" (a) The Lewis gun is an automatic rifle, very
" light, easily carried . . . not capable of sus-
" tained fire. . . .

" (b) The machine gun (Maxim or Vickers) . . .
" comparatively heavy to carry and conspicuous
" when being carried . . . capable of sustained
" fire . . . now part of the brigade, and not
" battalion, organization. . . .

" (c) Many instances have been brought to notice
" in which our infantry assault has been arrested
" by the fire of hostile machine guns which have
" escaped the previous bombardment. Even if
" accurately located, it has been found very
" difficult to bring sufficiently accurate artillery
" fire to bear on them, and so knock them
" out.

" The Lewis gun, owing to its lightness and
" invisibility, may provide the solution to this
" problem. It is suggested that Lewis gunners,
" either under cover of darkness, smoke, or
" artillery bombardment, may be able to creep
" out into No Man's Land and establish them-
" selves in advance of our assaulting troops in
" saps, shell-holes, ditches, crops, long grass,
" etc. From these positions, where it will be
" difficult for them to be detected, they will be
" able to fire on enemy emplacements, loop-
" holes, and parapets generally, and so assist the
" infantry to advance. . . .

" Some machine guns may also be usefully
" employed to search the enemy's communica-
" tion trenches by means of overhead fire from
" the rear. . . .

" The tactical training of all Lewis gun

M

" detachments and machine gun companies
" should be carried out with the above principles
" of tactical handling in view."

No more sound doctrine for the employment of automatic rifles and machine guns could have been advocated.
Yet, in scarcely any instance is there a record of effect
being given to these well-considered instructions, which
remain as the guiding principles for the tactical
handling of Vickers and Lewis, or Bren " guns."   On
the contrary, the two weapons continued to be regarded
as identical, the Lewis being but a lighter form of the
heavy gun in considered terms.   The Fourth Army
Commander laid down a tactical policy subsequently so
successfully developed by the Germans in 1918 under
the name of " infiltration tactics."

The question at once arises why these principles,
as formulated vital to the success of offensive operations, were not incorporated both into the training
of brigades and divisions, and into the tactical scheme
of operations themselves.   In the training schedules of
the time, there is no trace of any orders and schemes
wherein machine gun companies with the infantry
battalions of their brigades conducted combined tactical
schemes, though there was ample opportunity, both
prior to the opening of the battle and later, when the
wisdom of General Rawlinson's memorandum had been
more fully demonstrated by tangible proofs.   Nor is
there any evidence of any conferences, Army, Corps,
Divisional, whereat the special role of machine guns
and automatic rifles could be carefully discussed among
and explained to infantry and machine gun commanders.

The experience of the Guards machine gun
companies at the battle of the Somme is characteristic

of what was the usual practice. "The role assigned to
" the machine gunners," writes a former officer of the
Guards Machine Gun Regiment,[1] "was simply to con-
" solidate the objective when reached and to resist the
" inevitable counter-attack. Little was said of the
" possibility of their assisting the attack by covering
" fire. Machine gun sections were allotted to each
" infantry wave ; they were to advance by more or less
" definite routes and establish themselves at more or
" less definite points on the different objectives. There
" were no machine gun sections actually in the leading
" waves, but they followed close upon support. Train-
" ing on these lines was a simple form of drill, which
" left nothing to individual initiative."

Writing of the attack upon the Flers Ridge, battle
of the Somme, Major Wright continues : " On 15th
" September, this method of attack was adopted. The
" results of the attack made by one brigade were
" glorious but disastrous. A large number of machine
" gun teams got forward into the leading waves of the
" infantry where they were exposed and defenceless.
" Half the guns of the Company were put out of action
" and all the officers became casualties. Such teams as
" survived with their guns got into useful positions and
" were able to give a good account of themselves in
" keeping down hostile movement and assisting the
" advance of the division on the right by covering fire,
" but the casualties suffered were out of all proportion
" to advantages gained or casualties inflicted. In
" another brigade there were fewer machine gun teams
" involved in the attack, but their experience was a
" similar one and they achieved their results with a

[1] 'Machine Gun Tactics and Organization,' by Major R. M.
Wright, M.C., " The Army Quarterly," January 1921.

" heavy proportion of casualties. The second attack,
" made by the Division on the 25th September, taught
" the same lesson less cruelly, for machine gun company
" commanders were allowed more discretion in getting
" guns forward and they did not try to take trenches
" before the infantry had established itself in the
" position. It was made clear once and for all in these
" two days that, however definite the infantry plan
" might be, machine gun sections could not move
" forward with the infantry in accordance with a fixed
" time-table until it was known that the enemy's
" infantry and machine guns had been overpowered.
" . . . Machine gunners must not be tied too closely
" to the infantry they accompany and their commander
" must be allowed some latitude in choosing time and
" route for his advance, in order to avoid exposing his
" guns either to the weight of the artillery barrage, or to
" direct machine gun and rifle fire at close range."

The casualties among machine gunners on the
Somme were abnormally high. Undoubtedly, this was
the direct result of the tactics adopted. The problem
of how to employ machine guns in offensive operations
had yet to be solved.

The greater problems of how to co-ordinate riflemen—scouts, skirmishers, snipers ; automatic riflemen—the spear-point of attack ; bombers, bayonets—
the main infantry assault ; machine gunners—massed
fire-power and the foil to the counter-attack—had
scarcely been considered in the light of the potentiality
of the various weapons and their use upon ground.
The co-ordination of machine gun fire with that of
artillery was as yet beyond imagination.

The Germans, who, after the opening of the bombardment on 23rd June, erected notice boards on their

parapets, were realists—" Come on. We are ready for you " was the welcome from the machine gunners. Within three hours the 8th Division had lost 218 out of 300 officers, and 5274 out of 8500 men who had gone " over the top." This division was opposed by the 180th German Infantry Regiment, who only momentarily failed in holding any part of their line, while the total losses of this regiment amounted to no more than 8 officers and 273 other ranks, killed, wounded, and missing. Colonel Boraston, Lord Haig's first biographer, who served as his Private Secretary at G.H.Q., records : " the events of 1st July bore out " the conclusions of the British Higher Command and " amply justified the tactical methods employed." Sir Douglas Haig, in fact, saw every part of the battlefield, except the sector where the 8th Division was engaged, a remarkable fact though failure was widespread.

An eye-witness account of a typical action on the Somme graphically describes the first attack on High Wood on the morning of 15th July 1916 :

" In the early morning, under cover of a thick mist, " the 100th Brigade was deployed in the valley some " eight hundred yards west of High Wood. A heavy " dew was on the ground and hung like pearls upon " each blade of grass. After the turmoil of the pre- " ceding night an eerie stillness pervaded the atmo- " sphere. No shot was heard, except in faint echo from " the flank.

". . . I, with my Company, was deployed behind " the Glasgow Highlanders, which with the 16th King's " Royal Rifles was to lead the assault upon the wood. " By 8.30 A.M. the Brigade had deployed into position " and lay down in the long grass awaiting the signal to " assault, timed for an hour later. . .

" I looked up suddenly. The mist was clearing,
" rising rapidly. The sun peered through, orange and
" round, topping the trees of High Wood. Then its
" rays burst through the disappearing mists, and all the
" landscape, hitherto opaque and flat, assumed its
" stereoscopic vivid form. The wood seemed quite
" near, just above us up the hillside. . . . The village
" of Martinpuich, jagged ruins and rafters all askew,
" broken walls and shattered fruit trees, looked down.
" . . . From my cover I scanned the landscape. Not
" a shot was fired. The men crouching in the grass must
" be visible to watchful observers in the wood, but all
" remained quiet. I glanced down at my watch. Ten
" minutes to go : the attack was timed for 9.0 A.M. . . .

" A wind seemed to stir the grass. . . . I raised my
" head as the Highlanders rose to their feet, bayonets
" gleaming in the morning sun. My eyes swept the
" valley—long lines of men, officers at their head in
" the half-crouching attitude which modern tactics
" dictate, resembling supplicants rather than the van-
" guard of a great offensive, were moving forward over
" three miles of front. As the attackers rose, white
" bursts of shrapnel appeared among the trees and thinly
" across the ridge towards Martinpuich.

" For a moment the scene remained as if an Alder-
" shot manœuvre. Two, three, possibly four seconds
" later an inferno of rifle and machine gun fire broke
" from the edge of High Wood, from the tops of its
" trees, and from all along the ridge to the village. The
" line staggered. Men fell forward limply and quietly.
" The hiss and crack of bullets filled the air and skimmed
" the long grasses. The Highlanders and Riflemen
" increased their pace to a jog-trot. Those in reserve
" clove to the ground more closely.

" Looking across the valley to my left flank I could
" see men of the 1st Queen's passing up the slope to
" Martinpuich. Suddenly they wavered and a few of
" the foremost attempted to cross some obstacles in the
" grass. They were awkwardly lifting their legs over
" a long wire entanglement. Some two hundred men,
" their Commander at their head, had been brought to
" a standstill at this point. A scythe seemed to cut
" their feet from under them, and the line crumpled
" and fell, stricken by machine gun fire. . . . Up the
" slope before me, the line of attack had been thinned
" now to a few men, who from time to time raised
" themselves and bounded forward with leaps and
" rushes. . . .

" My orders were to move forward in close support
" of the advancing waves of Infantry. I called to my
" Company, and section by section in rushes we were
" prepared to move forward. As we rose to our feet
" a hail of machine gun bullets picked here an individual
" man, there two or three, and swept past us.

" On my right, an officer commanding a section had
" perished and all his men, with the exception of one
" who came running towards me, the whole of the front
" of his face shot away. On my left two other sections
" had been killed almost to a man, and I could see the
" tripods of the guns with legs waving in the air, and
" ammunition boxes scattered among the dead.

" With my runner I crept forward among the dead
" and wounded, and came to one of my guns mounted
" for action, its team lying dead beside it. I seized the
" rear leg of the tripod and dragged the gun some yards
" back to where a little cover enabled me to load the
" belt through the feed-block. To the south of the
" wood Germans could be seen, silhouetted against

" the sky-line, moving forward. I fired at them and
" watched them fall, chuckling with joy at the technical
" efficiency of the machine. . . .

" The attack of the Rifles and Highlanders had
" failed : and of my own company but a few remained.
" My watch showed that by now it was scarcely ten
" o'clock. . . . A new horror was added to the scene
" of carnage. From the valley between Pozières and
" Martinpuich a German field battery had been brought
" into action, enfilading the position. I could see the
" gunners distinctly. At almost point-blank range they
" had commenced to direct shell-fire among the
" wounded. . . . Anger, and the intensity of the fire,
" consumed my spirit, and not caring for the con-
" sequences, I rose and turned my machine gun upon
" the battery, laughing loudly as I saw the loaders fall.
" I crept forward among the Highlanders and Riflemen,
" spurring them to action, giving bullet for bullet,
" directing fire upon the machine gun nests, whose red
" flashes and wisps of steam made them conspicuous
" targets. . . ." [1]

That tragic story amply illustrates how lines of
British infantry were flung against well-posted German machine guns, and in what manner machine
guns were mishandled. No provision was made for
covering fire. Even upon this ground might machine
guns, but especially automatic rifles, have been thrust
forward under cover of darkness to hold in check
and destroy the enemy machine guns so soon as they
revealed themselves. The British machine gunners,
with their nerveless weapons, so vital to the exhausted
troops, after the attack, in holding the position won

[1] Lieutenant-Colonel G. S. Hutchison, D.S.O., M.C., "Warrior,"
pp. 127-136.

against counter-attack, were deprived of their preliminary task in providing covering fire ; were then
exhausted, and hopelessly and purposelessly reduced in
strength by being sent forward with the first waves of
the attack before any ground had been gained.   This
was typical of what was done throughout the operations.
There were, however, gleams of sanity, if crudely
displayed, such as was illustrated by the same machine
gun company (100th) a month later.[1]

Meanwhile, in another sphere the last story of the
grim record of Gallipoli had been written.   The
Turkish machine guns had swept hundreds of British
soldiers to their death during the landing on the
beaches ; and it will be remembered that machine guns
are seldom destroyed by artillery fire.   But, on the other
hand, the Australian Official Historian, Dr. C. E. W. Bean,
in his careful and detailed story, records how the great
Turkish counter-attack of 19th May 1915 at Anzac was
largely repelled by machine guns : and of how the
dust whipped up by the Australian and New Zealand
machine gun bullets followed the retreating Turks in small
clouds along the parapets of the crowded communication trenches.   The second great Turkish counter-
attack of the 10th August on Chunuk Bair was solely
extinguished by the New Zealand guns at the Apex.[2]

No high military authority at Gallipoli seems to have
informed the War Office that the decisive factor in
offensive warfare was the machine gun.   The more the
student examines ground and maps and dispositions,
the more overwhelming appears this contention as
applied to Gallipoli.   In trench warfare it was assumed
that the success of the attack depended upon the 6-inch

[1] Pp. 185-186.
[2] John North, " Gallipoli : The Fading Vision," p. 118.

howitzer and generally upon artillery. This conclusion, as will be seen from the development of machine gun barrage fire in 1917, was not justified. Only one record exists of any attempt to use machine guns for covering fire. The 11th Division attacked the W Hills on 21st August. " Twenty-two machine guns were massed on " Chocolate Hill to support the advance of two battalions " of the 32nd Brigade . . . but these guns had been " hurriedly collected and there had been ' little time " to organize their fire.' Their preliminary bombard- " ment failed to touch the Turkish forward trench, and " these two battalions were met by an unshaken " garrison."[1]

This was the year (1915) in which Mr. Lloyd George demanded the rapid increase of machine guns and wherein also the officer commanding the Machine Gun School at Wisques complained without just cause that none of Sir John French's staff came even to visit the school. Of what use numbers of machine guns, it may be asked, if the Higher Command would not give instructions how they were to be employed. Yet, General Sir Ian Hamilton had been Commandant of the School of Musketry at Hythe and had witnessed the exploitation of machine guns in attack and defence in Manchuria in 1904–5. Gallipoli must have reminded him of Port Arthur : but machine guns were forgotten.

On the subject of machine guns Dr. C. E. W. Bean[2] notes: " The men were not raised for them, and the " machine gun officer of the regiment and the sergeant " of its machine gun sections were those specialists who " trained certain of the men in the use of the regimental " guns ; whereas the artillery, engineers, and army

---

[1] John North, " Gallipoli : The Fading Vision," p. 182.
[2] " Official History of Australia in the War of 1914–18," vol. i. p. 57.

" medical corps were corps which drew upon specialists
" in the general population, so far as these could be
" found." After the landing, machine guns were
organized in brigades, and certainly their effectiveness
for defensive purposes was evident throughout the
whole course of the campaign.

There is, however, one notable exception to forgetfulness of the role and utility of this supreme weapon,
a forgetfulness pardonable having regard to the weight
of the artillery bombardment. When Captain Edward
Unwin, R.N.,[1] rigged up the s.s. *River Clyde* for the
landing, he placed a battery of machine guns, carefully
protected by sandbags, in the bows of the vessel.
These guns, according to the Official History, were
" the means of saving hundreds of lives." Captain
Unwin relates that the higher military and naval
authorities had entirely overlooked the necessity of
providing immediate covering fire and that it was only
by a stroke of good fortune that this battery, belonging
to the Royal Naval Division, arrived in time to meet
his urgent request.

In France, following the failures of the Somme, the
views of machine gun officers with battle experience
began to prevail.

The sanguinary operations on the Somme had been
its " baptism of fire " for the Machine Gun Corps.
Lessons had been learned at a high cost in casualties :
these lessons contributed immensely to the *esprit de
corps*, the knowledge and wisdom of the Corps, even
if they failed equally to impress themselves upon the
Higher Command. By the opening of the year 1917,
each machine gun company had become a well-knit

---

[1] Captain Edward Unwin, V.C., C.B., C.M.G., awarded the V.C.
for his valour in command of the *River Clyde*.

unit, technically efficient, which could hold its own beside any infantry battalion in and out of the line. Companies varied, of course, with their command, but it being held in mind that the Corps consisted of picked men, a machine gun company uniformly presented as fine an armed body as could be found in any division.

It must be noted that the officers for the Corps were not selected for any special abilities and aptitude which would enable them to attain to proficiency as machine gunners. Though it had long been realized that a special type of brain and training were necessary both for engineers and artillery, it did not occur to anyone that the machine gun officer, whatever his other qualifications, must also be a ready mathematician, possess an instinct for map-reading, and have a mechanical bent. Owing to an entirely haphazard method of posting officers to the Machine Gun Corps, it was often found that they were deplorably lacking in those vital departments of general education which form the essential background to the quick grasp of the principles of machine gunnery. Both in the selection and training of officers, those deficient in mathematical knowledge and mechanical instinct cannot be made into efficient machine gun officers. As the need for covering fire, and the more scientific use of machine guns, impressed itself both upon the fighting units and the staffs of the training centres, the need for a higher inspectorate in the field for the furtherance of the science itself and for the elimination of unsuitable direction became clearer. During the year 1917, therefore, a machine gun officer was appointed to the staff of each corps and, later, divisional machine gun officers were also appointed.

The battle of Arras in the spring of 1917 brought

with it no new tactical organization nor method, though there was a tendency by most brigadiers to allow greater freedom and initiative to company commanders in the disposal of guns. The assaults upon the formidable Hindenburg Line between the river Scarpe and Marcoing, notably on the high ground between Fontaine les Croisilles and Bullecourt, were frequently covered by the fire of batteries of guns. These were disposed either for long-range action up to 2000 yards, or were dug into the ground in advance of the British posts under cover of darkness to flank the German front and support line, and to engage German machine guns when they opened fire upon the advancing waves of infantry.

The German machine guns were placed in concrete emplacements impervious to shell-fire. Even after prolonged bombardments by artillery of all calibres, these concrete strongholds weathered the storm, and were fed with men and ammunition from deep shafts communicating with galleries beneath. Aerial photographs which show conditions of complete destruction of trenches and other defences reveal the machine gun emplacements as unscathed. The British attacks proved immensely costly : and the tactics employed were of the same character as those which marked the Somme offensive—waves of heavily laden infantry, following a creeping artillery barrage.

A notable exception, worthy of record, was the ruse employed by Major-General R. J. Pinney, commanding the 33rd Division, in the capture of the front and support German lines between Bullecourt and the Sensée River, in May 1917, after several fruitless attempts. The 100th Brigade deployed in darkness on tapes 80 yards from the German lines, their accoutrements muffled with rags, following a careful rehearsal behind the lines. Ammunition for machine guns was driven up the Sensée Valley to a chalk quarry, the animals' hooves and the wheels of the vehicles being similarly muffled with blankets. The machine gun personnel was divided into two. One half, armed only with bombs, in groups of four, with an officer or an N.C.O., secreted themselves in front of the infantry, camouflaged with grass, or in imitation of the unburied dead among whom they lay, the objective being to rush the concrete machine gun strongholds and turn the German weapons upon the defenders. The other half of the company manned two-, three-, or four-gun batteries, four guns being held in reserve to be hurried to the objective as soon as captured.

The attack did not follow the usual routine of an assault at dawn, and beyond a stray shell here and there fired to deceive the enemy, not a shot was fired. At 9 A.M., by which time the sense of morning alarm would have vanished, the battalions rose to the assault, and rushed the front line. The Germans were caught off their guard, at breakfast, or asleep in their dugouts; while the men of the 100th Machine Gun Company, having hurled bombs through the windows of the concrete emplacements, leaped to take charge. Manning the German weapons, they raked the front trenches and parapets of the support line as the enemy rushed to arms. Many prisoners were taken, and the assault was carried out with only two casualties in the 100th Brigade. The casualties inflicted upon the counter-attack which attempted to develop, both from the rear batteries and from the direct fire of German machine guns turned against their former owners, were very heavy.

With the Canadian corps, however, rests the

honour of having first effectively co-ordinated machine guns for the task of covering fire. The four Canadian divisions under Sir Julian Byng were grouped for the difficult task of capturing Vimy Ridge, a long gradual slope which reaches a height of 450 feet at its summit. Canada had already shown some independence in its machine gun organization, going so far as to arrange a mechanized force of motor machine guns, while Colonel Boyle, from Klondyke, had equipped a unit from among his own miners at his personal expense, commanding with unusual independence.

As early as 15th January 1917, Sir Julian Byng had written requesting " authority for the formation of a " Canadian M.G.C. on similar lines to that of the British " Service." He reported, " the situation as regards the " supply of personnel, conditions of service and pro- " motion is highly unsatisfactory and has resulted in ex- " travagance and inefficiency." By 4th May the Canadian Machine Gun Corps had come into being, due no doubt to the purposeful language with which the memorandum concluded : " I attach the greatest importance to this " step being taken without delay. As things are at " present the M.G. companies of the Canadian corps " must inevitably break down during active operations."

The Canadian Machine Gun Corps lost no time in bringing itself to a high state of efficiency. Neither directed nor prejudiced by a command with pre-conceived notions got from South Africa and man-œuvres as to the purpose of weapons, the corps at once developed a highly scientific and closely co-ordinated scheme of mutual support among its companies. When such training came to the test, upon ground admirably suited to the purpose, the machine guns rendered services of the highest value, as assault

weapons covering the Canadian attack. The capture of
Vimy Ridge, with 70 officers and 3500 other prisoners,
was a notable exploit as a feat of arms, and it marks
the first comprehensive use of machine guns grouped
in batteries for indirect overhead fire in support of an
infantry assault.

With the experience of Vimy, 4 officers and 60 other
ranks of the Canadian Machine Gun Corps arrived at
Camiers on 4th June, to carry out a series of experiments
in barrage firing : while preparations were already far
advanced for a scheme similar to that so successfully
employed at Vimy in conjunction with the attack
upon Messines Ridge by the Second Army. Sir
Herbert Plumer's attack was executed on 7th June 1917.
The machine gun barrage scheme was the most comprehensive hitherto envisaged. 7200 prisoners fell into
British hands ; 67 field-pieces, some of them of large
calibre, 294 machine guns, and 94 trench mortars :
while the total British losses were about 16,000. The
German figures do not, of course, include those killed
and wounded.

The IXth Corps Report upon the battle of Messines,
issued on 7th July 1917, demonstrates how machine gun
fire was organized for this successful set-piece operation,
and states the results :

" Operations—Messines—Wytschaete Ridge. From
" the middle of April, 18-pdrs. and M.G.'s were used
" at night to prevent the enemy from repairing the
" damage done to his defences. On 27th May this was
" intensified and a deliberate scheme of night firing to
" interrupt the enemy's communications was instituted,
" which on 31st May became a general barrage by both
" artillery and machine guns on hostile lines of approach;
" and appears to have been very successful in interrupt-

" ing the enemy's supplies and in making the reliefs of
" troops in the line difficult and costly. . . .
     " The machine gun barrage in advance of the
" creeping artillery barrage throughout the attack is
" reported both by our own troops and by prisoners
" to have been very effective. . . . The barrage ex-
" tended to great depth, which is considered to be the
" reason why so few casualties were inflicted by hostile
" machine gun fire, the hostile machine gunners being
" unable to bring up their guns and employ indirect
" fire through our barrage."

The organization of a machine gun barrage implies
forethought, initiative, and careful consideration of a
high order. The ground must be surveyed, its topo-
graphical features scrutinized. Special maps have to
be prepared. Intelligence reports and aeroplane photographs must be continually studied. The desired
barrage lines must then be plotted upon the map. The
next procedure is to site gun positions upon the map
from which such objectives can mathematically be
obtained. The ground must then be reconnoitred in
order to find gun positions, subscribing to those already
map-plotted, but which possess also the necessary
tactical requirements of concealment, field of fire,
communication. The exact positions of guns must then
be plotted upon the map, and the barrage lines worked
out again for each group of guns, and each gun, in
detail. Aiming marks, both for day and night firing,
have then to be set out on the ground, and the emplacements prepared with a solid base, cover for teams, and
camouflaged against observation.

All this work is preliminary to other organization
which falls upon all ranks of a machine gun unit. The
teams themselves must be carefully disciplined in the

N

carrying-out of fire orders, and be mechanically proficient. Spare barrels and other parts have to be
organized in readiness ; belts dried and filled, belt-
filling machines installed. Hundreds of thousands of
rounds of ammunition have to be transported by
limber, pack, or by mechanical means to the gun
positions : in exposed places they must be man-handled,
or the final distribution made under cover of darkness.
Tracks to and from gun positions must be obliterated
to avoid aerial observation. Provision must be made for
the supply of water for cooling purposes. Not only
must detailed orders be prepared for the major fire
schemes, but similar orders in greater detail must be
issued for every gun team. In addition, the ordinary
battle routine for casualties, rations, forage must be
ordered.

The responsibility which falls upon the machine
gun commander in such operations is, therefore, by
no means light. Not only must he be prepared to
carry through the barrage programme; he must also
be ready to meet any contingency which the events
of battle may produce : to engage and throw back
the enemy with direct fire in case of strong counter-
attack, to change the lines of barrage to meet an
S O S call or protect a flank left in the air ; or to
move forward, as a unit, with transport, where an
assault has proved so successful as to envisage further
progress. In short, an effective and comprehensive
barrage scheme cannot be introduced to cover the
assault by infantry in a major operation except with
full and adequate preparation. Granted the necessary
time, as was demonstrated, the effect of the machine
gun in co-operation with artillery may prove devastating
to the defence.

CHAPTER VIII

DEVELOPMENT OF BARRAGE FIRE

1917

Forward and supporting guns—Command of a machine gun company
ideal—Invidious position of Divisional Machine Gun Officer—
Co-ordination of barrage guns—The need for executive authority
—The dual role of machine guns in battle—Command in the
field—German change of tactics—Critical importance of
machine gun S O S barrage—First barrage schemes—SS. 192
—Machine Gun School, Camiers—Machine Gun Training
Centre, Grantham — Evolution of mathematics — Archibald
McLean—British fire technique and German tactical disposi-
tion—German machine gun organization—Demonstrations at
Camiers—Technical difficulties in field work—Menace of
machine gun barrage.

THE operations at the third battle of Ypres, July to
November 1917, provide no striking novelties in the
tactical employment of machine guns. The principles
had already been generally agreed throughout the
Army, though there were yet to be found many variations in their application. Moreover, the persistence by some corps and divisional commanders in
disregarding the lessons from previous experience remained marked ; and, indeed, in some instances was
continued until the Armistice. The experience of the
battle served to re-emphasize the conclusions to which
those familiar with the weapon had already arrived.

The principle of dividing the guns available for battle into two groups, " forward guns " and " supporting guns," each group under different tactical control, had been adopted. The " forward guns " were frequently divided also into two further groups, styled " mobile guns " and " mobile reserve guns." The duty allotted to the former was " closely to support " the attack of their respective brigades "; [1] that of the latter to be under the control of the G.O.C.'s of assaulting brigades. In some cases machine gun sections of four guns, or sub-sections of two guns, were attached to infantry battalions, under the direct orders of the infantry commander. In others " machine " gunners were given certain objectives to go to in the " ground captured by each battalion."

A certain vagueness in direction often appeared as the result. The divisional machine gun officer, nominally in command of the fourth, reserve, machine gun company, allotted to all divisions in the late summer and early autumn, was also responsible for the training and tactical disposition of the three companies attached to each brigade within the division. In certain instances the D.M.G.O. was able to exercise a real authority : in others the appointment was hotly resented both by brigadiers and by the officers commanding brigade machine gun companies.

The command of a machine gun company was as nearly the ideal fighting unit as it was possible to imagine. The commander was interested with the same problem in administration and organization as in an infantry battalion. The unit, in personnel and transport, was large and self-contained. The rank and file were picked

[1] Notes on Machine Gun Tactics, No. 1, 1917.

men, with an added variety of specialists ; while the company commander was practically his own master, especially when serving a sympathetic brigadier who understood the weapon, its potentiality and tactical uses. Moreover, the commander possessed the added advantage of the whole brigade area in which to manœuvre and dispose his guns in place of the far more restricted terrain controlled by an infantry commander. To a man with fighting instincts and who found pleasure in the leadership and comradeship of a well-knit unit, the command of a machine gun company was an enviable one. To find himself under the orders of a divisional officer who most often had commanded a brigade machine gun company in the same division, with all the natural jealousies, born of pride and petty quarrels in taking over in the line and in billets, proved often most vexatious to a machine gun company commander. In such circumstances, the brigade machine gunner sought the protection of his brigadier, against " interference " ; and the latter was often only too willing to fight as an ally of one whom he regarded as the linch-pin of his own special preserve. The intrusion of the divisional machine gun officer implied that the control of machine guns in battle was to be taken from the control of the brigadier. That was enough.

The position of the Divisional Machine Gun Officer was in fact ludicrous. Commanding the divisional company, his duties were such that he could give little time or attention to its individual training ; while, once in battle, the command became merged in larger schemes of organization. Yet, the D.M.G.O. was possessed of no executive authority over brigade machine gun companies, unless so endowed by a forceful and

understanding divisional commander. In the Army one
gives or receives orders : one neither gives nor receives
advice. The appointment of D.M.G.O. was advisory,
and it was left to each officer appointed to make what he
could of the job. The events at the third battle of Ypres
determined the matter.

The disposal and ordering of the forward or mobile
guns, with their reserve, by general agreement, remained with the assaulting brigadiers. In one division,
for example, 64 guns would now be available ; while
even more, from divisional reserve, might be added to
increase the density of fire. A division attacking upon
a two-brigade front would require perhaps 16 mobile
guns, 8 to each assaulting brigade, to go forward with
infantry and act as defensive pivots during consolidation against counter-attack. There remained 48 guns,
possibly more, whose duty, it was now generally agreed,
was to provide the overhead barrage and S O S fire,
and subsequent consolidation in depth.

Co-ordination of the barrage, or supporting guns,
implied at once that executive powers of command
must be accorded to the D.M.G.O. both in devising
the fire scheme and during the battle. The organization of the fire scheme entailed, also, that of ammunition supply, the ordering of transport, and all the
detail involved in such matters as casualty replace-
ments, reliefs, spare parts, rations. This meant that,
in fact as well as in theory, the D.M.G.O. must be
invested with full executive authority. So much was
conceded. In the last resort there were few, if any,
who would be found to question the authority of an
appointment, ordered by the Higher Command, of an
officer chosen obviously for his special ability and experience of machine gunnery. Having regard to the

dual role which machine guns may be called upon to play at any time in battle—that of direct fire, as mobile, or forward weapons ; and that of barrage batteries, either to contribute a creeping barrage when covering an assault, or the S O S barrage during consolidation and, if called upon, to break up threatened counter-attacks—sheer necessity demanded that all the machine guns within a division, the largest self-contained tactical unit, must be under the authority of one commander.

Moreover, the idea that certain guns, usually the mobile or forward guns, could be taken arbitrarily from the command of the divisional machine gun officer and placed directly under that of a brigade or battalion commander, suggested a weakness in direction and organization and a lack of faith in system which had only to be realized to be apparent. The swaying backwards and forwards of a hard-fought battle, with its assault and counter-attack, produces situations wherein forward guns may be overwhelmed, and may be short of ammunition or personnel ; while barrage batteries may be forced to forsake the barrage or harassing role, and adopt that of direct-fire units of two guns, moved hither and thither, irrespective of battalion, brigade, and even divisional battle areas and boundaries, in order to give the most effective fire-support.

Barrage batteries, whose fire orders form part of a large divisional plan—sometimes extending to a corps front in its content—being co-ordinated with artillery, must necessarily be under the absolute direction and control of one executive commander. From the two roles which guns have often to play in one operation, it is no less desirable, even necessary, that all the divisional machine guns should be under the command of one authority.

With the ground of the whole divisional area available for manœuvre, disposition, and organization, the D.M.G.O. possessed unique facilities for gauging the ebb and flow of battle. Although nominally placed at divisional headquarters, in many instances, after completing his fire-plans with the divisional and artillery staffs, the D.M.G.O., not being a staff officer, was at liberty to direct his guns in action on the divisional front. Indeed, the presence of the virtual commander was, and would always prove to be, undoubtedly an asset of high value both to morale and to the direction of fire.

The operations at Ypres, due especially to the nature of the terrain and the comparative immobility of artillery, marooned in a sea of mud, gave to machine guns a role in battle even more important than at any previous period of the War. Despite the most exhausting conditions, machine guns, complete as fire-units, remained mobile. A most important tactical lesson derived from these operations, also, was " the " advisability of considering the machine gun S O S " barrage a permanent portion of all defensive schemes, " owing to the *rapidity* with which such machine guns " can open fire.

" Central control, flexibility and rapidity of action " are the three great desiderata of machine gun " barrage fire, and the operations of the third battle of " Ypres have supplied a most valuable training ground " for the realisation of these lessons in the most trying " conditions." [1]

[1] Tactical Summary of Machine Gun Operations, No. 1, Oct. 1917, (G.S.) 6.

During the month of October, the Germans changed their defensive dispositions in a way which very closely affected the tactical employment of machine guns on both sides. Instead of the thinly held front line defended in depth by nests of machine guns and mazes of wire which afforded gaps through which his counter-attacking divisions could sally, the enemy placed more reliance on a concentration of troops in the forward area liberally supported by machine guns, both heavy and light, the latter, although of the same mechanical construction as the heavy guns, corresponding with the Lewis gun. The German counter-attacks were therefore delivered much sooner than previously, and by troops much closer forward. By the end of this month the enemy, no doubt as the result of the heavy casualties incurred by such concentration of reserves in the forward zone, reverted to a middle policy of keeping his main counter troops well in the rear, and at the same time maintaining additional fire-power in the front line, especially light machine guns, the weapon in correspondence with the automatic rifle. These changes affected British machine gun tactics in two ways. The importance of the task assigned to the machine guns sent forward to cover consolidation in the neighbourhood of the final objective was increased. Secondly, an *immediate* response to S O S calls became a factor of critical importance.

Barrage fire had been extensively used in the later stages of the battle of the Somme, 1916. Many factors in barrage work which later became common knowledge had not then been learned nor indeed considered. In the further attack upon High Wood on 24th August, a somewhat amazing exploit was carried out by the 100th Machine Gun Company. Ten guns were grouped in Savoy Trench, from which a magnificent view was obtained of the German line at a range of about 2000 yards. Two companies of infantry were lent for the purpose of carrying ammunition and water to the battery position during the previous night, when the machine guns were installed, and camouflaged with netting. The operation orders read that " rapid fire " is to be maintained continuously for twelve hours, " to cover the attack and consolidation."

The 100th Infantry Brigade had been engaged in the first assault upon High Wood, on 16th July, an attack which was repulsed with the heaviest losses, due largely to lack of artillery preparation and support. For the new assault, with limited objectives, the brigadier was determined that nothing should be lacking in effective covering fire. It is to the credit of the gunners and of the Vickers gun itself that the orders were fulfilled to the letter. During the attack on the 24th August, 250 rounds short of one million were fired by the ten guns. Four 2-gallon petrol tins of water, the company's water-bottles, and all the urine tins from the neighbourhood were emptied into the guns for cooling purposes, an illustration of the amount of water consumed ; while a party was employed throughout the action carrying ammunition. Strict discipline as to barrel-changing was maintained. The company artificer, assisted by one private, maintained a belt-filling machine in action without cessation for twelve hours. A prize of five francs to each of the members of the gun-team firing the greatest number of rounds was secured by the gun-teams of Sergeant P. Dean, D.C.M.,[1] with a record of just over 120,000 rounds. The action

[1] Later Major P. Dean, M.C., D.C.M., now of the Royal Tank Corps.

was a remarkable performance in itself, if prodigal in its expenditure of ammunition. Nevertheless, the assault was a brilliant success, the operations being difficult, and all objectives were taken within a short time. The machine gunners sustained one casualty, while prisoners examined both at divisional and corps headquarters reported that " the effect of the machine gun barrage " was annihilating. Counter-attacks endeavouring to " retake the ground lost were broken up whilst being " concentrated east of the Flers Ridge and High " Wood."

The first machine gun barrage demonstration along lines which marked those of subsequent operations was carried out on 18th February 1917, covering an attack by the 4th Division opposite Bouchavesnes on the Somme, when forty-eight guns of the 4th and 33rd Divisions were grouped in batteries in one area. The " shoot " was organized by Lieutenant-Colonel R. G. Clarke, 15th Corps machine gun officer, himself a pioneer of the pre-War era at Hythe. In order to achieve success no ground was suitable for the siting of the batteries other than an area within full view of Mount St. Quentin, a dominating observation point for the enemy. With snow on the ground, the guns, although concealed, were soon spotted. It is interesting to note, however, that although shells fired at the batteries actually pitched among the guns, they ricochetted off the hard frozen ground and burst against a bank about fifty yards in rear. No casualties were sustained during the action.

Combined actions by batteries of machine guns so far had resulted from the determination of individual machine gun company commanders to attain the maximum fire-effect from their weapons ; or were demonstrations, largely inspired by the G.H.Q. Machine Gun School. During September 1916 the school was visited by His Majesty King George V. The machine gun school proved by carefully arranged demonstrations on the sands at Camiers that well-directed and well-controlled machine gun fire could be almost annihilating in its effect at ranges up to 2500 yards, even when the fire was indirect and unobserved, provided a sufficient number of guns could be brought into action. These demonstrations supported, for example, the less mathematically precise " shoot " of the 100th Machine Gun Company on 24th August 1916. As a new principle machine guns were, therefore, to be organized in batteries of four to eight guns, and the fire of these batteries was to be controlled, distributed, or concentrated in accordance with the principles which governed the action of a battery of artillery, with variations prescribed by the character of different weapons. The range of machine guns was limited to 2500, at the most 3000 yards, but the effective beaten zone, on the other hand, was both deeper and more intense while fire itself was more sustained. In effect, the machine gun was officially accorded a new role, secondary to that of an infantry pivot, but one which was to gather importance as its technique came to be understood and appreciated not only by the personnel of the Machine Gun Corps itself, but by the Higher Command. The machine gun text-books were re-written from this point of view ; and that which came to be popularly known by its official nomenclature of " SS. 192 " became the "machine gunners' bible."

Machine guns were gradually assuming recognition as a separate arm, an intermediary between the infantry rifle with the automatic rifle and field artillery.

The theories expressed themselves as cones, or bands, of fire, which according to the range and slope of ground upon which the target was situated varied both in length and breadth, but by setting guns by means of a large-scale contoured map, for range and angle of fire, together with the use of compass and clinometer to give effect to the map-readings, could be made to interlock in depth or width, or both, according to the number of guns used, thus producing an impenetrable zone of fire upon any given area.

Throughout the year 1917 both the machine gun school at Camiers, whose title was changed to that of G.H.Q. Small Arms School on 31st May, and the Machine Gun Training Centre at Grantham, were preoccupied with exhaustive experimental work. At the former, Major G. M. Lindsay of the Rifle Brigade, graded as G.S.O.2, was appointed Chief Instructor from Grantham on 28th May, under Colonel J. K. Cochrane, who had been G.S.O.1 of the 55th Division, as Commandant. On 3rd June Major Lindsay was created a Companion of the Distinguished Service Order. The following day there arrived at Camiers four officers and sixty other ranks of the Canadian Motor Machine Gun Brigade " to carry out a series " of experiments in barrage firing." It may here be noted that the Canadians had already made considerable advances in the technique of barrage fire, and the machine guns of the Canadian Corps were already organized for the purpose. Their selection for this experimental duty was, therefore, not the result of caprice.

At Grantham a studio had been instituted as part of the establishment, in which professional artists, under Mr. Handley Read, an officer of the Machine

Gun Corps, were employed in painting pictures of battle actions used for instructional purposes. The Senior Instructional Staff at Grantham who developed machine gun mathematics were Colonel Charteris, with Major M. E. Denny, the well-known engineer of Clydebank, and Majors G. F. H. Satow, Cox, Rathbone, Ian Hay Beith, and Ball, son of Sir Robert Ball, Astronomer Royal.

Up till 1917 machine gun officers in the field, using improvisations, had been more or less satisfied with following a guiding star, which frequently implied no more than " trusting to luck." That they might thus attain to the " glorious haven " of which Dante so nobly spoke in his lines " *Se tu segui stella, Non puoi fallire a glorioso porto*," is well proven by a story told by Major R. M. Wright, M.C., late of the Guards Machine Gun Regiment, of an experience early in 1916 :

" A new target having been selected for harassing fire
" one night, the necessary calculations were made by
" the officer concerned and submitted to company
" headquarters for verification. In the meantime,
" without waiting to hear if his calculations were con-
" sidered correct, the officer passed on the directions
" and elevation to his guns, and some two thousand
" rounds were fired. It was eventually discovered
" that the compass direction chosen was about thirty
" degrees out, owing to the fact that the officer had
" subtracted instead of adding his ' magnetic deviation.'
" The bullets had gone into the blue, fortunately on
" the enemy's side of the line, and it appeared that two
" thousand rounds of S.A.A. had been wasted. It so
" happened, however, that a German prisoner was
" taken that night, and in the course of his examination
" at brigade headquarters he said that some men of

" his company who had been at work digging a new
" trench had been heavily fired on by one of our
" machine guns during the night and had suffered
" casualties. The brigadier congratulated the company
" commander on this result of his fire ; the latter saw
" no reason to confess in reply that the two thousand
" rounds which were all that he had fired that night had
" hit their target by good luck and bad calculations." [1]

Undoubtedly much of the " harassing fire," indirect shooting, in the early days was ill-directed ;
not usually as the result of gross errors in calculations
but owing to the imperfections of the technical appli-
ances available. In order to provide a permanent remedy
against such errors and to ensure that, with the maximum
effect, large numbers of guns could be used together, not
merely for harassing but in large-scale operations, the
staffs of Grantham and of Camiers jointly and severally
laboured to make more efficient the machine gunner's
working tools.

In the Grantham studios during 1917 was employed a junior officer, severely wounded on the Somme,
named Archibald McLean. He possessed the qualifications of A.R.I.B.A. and was an engineer, also, with
much railroad and steel experience. He was asked if
it would be possible to design a graph to do all the work
of the Quadrant Elevation tables. McLean, now in
his element, was designated " O.C. Graphs " ; and,
wrapt up in his task in the studio, produced the graph
which was passed as perfect by a board of senior officers.
Graphs for cones of fire upon sloping ground and for
other aspects of machine gunnery were produced by
McLean and incorporated in " The Machine Gun
Pocket Book," the *vade-mecum* of every officer of the

[1] " Army Quarterly," vol. i. No. 2, January 1921.

Machine Gun Corps. When the graphs were completed, McLean handed his work to Lieutenant D. H. Corsellis, who embarked for Camiers, with the thirteen exhibits prepared by 2nd Lieutenant McLean, in order to explain and demonstrate to the instructional staff of the G.H.Q. Small Arms School.

Archibald McLean was responsible also for making a working model of the lock of a machine gun which was photographed by operators of the Gaumont-British Company, the subsequent film of which was the first of all instructional films used in the Army. Captain Corsellis [1] too, a brilliant young barrister who had lost an arm in action, continued his work and conceived the idea of a sliding graph upon the principle of a slide-rule to perform the same work as the original graph. McLean worked up the first model in celluloid, and this was later sold to officers at the price of seven shillings and sixpence. The distinguished work of Major M. E. Denny in the background was felt everywhere.

It can be affirmed that those primarily responsible for the conception and development of machine gun mathematics and the technical implements which served as the essential " ready reckoner " in the field were Colonel N. K. Charteris, C.M.G., D.S.O., Lieutenant A. J. McLean, Captain D. H. Corsellis, and Major Rathbone. Their work was the foundation of, and made practicable the grandiose, and most effective, machine gun barrage schemes which played their part in the successful attack at Messines and during the operations at the third battle of Ypres and Cambrai. The diagrams and graphs prepared by Archibald McLean in celluloid remain in the Imperial War Museum.

[1] Killed as pilot in a flying accident, 1931.

On 18th August 1917, the Commander-in-Chief, Sir Douglas Haig, together with some 130 General officers, attended the School at Camiers to witness a demonstration of barrage fire. During the succeeding months 300 senior Staff officers, together with representatives of the French, Belgian, Italian, American, Danish, and Japanese armies, witnessed similar demonstrations.

The history of machine gunnery from this date is almost exclusively that of the development of British fire-technique and of German tactical disposition. In one vital matter did Germany show its initiative and a tactical lead, namely in recognizing the true role of the automatic rifle. It was clear that the German High Command was much impressed with the new and more purposeful methods of British machine gunnery as exemplified first by the Canadian Corps at Vimy ; and repeated in a far more ambitious plan, co-ordinated over the whole front of attack, by the Second Army at Messines. There can be little doubt also that, both from the Intelligence service and from prisoners of war, Germany had closely watched the development of British machine gunnery, remembering perhaps that the German Staff had obtained its first lesson in machine gun fire-tactics from British sources. But, as tacticians, the Germans remained the masters of the battlefield because, while the British army adopted the rigid machine gun dispositions which Germany rejected in 1917, General Ludendorff revolutionized the German tactical control of its machine guns by the introduction of a " fluid " tactical control and disposition in the battlefield.

Up till September 1917, although possessed of a vast superiority in weapons, the Germans had not

o

employed barrage machine gun fire as part of the machine gun defence or attack. German prisoners captured early in November stated that " barrage and " indirect fire is now being taught to all men in the field " as far as possible. One man from each machine gun " company is being sent to the Deutsche Gewehrfabrik, " at Spandau, for a course including instruction in " machine gun construction and in barrage and in- " direct fire." Further, a graph captured during the same operations was almost a facsimile of the clearance graph used in the British army, but it appeared to contemplate the putting on of elevation by some form of tangent sight method.

The normal German establishment at this date was 8-12 heavy, sled-mounted guns for each battalion machine gun company ; that is to say, 72-108 guns to the division ; and 2-3 light, bipod, or barrel-rested, guns per company, amounting to 72-108 for each division. The latter, it is again emphasized, did not possess the essential characteristics of the machine gun, and was equivalent to the automatic rifle (Lewis gun). An important note was issued by the British General Staff in October 1917, reiterating the need for discrimination in considering automatic infantry fire arms. " There still appears a tendency in some divisions to " use machine guns for work that is essentially the role " of riflemen or Lewis guns, namely, to deal with snipers, " infiltration, or early small local counter-attacks. The " tendency is dangerous in so much as it weakens the " machine gun defence in depth against the larger " counter-attacks which develop later." [1]

The average number of guns of each German

[1] " Tactical Summary of Machine Gun Operations," No. 1, 1917, SS. 201.

division was 90 heavy and a similar number of light guns. In addition Germany had formed 90 independent machine gun " marksman " detachments (Maschinengewehr Scharfschützen), each of three companies. The establishment of these companies was similar to that of battalion machine gun companies, producing a further 3240 machine guns organized for attack or defence, detailed as Army troops and held as a reserve, and allotted as required to different sectors of the front.

The British General Staff " Summary of Machine Gun Operations," October 1917, in its concluding remarks, makes this decisive and emphatic statement:

" The development of rapidly produced barrage fire " by organized machine gun batteries will be an " essential feature of any successful effort at pushing " forward under conditions of open warfare to exploit " an initial success when adequate field artillery " support is lacking.

" For this reason, it must be realized that the " development of scientific machine gunnery is as im- " portant from an open or semi-open warfare point of " view as it is from a trench warfare point of view, and " this should be very carefully considered in the winter " training of all machine gun companies."

The mind of G.H.Q. was in fact already made up. The battalion organization, being carried on in fact if not in name, had already the unofficial approval of the War Office. The bearing of the instruction contained in SS. 201 is, therefore, of high importance when the conduct of machine guns in the two distinct phases of defence and attack, in both semi-open and open warfare, come to be considered.

Certain very important practical factors, however, were immediately presented. It was one thing to fire a successful barrage demonstration upon the sands at Camiers, where all the conditions were favourable ; it was a vastly different matter to attain such results on the battlefield. At Camiers, the instructional staff possessed all the advantages of well-equipped drawing offices, draughtsmen and instruments ; the advantage of being able readily to observe fire as bullets struck the sand ; perfectly tested instruments for laying guns and gauging wind ; admirable means of communication ; ample time in which to work out a " shoot " to a rigid time table, with its variations of switch, lift, creep, bracket ; and not least gun teams consisting of officers and men, highly trained, perfectly fed, clothed and rested, subject to no retaliation.

On the battlefield, without observation and registration, it is almost impossible to be accurate, though a high degree of accuracy may be secured. Wind, temperature, barometer all have an appreciable, and, under ideal conditions, calculable effect upon the flight of a bullet. In battle conditions, however, the calculations were seldom worked out and only rough allowances made for such disturbing influences, the facts concerning which were often unascertainable.

In addition to errors due to weather conditions, further possibilities of error occurred as a result of the difficulty of locating exactly the position of the " directing gun " and laying out a line of fire by means of a compass or aiming-mark. The artillery often experienced difficulties of a similar character, but ordinarily the first sighting shot of a field piece was made on rough calculations and the necessary alterations were made by simple direct observation of the result. The artillery usually possessed, moreover, the services of an expert field survey company to assist in

Imperial War Museum

MACHINE GUNS OF THE CANADIAN CORPS IN BARRAGE
POSITIONS, VIMY, APRIL 1917

Photograph by the Author

OBSERVATIONS WITH CLINOMETER AND BARR & STROUD
RANGE-FINDING INSTRUMENT, WHEN SITING A BATTERY
OF MACHINE GUNS, YPRES SALIENT, SEPTEMBER 1917

laying out the initial lines of fire. The officers of machine gun companies had usually neither the scientific minds nor certainly the technical materials of such expert assistance.

In discussing the " basis of fire-control rules,"[1] the War Office has now recognized the effect of errors. " There is no quick reliable means of determining the " range exactly, nor of estimating with precise accuracy " the effect of climatic conditions. Errors, both of " direction and of elevation, must therefore be expected. " The procedure is to define round the target an area " allowing for reasonable errors of direction and eleva- " tion, and to apply fire over the whole of this area. " . . . As these errors (1. Wrong estimation of wind ; " 2. Slight inaccuracies of aim, wear in the mounting, " drift, etc.) may act either way, it will be necessary to " engage an additional area on either side of the target. " Lateral errors will not normally be great, but it must " be remembered that the beaten zone is narrow and " does not give much assistance in overcoming them. " The error increases in proportion to the range, and " therefore a greater width will require to be engaged " at long ranges than at short."

A factor which contributed to error during the Great War, notably at Ypres and in the later stages of the Somme operations, which may often be overlooked, is that of sinking of the tripod. In the heat of action the subsidence of the platform may sometimes be forgotten. In order to forestall such an event, one which might seriously interfere with accuracy, the guns of the machine gun batteries of the 33rd Division covering the infantry attack on 25th-26th September 1917, beside Polygon Wood, were fixed upon wooden platforms to

[1] Small Arms.

prevent the tripod legs from sinking into the mud. When the barrage batteries moved forward according to the ambitious operation order, new platforms were awaiting them, which had been placed in position under cover of darkness a day prior to the battle.

It is not improbable that these platforms were observed from the air, for, when later occupied by the batteries, they were subjected not only to severe machine gun fire from the air by machines flying in line and diving over the batteries, inflicting the most severe casualties, but also to heavy artillery fire. As a subsequent chapter demonstrates, in a detailed account of a remarkable machine gun action, barrage batteries, unless very well concealed, were frequently severely harassed by hostile aeroplanes which adopted a special formation for the purpose. The machines advanced in two lines, one above the other. The upper line provided protection while observing results. The lower line would dive, machine by machine, sweeping sometimes only a few feet above the battery positions, while directing machine gun fire upon them. It was found that the protection of Lewis guns to a flank was invaluable against hostile aircraft. Alternatively, a machine gun with each battery, mounted for anti-aircraft, was used. During the heat of the battle instanced, hostile aircraft were almost immune from counter measures ; and had it not been for the exceptional courage and determination of the machine gunners the aircraft action would have proved decisive.

Where a battery is moved forward during battle it is probable that such considerable movement will be observed. It was found that to move in file, each section officer proceeding in advance to indicate the next battery position, was a satisfactory tactical formation. Preparation of battery positions with belt-boxes, ammunition, water, aiming marks and camouflage nets, or canvas, erected upon rabbit wire, is a precaution which should never be neglected. Immunity from directed artillery fire and aircraft harassing will always provide that condition of comparative harmony in battle in which fire-direction and control can be carefully exercised.

Although a high degree of accuracy in respect of the target is necessary for artillery fire, such absolute definition with machine gun fire is not so essential. The effective beaten zone within which 75 per cent of the bullets fall from a machine gun firing at 2000 yards is an area 70 yards long and 20 feet wide ; while, owing to the steepness of the trajectory at this range, the bullets have an excellent effect upon enemy troops in shell-hole defences, indeed in body cover of all kinds. The objective of all covering fire, whether artillery or machine gun, is to enable the infantry to advance. This is achieved by the infliction of casualties, by forcing the enemy to " keep his head down," by the prevention of concentrations for the counter-attack, and by rendering ineffective the shelter in which reserves are being held. Infantry officers and men who were sometimes sceptical about the value of barrage fire were inclined to overlook these technical details. But as was most aptly said by Major R. M. Wright, M.C., of the Guards Machine Gun Regiment: " Even the most sceptical " infantry officers have occasionally been heard to say " that they were comforted during an advance by the " sound of machine gun bullets passing over their " heads towards the enemy, and at least there was " never any complaint made of short shooting." [1]

[1] ' Machine Gun Tactics and Organization,' by Major R. M. Wright, M.C., " The Army Quarterly," January 1921.

An enemy is almost always obliged to keep his reserves, whether to reinforce a threatened line or for counter-attack, within 2000 yards of his front defences. Any form of covering fire is, therefore, valuable. It has a moral effect upon the enemy's troops, and, as is shown from the examination of prisoners published in Intelligence summaries during the War and from the detailed histories of German regiments, sometimes the heaviest casualties were inflicted. Moreover, an enemy cannot observe a machine gun barrage as can sometimes be done by intelligent observation of an artillery barrage. During the War, men of fighting experience developed a shell sense, and in the advance became adroit in the avoidance of shell-storms without losing direction, whereas it was quite impossible to anticipate or avoid the unseen menace of the machine gun barrage. Nor is this an unimportant point. Even with mechanized forms, counter-attacks require preparation not too far behind the battle zone and cannot, unsupported, penetrate the defensive line too far in depth.

CHAPTER IX

LESSONS FROM YPRES
1917

Eye-witness account of the Menin Road–Polygon Wood battle, 25th-26th September—Corps machine gun scheme—Attack and counter-attack—Mobility of batteries—Vickers and Lewis weapons—The Cambrai battle—Tanks—Sir Hubert Gough's opinion—Weapons separately considered—Machine guns at Cambrai—Importance of local protection—Canadians at Passchendaele—The new German defensive tactics—Comparison with disposition of Roman legions—Functions of the "Kampf Truppen Kommandeur"—Dual role of machine guns—Their two functions considered—Machine guns have tactics of their own—British defensive tactics of March 1918 compared with German tactics in autumn of 1917—Factors contributed by machine guns and automatic rifles.

AN eye-witness account of the action on the Menin Road, the operation on 25th-26th September, shows something of the ardours of the third battle of Ypres :
" The third battle of Ypres bit three miles farther
" east into the German defences, but it was a victory
" with no sweets. The enemy gave only a crumbling
" mud honeycomb filled with sticky gaseous slime. . . .
" At no stage in war were the courage and endurance
" of man tried more highly. . . .
" God knows what cynical wit christened those splin-
" tered stumps Inverness Copse or Sanctuary Wood.
" Who named that stinking quagmire Dumbarton Lakes ?

" And who ordained that those treacherous heaps of
" filth should be known as Stirling Castle or North-
" ampton Farm ?

" The maps with which I was presented prior to
" battle betrayed nothing of the chaos, which at every
" yard of reconnaissance or attack mocked the eye.

" We arrived at the rendezvous. I drew rein, dis-
" mounted, gave my men leave to slumber beside the
" waters on the northern shore of Dickebusch Lake.
" . . . Limbers almost axle-high in muck, men sweat-
" ing from the smallest effort of movement, yet chilled
" with cold rain-laden wind. Even at this point of
" concentration, at least recognizable in form, men
" could but squat and huddle, while sheer fatigue freed
" them from consciousness. And so they slept on the
" eve of battle.

" Already orders had been issued for a second attack
" upon the Ridge to include the capture of Polygon
" Wood, the Reutelbeeke and Polderhoek Château on
" the 33rd Divisional Front. . . .

" Very little time was available for reconnaissance
" and for the dumping of ammunition in the forward
" area. It seemed inconceivable that those who were
" directing operations could so blindly continue to
" issue orders to troops, whose fatigue was so great
" and whose casualties were so heavy in the task's
" execution that nothing but almost superhuman
" courage urged them to fulfil this futility.

" With my groom next day I rode forward, my
" mount slithering and stumbling upon baulks of
" timber, logs torn from woods and copses to make a
" track for tanks and artillery. Beside a burrow,
" belching smoke, and smelling sweetly of savoury
" cooking, I handed my horse to the groom, and

" surveyed a map. At Holybone I had arrived. Two
" bedraggled signallers, sitting in smoke, curtly told
" the groom to remove our horses. He wandered sadly
" a little way back along the track while a German
" aeroplane hovered far overhead.

" I walked on to the east, then set my map. Gone
" were the châteaux, farms, and woods of which it
" spoke. To the east nothing but pools of yellow un-
" dulations. I guessed the quality of the churnings
" along the horizon, and often round and about shrieked
" and dived great shells heaving volumes of mud into
" the air, accompanied by clouds of spray. I would
" watch the shells plunge. So deep, so yielding was
" the soil in its embrace that seconds passed before
" impact against anything solid which might detonate
" the metal mass. Then, as if by some angered reptile
" of the nether world, the earth's surface would heave
" and spout and flash with fire, emitting black fumes
" before delivering itself of a tempestuous diarrhoea.
" A shower of gangrenous metal and yellow mud.

" With the aid of a compass I learned the general
" direction of the attack objective. We would go east
" from astride the Menin Road by Herenthage Château.
" I noted a derelict tank—thank heavens for that land-
" mark—and an unburied corpse or two, which marked
" the track from Holybone. Then I returned to my
" horses. The map sheet was a fair deceiver. But a
" bogged tank, unburied dead, and a spray vomiting mud
" along the horizon gave me the lie of the land. To this
" battle-ground on the morrow would I lead my troops.

" I was unfortunate, for as a machine gunner I had
" to play the dual role of infantry and artillery. In
" consequence, with my gunners, I fought in two con-
" secutive actions. According to custom the divisional

" artillery remained in action to cover several phases
" of infantry assault. Thus it covered several divisional
" waves of assault. The infantry division was, on the
" other hand, involved in but one phase of assault with
" prescribed objectives, after the capture of which
" some fresh division would go through its forward
" posts and continue the assault. That was the infantry
" function if the attack went according to plan. But,
" with the exceptions of Plumer's attack at Messines,
" and that of Byng upon Vimy Ridge, both very limited
" objectives, no major British attack ever fulfilled
" expectations. Usually, therefore, the infantry divi-
" sion, after a few hours, or a day or two at the
" longest, was relieved after being held up or almost
" annihilated.

" Machine gunners, like infantry, moved on their
" feet, and fought with the front waves of assault or
" became the rallying points in defence.

" The capacity of the Vickers gun, providing not
" only the most powerful direct fire, but a controlled
" bullet-storm, fired at long ranges over the heads of
" the assaulting waves of infantry, realized for the
" Machine Gun Corps a role, also, akin to that of
" field artillery. Every machine gun company not re-
" quired for the first waves of assault and consolidation
" with its own division was now detached to give
" covering fire to the assault of other divisions.
" Grouped under the direction of the corps or divi-
" sional machine gun officer, guns and gunners were
" placed in barrage positions some twelve or fifteen
" hundred yards behind the objective line. Gun teams
" were occupied for some days prior to the attack in
" bringing ammunition up to the barrage positions.
" These often, owing to the fire-angle necessity im-

" posed by topography, were in exposed positions,
" and always in the very middle of the enemy's heaviest
" counter-barrage. The siting position of the machine
" gun batteries was the area in which reserves to the
" assault would be concentrated, and here fell the
" greatest storm of enemy shell-fire.

" Nevertheless, following most successful experi-
" ments on the sands at Camiers, where was situated
" the Machine Gun School, and since the later stages
" of the Somme battle, the practice of concentrated
" overhead machine gun fire rid the infantry of its
" first nervousness, and they were appreciative of its
" devastating effect.

" By the opening of the battle of the Menin Road,
" known as the third battle of Ypres, G.H.Q. was
" deeply impressed with the power of machine guns
" in this apparently new role, although the possibilities
" had been explored at the School of Musketry at Hythe
" prior to hostilities.

" I found myself, therefore, in command of the four
" divisional machine gun companies, grouped with
" others in support of the 23rd Division, whose infantry
" attack upon Inverness Copse and Polygon Wood,
" with the added objectives of Passchendaele and
" Westroosebeke, was to precede the passage of the
" 33rd Division into the open country beyond.

" I had made my first reconnaissance on the
" morning of the 18th September. From the following
" day until the 27th we were occupied in transporting
" hundreds of thousands of rounds of ammunition to
" the barrage positions. Over the very slushy ground
" it required two men to carry each ammunition box.
" The Divisional Ammunition Column sent up no less
" than 700,000 rounds on pack mules as far as Holybone,

" a considerable feat of organization and patience.
" From this spot, under sudden and violent shell-
" storms, or subject to the annoyance of being sniped
" by field-guns, my machine gunners man-handled
" the boxes across a mile of shell-pocked land to the
" positions. The burden was most severe, following,
" as it did, a march from bivouacs over the broken,
" pitted, mud-covered track of eight miles.

" No troops were more sorely tried than were
" machine gunners in this most exhausting of all
" battles on the Western Front. . . .

" The struggle for the possession of Inverness
" Copse had continued with great violence. The wood
" had been captured, but the enemy succeeded in
" retaking it, and threw back our line on to the Stirling
" Castle Ridge. The attack for the 20th had been
" admirably planned, the troops for the assault lying
" in readiness well in front of the ridge, in what had
" been the enemy's line. At ' zero hour ' troops of the
" Northumberlands and Durhams swept forward with
" great violence and courage ; and, suffering very few
" casualties, overwhelmed the machine gun posts in
" Inverness Copse, bayoneting the German gunners
" at their posts, driving through to the eastern side of
" the wood which was their first objective. They con-
" solidated the line to the east of it, on the edge of the
" boggy morasses, over which it was extremely difficult
" to pass. Moreover, the wide area of the lakes was
" quite impassable. Before the assault could be con-
" tinued, it was necessary to accomplish a wide turning
" movement. The troops for assault must be massed
" to the north-east of Inverness Copse, to permit
" them to sweep down to the south, past the northern
" extremity of the lakes ; and from this position assault

" the Tower Hamlets Ridge. Under cover of a smoke
" barrage this was done in little under an hour. The
" movement completed the first and second phases of
" the attack.

" The position of my machine gun batteries lay in
" the middle of the German barrage line, and I suffered
" very heavy casualties, losing during the morning the
" officers commanding each one of my companies and
" many valuable N.C.O.'s and men. The capture of
" Inverness Copse and the isolation of Dumbarton
" Lakes was a complete success. Tower Hamlets Ridge
" to the south-east had been stormed and taken by
" London troops, and the ground to the north was now
" freed for the further assault upon Polygon Wood, the
" Reutelbeeke, and Polderhoek Château.

" My command was in an evil case. Having
" completed its role, which I have compared to that of
" artillery, now depleted in men, and without tried
" commanders, we were to play a more important part
" as infantry accompanying the assault. The men were
" nearly exhausted. . . .

" Whatever losses I had incurred, the orders to
" advance were clear and concise. The barrage position
" of the guns was to be moved forward, so soon as the
" Tower Hamlets Ridge had been gained, to the edge
" of Inverness Copse. This movement implied not
" only carrying the guns forward a further mile over
" territory ankle-, sometimes knee-deep in slush, but
" bringing up also a further half million rounds of
" ammunition to serve the guns for the coming fight.
" The task was probably the most arduous which those
" under my command were ever asked to perform.
" Under heavy fire, in which fresh casualties were
" sustained, by nightfall guns and ammunition had

" been placed in their new position, and sighted to
" fulfil the new barrage chart.

" Such a barrage impels the utmost precision on
" the part of the commander ; and is a matter of
" mathematical delicacy for gun commanders. Having
" regard to the almost endless stream of bullets, death-
" dealing, delivered by each machine gun, the slightest
" inaccuracy in the calculation of angle or time is
" fraught with the greatest danger to troops advancing
" under cover of machine gun fire. This danger is the
" greater when it is remembered that the machine gun,
" unlike artillery weapons, has no fixed platform, and
" the agitation of the gun in action, without a sure
" bed to the tripod legs, will cause it to lose elevation.
" Not only was it necessary in the short time available,
" therefore, to bring guns and ammunition to their
" allotted station, but it was imperative to shore them
" up against sinking into the ground. My reserves had
" been used up, and there remained but half the
" numbers of my command, three men for each gun
" team. Of the four companies at my disposal two
" were allocated to go forward with the first lines of
" the assault and two, with sixteen guns, to cover the
" infantry with barrage fire from the edge of Inverness
" Copse.

" In reply to my telegram announcing heavy
" casualties, during the night three reserve officers
" tumbled into my new headquarters, now posted on
" the lée side of a derelict tank, one of whom was to take
" over command of one of the companies destined for
" the assault. He was almost fresh from the Machine
" Gun Training Centre at Grantham, and had never
" served before in the Ypres Salient.

" The ferocity of the cannonade defied the senses.

" The British batteries poured an incessant stream of
" shells overhead preparatory to the further attack on
" the morrow. The German artillery in titanic support
" of strong counter-attacks delivered by Bavarians
" hailed a most violent bombardment upon our support
" line and communications. So tremendous was the
" roar that its sound could clearly be heard in Boulogne,
" and even across the Channel in Kentish seaports and
" villages. The ground heaved and rocked. A tornado
" of earth clods and flying mud, splinters of timber,
" bricks and hot metal whistled all around. The swish
" and sigh of our own shells overhead was accompanied
" by unceasing crashes as the German shells thundered
" a gigantic defiance.

" We lay beneath the storm waiting for the dawn
" at whose first gleam the attack of my own division,
" which had come into line, was ordered. Short of
" responsible officers, my command of trained experts
" seriously reduced by casualties, and ever diminishing,
" during the night I appointed a private soldier who
" had already won the D.C.M. at Loos, a man of high
" intelligence and imperturbable pluck, to take com-
" mand of one company for the first assault. . . . The
" men, bewildered by the violence of the counter-
" bombardment, rallied at once to his singular coolness,
" grasp of essentials, and rapid orders. They knew him
" already as a fearless leader. Now as the tactical
" commander, N.C.O.'s and men alike rejoiced in his
" leadership.

" A further machine gun company detached from
" its own division had reported to me. The unit was
" fresh, its commander eager. I took this company,
" heavily laden with ammunition and guns, towards the
" Reutelbeeke in the hell of night, fortunately without

P

" loss. It was disposed in groups of four guns in an
" area almost free from fire, immediately behind the
" leading companies of the 98th Brigade. The barrage
" batteries being positioned, there was yet time to
" dispose the remaining company for the assault with
" the 100th Brigade. . . .

" At 3.30 A.M., just before dawn, the extraordinary
" happened. With outstanding gallantry the Germans
" attacked, two divisions,[1] just as we ourselves were
" preparing to leap to the assault. Almost simul-
" taneously both barrages lifted. The heavy bombard-
" ment sailed over my head to crash upon the com-
" munications and was replaced by a ferocious deluge
" of shrapnel and high explosive. ' Zero hour,' the time
" for action, had not yet arrived for my batteries. A
" comparatively clear view could be obtained across the
" Reutelbeeke valley and up the opposing slopes.

" I witnessed an astonishing sight. Dense masses
" of German troops were pouring down the hillside
" against our brigades waiting to assault. Suddenly
" the independent machine gun company's batteries
" opened fire. The range was almost point-blank.

" The commander so skilfully directed the fire of
" his company that, by holding it until the German
" officers, at the head of their troops, had topped the
" ridge and advanced down the forward slope, he could
" see the massed formation behind, coming over the
" ridge, as low down as the knee. As each mass
" advanced in this manner, he opened fire upon their
" ranks. The enemy was thus so far committed to the
" assault that he could not retire, but must advance.
" Low-flying aeroplanes, however, soon detected the

[1] 229th and 230th Reserve Infantry Regiments, 50th Reserve
Division, Wytschaete Group, 4th German Army.

" battery and both by machine gun action and directing
" artillery fire upon the gunners the enemy inflicted
" very severe casualties among them. So heavily did
" this company suffer that its commander, who with-
" drew his company in perfect order to a new position,
" was assisted only by his one surviving officer, who was
" badly wounded, and one N.C.O.

" During the action the German counter-battery
" bombardment was so fierce that despite a preponder-
" ance in our favour, guns of all calibres being locked
" almost wheel to wheel along the whole front, and in
" several lines, our artillery could appreciably be felt
" to grow weaker and weaker. Every form of com-
" munication had disappeared early in the day. The
" only possible means left was that of runners ; but
" as it took a runner nearly three hours to reach the
" imagined front line from the brigade headquarters
" at ' Tortops,' the direction of the battle became an
" impossibility. . . .

" The S O S signal was seen at every point along
" our lines. Our guns of all calibres and machine guns
" immediately opened fire. Following the bombard-
" ment, the enemy attacked in massed formation upon
" our lines, no less than six divisions being used in
" this attack upon our divisional front. On the right
" the posts of the 1st Queen's were overwhelmed, the
" enemy debouching from the village of Gheluvelt
" armed with flame-throwers. The stream of burning
" oil thrown from these devilish weapons reached a
" length of thirty yards and many feet in the air, and
" set fire to the trees, which being as dry as tinder
" immediately took fire. . . .

" The men of the 1st Middlesex and the 93rd
" Highlanders on the left flank met the Bavarian wave

" with Lewis guns, bombs, and at the point of the
" bayonet. The resistance was insufficient and the
" attack swept on.

" With such energy was the attack pressed that the
" whole of our line was thrown back. For some hours
" uncertainty prevailed. It was impossible to know the
" position of our own troops and how far in the German
" attack had penetrated. Commanders of all forma-
" tions from those of brigades, even down to platoons,
" were out of touch with their commands and with
" their flanks. The enemy, possessed of the advantage
" of ground, seems to have been in no such dilemma,
" for the bombardment lifted, and, as it seemed, with
" an even greater ferocity smote our communications
" and every approach to the beleaguered line. British
" batteries, which in the rear kept up a hurricane fire
" from their deep formation, possessed of no new
" information, although themselves now under the
" heaviest shell-fire, brought down the barrage line
" with the object of stemming any further infiltra-
" tion. . . .

" The plans for the original attack had now been
" abandoned, and until some definite news was received
" concerning the situation, I ordered my batteries to
" cease fire and to recondition themselves for further
" action. We buried our dead, twenty-seven of them,
" in graves already prepared by shell-bursts, marking
" each position with a rifle, thrust bayonet first into the
" ground, a steel helmet covering the butt, the
" common practice. The idle teams fell to the task of
" refilling ammunition belts and changing worn gun
" barrels for renewed action. . . .

" Late in the afternoon it was determined to renew
" the assault, for by now it was plain that the German

" counter-attack had been only partially successful, and
" it was thought that the enemy reserves would be
" weakened. Fresh troops from the brigade in reserve,
" two battalions of Scottish Rifles and one of Royal
" Fusiliers, came up platoon by platoon in shell forma-
" tion, even so sustaining heavy losses during the
" earliest stages of the advance. All day the enemy
" bombardment continued at the height of its fury.
" Beyond Polygon Wood the Australians, fresh troops,
" threw themselves to the assault. They stormed across
" the pitted ground, and as they advanced, taking
" numbers of prisoners, they reached the companies of
" Middlesex and Argylls, who, sustaining their posi-
" tions, had fought off eleven German attacks which had
" sought to oust them. So successful was the renewed
" drive through the posts where our infantry had held
" the German attack that the supports were able to
" carry forward to the original divisional objective.
" For one British division the achievement of this
" battle was a notable feat of arms, contributing lustre,
" not alone to the regimental records of those who had
" participated in it, but to the Salient, in which British
" warriors had already set up new records in British
" chivalry and courage. Not only had we withstood
" the fierce attacks of superior forces, but overwhelming
" them, had carried all the objectives planned for our
" own assault.

" So far as my own division was concerned, for the
" moment, the battle was at an end. We had yet to
" withdraw guns, ammunition boxes and equipment.
" But at dawn exhaustion possessed both sides, and I
" was able to bring mules right up alongside the gun
" positions and load the material without further dis-
" turbance. Even a German aeroplane, which swooped

" down to examine the labour, flew on without a
" greeting of machine gun fire.

" I brought out of action but one-third of the men
" who had first rested beside the lake at Dickebusch.

" And the soldier, who as a private had commanded
" a company in the assault, was awarded a Bar to the
" Distinguished Conduct Medal and a direct Com-
" mission in the field. I promoted him to the rank of
" captain and he continued to lead the company which
" he had so well commanded.

" The stout-hearted resistance of the 25th, in which
" already the division had sustained five thousand
" casualties, and the victorious attack on the 26th, in
" which all objectives were reached, was a triumph for
" all arms."

The independent company referred to in this
narrative was the 207th commanded by Captain A. M.
Gelsthorpe,[1] who received the D.S.O. as an " immediate reward."

Captured German documents showed what efforts
the enemy made on the 25th September against the
front held by the 33rd Division between the Ypres–
Menin Road and the south edge of Polygon Wood.
The attack by the 50th Reserve Division was made
while the 33rd British Division was actually relieving
the 23rd Division. The Germans had started a tremendous bombardment at 5.15 A.M. on the morning
of the 25th September. The enemy artillery concentrated to cover the attack consisted of 27 field artillery
and 17 howitzer batteries, 15 heavy howitzer and 5
batteries of high-velocity guns of long range. In
addition, the artillery of neighbouring divisions contributed support with counter-battery work. The

---

[1] Afterwards Bishop of West Africa.

.303-INCH VICKERS GUN MOUNTED ON POST FOR ANTI-AIRCRAFT WORK — IN ACTION.   TYNE   COTT,   YPRES
SALIENT, DECEMBER 1917

GERMAN 'HEAVY' MACHINE GUN IN ACTION, 1918

Germans attached the utmost importance to the success of the counter-attack.

The British front line taken over by the 33rd Division ran from the southern edge of Polygon Wood to the Reutelbeeke-Veldhoek trench to Carlisle Farm, known to the Germans as *Wilhelm Stellung*. The objectives ordered for the 33rd Division on the 26th were from 500-1000 yards in advance of this line, through Cameron House and Jut Farm. In ordering the counter-attack for the recapture of the *Wilhelm Stellung*, Major Hetthey, commanding the 3rd Battalion, 229th R.I. Regiment, laid down: "The newly won line is to be held as our front line at all costs." Not only did the 33rd Division repel the formidable attack of the 25th; but, despite the heavy casualties of the preceding day, succeeded in attaining the whole of its objectives with the exception of a small part on the right flank.

The elaborate machine gun barrage scheme, involving the advance of 48 guns to new positions some 800 yards ahead and laying out their lines of fire, was fired to its completion, in addition to the engagement of targets with direct fire during the German counter-attack and the answering of many S O S calls. Although there was no Corps scheme, Lieutenant-Colonel H. F. Bidder, D.S.O., the Corps Machine Gun Officer, arranged for five additional machine gun companies to be available. The corps front was 3400 yards long. It was covered by 136 machine guns, each with a frontage of 25 yards. The enemy attacked three times, with a final bid to wrest the ground gained from British hands between 4 P.M. and 7 P.M. on 26th September. Twenty-two German officers and 499 others were captured in the fighting.

A man of the 12th Company, 3rd Battalion, 229 R.I.R. stated that " The losses in the front lines were " heavy, but heavier in the reserve positions," a testimony to the efficacy of the machine gun barrage. The 10th Corps Intelligence Summary (No. 533, 27.9.17) stated : " All prisoners agreed in saying that " they had far more casualties from shrapnel and " indirect machine gun fire than from high explosive, " especially in these shell-hole positions " ; evidence which demonstrates the advantage of the steep trajectory barrage from long range machine gun fire.

The Field Marshal Commanding-in-Chief telegraphed, " Success constitutes a complete defeat of the " German forces opposed to you " : and Sir Herbert Plumer, " Heartiest congratulations, and especially to " the 33rd Division whose successful attack following a " day of hard fighting is deserving all praise." In this action Pte. Peter Dean, who, as a machine gunner had already won the D.C.M. at Loos on 25th September 1915, made it an anniversary, and was awarded the rare honour of a Bar to the D.C.M. and his "direct Regular " Commission in the field." In 1918 he was again awarded for gallantry in action, receiving the Military Cross.

As the third battle of Ypres pursued its desperate course farther and farther into the slime of Passchendaele, the tasks of machine gunners became always more arduous. The machine gun batteries, recognized by the enemy to be the veritable hornets' nests, whose fierce fights and furious stings continually frustrated every attempt by the Germans to concentrate and bring up reserves for the counter-attack, became the object of special aerial reconnaissance both between battles and during their progress. The batttery positions were

swooped upon by lines of low-flying aircraft, their teams
subjected to heavy machine gun fire by one machine after
another ; while " spotting machines " would indicate
battery positions by means of a rocket, observe for a
ranging shot by artillery, after which the machine gun
battery area would be subjected to heavy shelling.

In summarizing machine gun operations during the
third battle of Ypres, the First Army emphasized that
" forward guns can assist the advance of the infantry
" more by bringing to bear direct overhead fire than by
" advancing with the infantry." G.H.Q. declared :
" The Lewis gun is the natural link between the
" Vickers gun and the infantry, and it is impossible to
" know whether both types of automatic weapons are
" being correctly and fully employed, unless their effort
" is regarded as a joint one."

In the Second Army, the instance is given that
" Vickers guns kept up overhead frontal fire upon an
" enemy strong point, while the Lewis guns crept to a
" flank and assisted the infantry to take the position."

Again, " Lewis guns were made responsible for the
" immediate front of the objective, while Vickers guns
" covered the flanks and more distant approaches." [1]
The experience of both Armies showed, therefore, a
correspondence in tactical lesson in the use of automatic
weapons.

Late in 1917, the scene changed from the quagmires
of Ypres to the chalk downs of Cambrai, little scarred
by shell-holes. Brigadier-General Hugh Elles with
Colonel Fuller had selected this terrain for the test of
tanks in battle ; the tactics and field organization of
the operation being based upon the potentiality and

[1] " Tactical Summary of Machine Gun Operations," No. 2,
November-December 1917, SS. 201.

manœuvreability of the tank, other arms being subordinated to its requirements. The attack was notable almost unique, for its element of surprise—a first principle, always recognized but so hard to achieve—and it was this factor which contributed to the unusual and astonishing success of an offensive undertaken, at an unusually unfavourable period of the year. Some emphasis is here laid upon tank tactics although they fall outside the scope of this volume, because, as already noted, the Tank Corps was the child of the Machine Gun Corps,[1] and is yet a mechanized transport for machine guns, although possessing battle tactics of its own. The Tank Corps entered the Cambrai battle in the teeth of opposition. Tanks had failed at Ypres, for reasons which the Higher Tank Command foresaw, but which were consistently ignored by G.H.Q. Sir Hubert Gough, Commander of the Fifth Army, had issued a most unfavourable report upon tanks which the Tank Corps historians " condensed into a simple syllogism : " (1) Tanks were unable to negotiate bad ground. " (2) The ground on a battlefield will always be bad. " (3) Therefore tanks are no good on a battlefield."[2] The report is reminiscent of the uncompromising attitude adopted towards machine guns prior to the War by certain officers : and the same error of thought and judgment is perceived.

It is of no avail to consider weapons, whether projectile or *arme blanche*, except in regard to ground. The nature and potentiality of weapons must be considered separately, and, thereafter, in co-ordination with those of other weapons, arms and services. The formula for every British attack had been the prolonged

[1] See footnote, p. 233
[2] Williams-Ellis, " The Tank Corps," p. 89.

artillery bombardment, followed by its churnings of ground, which made it impassable for vehicular or any kind of heavy traffic, often even, as in the later stages of the third battle of Ypres, almost impassable for infantry except upon timber tracks specially built for the purpose. Tanks had been used under grotesque conditions.

General Gough added that tanks, " being no longer " a surprise to the enemy, had lost their moral effect " and had no value used in masses."

The tank battle of Cambrai showed that the new weapon, used as a surprise in fog, over ground undisturbed by artillery preparation, and used in masses, could contribute marked success. That the battle of Cambrai did not conclude with its initial success was no fault of the tanks, but was partly due to alarming events in Italy, which led to the plans for exploiting the battlefield being damped down. Insufficient measures seem to have been preconceived, also, to hold the ground captured by little more than 4000 of all ranks of the Tank Corps, assisted by a proportionate number of infantry.[1] Weary troops, with quite inadequate reserves, met the inevitable counter-attack, conceived with ambition and boldness by General von der Marwitz.

In the battle which followed, the Machine Gun Corps was heavily engaged. The difficulties of the Corps were increased by the failure to send forward officers with the first attack to make a careful reconnaissance of ground. It was found, also, that the tank tracks could not be used by animals with limbers or as pack train, since the wire was trampled and not cut by tanks, and no sufficient provision had been made to open

---

[1] The tank battle achieved a penetration of 10,000 yards on a front of 73,000 yards in 12 hours, capturing 8000 prisoners and 100 guns.

up the way in rear of the tanks. The machine gun teams were short of ammunition and water ; while communication was faulty.

Generally, two ideas seemed to dominate the mind of the Higher Command. First, the machine gun is a defensive weapon : in consequence, except in rare instances, they were " not pushed forward with any " boldness, and they missed many good opportunities " on the first two days of the operations." [1] The result, in part, was failure to consolidate the ground even by tanks. In mechanized warfare, wherein it has been shown that tanks can take ground, machine guns must be in close co-operation, provided with a means of mobility equivalent to that of the tank, for the purpose of holding ground. Second, the conditions of the ground at Ypres, requiring a special organization for machine guns, which in consequence usually fought the attack from stationary positions in batteries with long range and indirect fire, moving rarely by big bounds, seems to have impressed the mind of the Higher Command with an insistence that machine guns must normally so fight. At Cambrai, in consequence, the machine guns were too far behind the attack.

When General von der Marwitz counter-attacked on 30th November 1917, his machine guns followed the attack " with exceptional speed." Realizing our error in tactical handling, G.H.Q. laid down : " It is neces- " sary to consider automatic fire-power as a whole and " to distinguish between the different purposes for " which it is required in the forward system. It is " required :—

" (a) To assist the infantry in clearing out enemy

[1] " Tactical Summary of Machine Gun Operations," No. 2 November and December 1917, SS. 201.

" parties and in silencing snipers and individual
" machine guns. This is the work of the Lewis gun.
" (b) To organize for defence the ground won.
" This is the work of the Lewis guns and Vickers guns
" together, the Vickers guns being reserved for the
" organization of the most important features, and not
" necessarily defending these features by being placed
" on them.
" (c) To engage enemy targets during the advance.
" For this purpose it is advantageous to have some
" machine guns (guns of opportunity) specially de-
" tailed, which have no definite responsibility in organi-
" zation, and which can therefore move where they
" please in search of targets. . . ."

G.H.Q. summarized the machine gun lessons learnt
during the period of attack as follows : " The more open
" the fighting becomes, the more necessary is it that a
" large number of machine guns be retained under the
" hand of the commander of the force for the purposes
" of covering the advance." A note should have been
added that a machine gun officer should be appointed
to the staff of each Army.

Despite failures, there are recorded some remarkable
achievements. A German machine gunner captured
on 20th November stated that " British machine gun
" fire in the neighbourhood of Fontaine-les-Croisilles
" was so intense that four machine guns were unable to
" come into action, and the teams remained in their
" dugouts during the attack." On 30th November the
group commander of the machine guns was at brigade
headquarters, and in touch not only with his brigadier,
but also with the O.C., Left Group, R.A., who had his
headquarters in the same dugout. Therefore, he had
" unique facilities for information of all movements :

" both batteries being in telephonic communication by
" direct wire to Machine Gun Exchange, which itself
" had a direct wire back to Brigade Headquarters."
On the morning of the 30th, the enemy was observed
massing about Quarry Wood and entering Mœuvres.
This was followed by a heavy bombardment and the
S O S call, whereupon all guns opened rapid fire and
" many direct targets were obtained, as the enemy came
" down slopes in wave after wave. . . . Throughout
" this day and night most excellent work was done by
" batteries, and the system of controlled and co-
" ordinated machine gun fire by the battery method
" was amply justified." The G.H.Q. report notes,
also, that " The foremost guns got good targets, but
" became isolated by the infantry's withdrawal, and in
" retiring suffered casualties in guns and men." This
most important lesson was unfortunately ignored, as is
instanced by the failure to give local protection to
machine guns in the battles of March and April both in
the Fifth Army and on the Lys.

It may be laid down as a principle, therefore, both
for the attack and defence, that " local protection must
" be provided for machine guns." In each machine
gun unit, marksmen snipers and bombers, men selected
both for courage and initiative, must be detailed to act
with each pair of guns. In static positions, such men can
be usefully employed in belt-filling, or as spare gun
numbers. In the attack they should be used as scouts,
in defence exclusively for local protection, with eyes
always searching for bodies of the enemy attempting to
creep within bombing distance of the machine gun
position. Although not provided for by the machine
gun battalion establishment, the commander of the
33rd Battalion pays the highest tribute to the work of

his scouts, especially selected, trained, and organized as a Scout Section attached to battalion headquarters, " with a high *esprit de corps*, peculiarly their own." [1] At Meteren in April 1918, the scouts, under an officer, received one Military Cross, 5 Distinguished Conduct Medals, and 29 Military Medals, a sufficient testimony to their value.

The G.H.Q. report upon operations concludes with the important injunction that " The more vehement the " anticipated attack or counter-attack of the enemy, the " more the balance turns in favour of adopting a " defence in depth by means of a grouped resistance on " the battery system." This is precisely what was not done by the Fifth Army in the grave operations which followed after the lull of the winter months.

The third battle of Ypres brought a general recognition of the role which machine guns should play in supplementing artillery fire. From this date divisional brigade and battalion commanders became accustomed to the principle of the machine gun barrage, but this is not to say that they always understood when, where, and how it could best be applied. At critical moments, however, there was always a call for the machine gun barrage. Many illustrations are available as evidence of the efficacy of barrage fire contributed by batteries of machine guns, and these have been contributed both from our own infantry and from enemy sources.

The 12th Canadian Brigade, for example, carried out a most difficult operation in the assault upon Crest Farm, Passchendaele, on 30th October 1917, but obtained and held all its objectives. The War Diary of the 72nd Canadian Infantry records : " The work of the " machine gunners attached from the 4th Canadian

[1] War Diary, 33rd Bn., Machine Gun Corps, 12th/19th April, 1918.

" M.G. Battalion is deserving of the highest praise . . . the
" barrage was of inestimable value. As soon as it was
" no longer possible to fire on this area, Lt. B. C.
" Montagnon moved the Vickers guns forward and
" placed them on a very commanding position on Crest
" Farm, from which not only the front of our own
" battalion could be enfiladed, but also that of the right
" and left battalions. The artillery and machine gun
" barrage was splendid, but subsequently much trouble
" was experienced and many casualties caused by the
" shooting by our artillery."

It will be observed that here is an admirable
illustration of the utilization of the dual role of machine
guns in one operation. During the first phase of the
attack, machine guns conformed to the role of artillery,
in the second the machine guns assumed that of infantry
and were able to produce that sustained, observed,
flanking fire, which is the supreme safeguard to a
captured position while it is being reorganized for
defence. The failure of the artillery to contribute
effective defensive fire was due to lack of observation.

The command of machine guns in action must be a
" battlefield command," while artillery direction necessarily is from the battery position aided by the forward
observation. Nor is observation always practicable,
owing to smoke, dust, darkness or even a casualty among
observers. The close defensive barrage by artillery,
following an attack, and where the location of our own
troops cannot be accurately known at the battery positions, as in this instance, may frequently, therefore, be
impracticable. On the other hand, that of machine
guns, whose mobility permits of their presence wherever
infantry can go, is always available.

There is therefore often a period of time, following

the preliminary artillery bombardment which will have proceeded according to plan, wherein the only effective, and possibly the only safe, barrage is that contributed by machine guns with the officers on the spot in the forefront of the battle. The machine gun batteries, which have played their part in co-operation with artillery in the preliminary bombardment and creeping barrage as one function, can then, their task completed, be reorganized as forward, S O S barrage guns, these former occupying commanding positions from which to break up the enemy counter-attacks.

The new German tactical disposition first exploited at Ypres appears almost as the reincarnation of the tactical formation adopted by the Roman legion.[1] The legion generally consisted of 4500 men—3000 heavy infantry, 1200 lighter armed (*velites*), 300 horse. The heavy infantry, in strength equal to the German regiment, or British brigade, were the backbone of the legion. For battle they were divided into 1200 *hastati*, 1200 *principes*, and 600 *triarii*. All were armed with the large shield, metal helmet, leather cuirass, short thrusting and cutting sword. The *hastati* and *principes* each carried two short heavy throwing spears (*pila*), while the *triarii* were possessed of long spears. In an engagement they were drawn up in three lines: *hastati*, *principes*, *triarii*. The procedure in fighting was that the front line discharged a volley of *pila* and then rushed in with the short sword, a sequence not dissimilar from the volley and bayonet charge of the eighteenth century. If this failed the second line went through the same process. The sub-organization of maniples of 120 men arranged in chess-board fashion

[1] I am indebted to Captain G. C. Wynne for having introduced to my notice this comparison. See p. 318.

Q

enabled the *principes* to pass forward through the *hastati*, and the latter to retire through the former. The third line *triarii*, armed with the thrusting spear instead of the *pilum*, formed a reserve.

The two forward lines were armed, therefore, with both missile and shock weapons, while the *triarii* were armed with shock weapons alone. A similar organization, in theory, usually exists in modern war, the systems of command on the battlefield being the vital difference between the German tactical idea and that of the British. The German front line was armed with rifle, automatic rifle, mortar bomb—missile weapons— and the bayonet and sometimes also the bludgeon and dagger—shock weapons. The second, supporting line was similarly armed ; the third line being held in reserve for " shock tactics," in attack or defence, using either the bayonet or its missile weapon, the bomb, as a shock weapon at short range. The bomb in reality should properly be defined as a shock weapon, although thrown; so, also, is the flame-thrower (*Flammenwerfer*).

The vital element of control and direction in action is that which so closely approximates the new German system to the Roman : and marked a difference, for British practice, which at first sight may seem slight, but which in battle is of critical consequence. The regiment is a self-contained entity consisting of three battalions recruited from the same district, with its officers, leadership, and systems of promotion common throughout the whole regiment : the command of companies, corresponding to the maniples of the Roman legion, being interchangeable between battalions as the tactical situation demands. In the Roman legion, the command was vested in six tribunes, who held command in rotation. In the practical issue of battle the tribune commanded all three lines of *hastati, principes,* and *triarii,* his position being not in rear, but in the forefront of the battle : and he took command of the whole or elements of the two rear lines as and when required. The British brigade rarely consisted of battalions of common origin, though this was so in the two Scottish, the Irish, and some Territorial divisions, and in the Canadian and Australian divisions. Nevertheless, not only was the battle position of the brigade commander often in rear, but the front-line battalion commander at practically no time exercised the authority of command over the troops of a supporting and reserve battalion.

The Roman system was such that the front-line commander continuously during battle ordered the tactical disposal of all troops on the battlefield, for the obvious reason that he alone would be immediately familiar with its ebb and flow. The new German tactical plan, ordered by Ludendorff in the autumn of 1917, displaced the tactics of rigid lines by those of fluid groups, which, even in trench warfare or that of shell-hole positions, regained the mobility of infantry, and secured for the forward commander an authority over his sector, both frontal and in depth, no matter what battalions or companies from the second and third lines he might call to its aid.

The British adopted from the Germans the rigid three lines of defence, command being retained in the hands of the brigadier or divisional commander. When, therefore, a battalion from the second or third line was called upon to contribute to the battle being waged by the front line, in practice, a system of dual command became apparent, depending ultimately for direction upon a third authority, the brigadier, or divisional commander not immediately present within the battle zone.

The Germans, on the other hand, vested all authority in the fight, for the time being, in the " Kampf Truppen Kommandeur," the officer who commanded the front-line (*hastati*) battalion, but who assumed full command over the second-line (*principes*) battalion and the third-line (*triarii*) battalion should he require their support. The commanders of the second and third lines were obliged to carry out the orders of the K.T.K. throughout the battle ; while the duty of the regimental commander (brigadier) was to supply reinforcements from the second and third lines at call, and to organize the artillery, engineer, and other services to the objectives of the battle. Such a system enabled far greater speed in taking advantage of tactical situations, " opportunities," as and when they occurred in the battle, while giving greater freedom to the regiment (brigade) commander to organize fire for the purpose of covering his troops, and to keep in touch with troops operating on the flanks. From his position further in rear he was admirably situated to do this, and could also advise the battle commander—K.T.K.—of the progress of battle and give timely warning of any danger to his flanks. The point to press is that the battalion commander of the front line exercised supreme battle command over all infantry formations within the sector during an operation, the higher command—the brigadier or divisional commander—guiding, rather than commanding, the battle from a position at the base point of the fire fan.

It is difficult to conceive of a battalion commander of an English country regiment assuming command of two companies of Highland troops, subsequently reinforced by a battalion of rifles : though this is not impossible. On the other hand, it would seldom be possible to dispose a battalion in such depth that the battalion itself could be made to constitute the three lines of front, support, and reserve, a system which would be difficult, also, to administer and supply in battle. The British system tended, markedly, towards rigidity, as opposed to fluidity of manœuvreability, in battle, a fact sufficiently illustrated by the retreat of the Fifth Army on the Somme in March 1918.

Machine guns are, so to speak, both "missile" and "shock" weapons. The year 1917 established the tactical principle, also, that the machine gun is both a weapon of *principes* and *triarii*, as it were the short and the long spear cast upon one haft. Its characteristics make it so. But the machine gun is not a weapon of *hastati*. The proper command, organization, control, and direction of machine guns depends upon the realization of this fact. The automatic rifle is at once a missile weapon and a weapon of *hastati*.

The realization of the essential differences in characteristic and therefore in tactical handling between machine guns and automatic rifles, no matter whether the latter may be Maxim-pattern light " guns," as used by the Germans, without a fixed mounting, Lewis, Bren, or other similar weapons, is, therefore, the key to their disposition in the scheme of attack or defence.

The automatic rifle belongs to the front line (*hastati*) in defence, and should serve the *velites*, the lighter armed men who under modern conditions are the skirmishers and scouts, the spear-point of the attack.

Confusion of thought on this matter must lead to chaos on the battlefield, where the effective handling of machine guns depends first, absolutely, both upon free selection of ground, without heed to the rigid divisions

of line as between front (*hastati*) and support (*principes*);
and, second, upon the indestructible cohesion of the
machine gun unit, never less than the section (platoon)
with its transport, as a single tactical entity.

Machine guns, as a new arm with tactics of its
own, were, therefore, the weapons which produced a
new factor in the age-old Roman organization. There
can be no doubt that the Roman legion retained its
mobility and capacity for manœuvre. The enormous
power of artillery, the use of wire entanglements, and
the introduction by one side—the German—of machine
guns on a mass scale, produced the stagnation of trench
warfare. Even when the British machine gun strength
matched that of the enemy, the Higher Command
had yet to learn tactics. Weapons were balanced :
the power to manœuvre again was alone required to
revivify the battlefield, and to reproduce fluidity among
the *hastati, principes*, and *triarii*. The German machine
gun organization disposed the automatic rifles (light
machine guns) with the *hastati*, allowing the heavy
machine guns to be disposed by the regiment commander—who was invariably accustomed to their use—
upon ground behind the *hastati*, and varying between
the *principes* and *triarii* according to the topography of
ground, the nature of the target, and the task of the
moment, whether direct individual fire or the battery
barrage.

The German dispositions of infantry were made to
depend upon the framework of the mobile machine gun
defence ; while the disposition of the British defence
was made to conform to a system of infantry lines. The
result was immediately apparent, for example, as at
Passchendaele, 1917, where the Germans held the battle
zone with posts of light " guns " (automatic rifles),

corresponding to *velites* in front of the *hastati* positions, as the outpost, distributed in shell-holes, while the *principes*, support, line became one of machine guns disposed so as to be able to contribute overhead, indirect fire, or interlacing bands protecting the front. In consequence, while the British infantry lines, to which machine guns were subordinated, were heavily manned with infantry, inevitably producing exhaustion and lowered morale, the German organization was enabled to retain the bulk of its men, fresh, in the support (*principes*) and reserve (*triarii*) positions, located usually in large group dugouts.

The German command in battle remained in the front zone, while the British command was produced to an extremity always farther back, in fact, in accordance with " the chain of command." It would appear that the fullest exercise of authority must be conceded to the " battle commander " to fight his battle. The higher command, up the ascending scale from brigade to division, corps, and army, having devised the battle plan, settled the objectives and ordered the troops and munitions for the purpose, once battle is entered, has one vital task remaining, namely, by every means possible to secure success. Reference back for authority is neither the easiest nor the most certain way of attaining this end. Authoritative orders for reinforcements, protective fire, artillery bombardment, the use of tanks to overcome centres of resistance or to destroy obstacles, must come from the front : and all formations must be subordinated to such orders. The higher command, in touch with the wider situation, can first effectively make practical the orders from the battle front ; and, judging a wider situation, can exercise its discretionary authority by calling for changes of direction, for a halt in operations, for further advance or retirement, in accordance with the situation on the flanks, or the availability of reserves of personnel and fire-power. Although the battle front commander (K.T.K.) will usually be an officer of subordinate rank, if it be granted that he is possessed of the qualities necessary to good leadership, the duty of the higher commanders is to supply his needs and to meet his calls, while in a more general sense directing the wider policy of the battle zone.

The new German tactical scheme enabled such a system of command, and contributed a fresh manœuvre-ability to the battlefield in defence. As the new tactical idea was considered from the aspect of attack, the " infiltration tactics," used with such success in March and April 1918, developed. Again, the Roman legion system persisted throughout. The " storm troops " (*velites*), armed with light machine guns (automatic rifles), were thrust forward with the utmost boldness, creating gaps in the immobile British lines into which both infantry, as the *arme blanche*, and machine guns, as shock weapons, were pushed, by the battle commander. Nearly everywhere these tactics were successful, not-ably against the Fifth Army, which, considering the whole zone in terms of lines only, and of lines which were abandoned one after the other, rather than as defensive zones mutually supporting, withdrew at the command of the authority farthest from the scene of battle. The machine guns of the Fifth Army, apart from being dispossessed of their essential unit mobility and ammunition supply, were also subordinated to the concept of the infantry line. As line after line was abandoned, therefore, the machine guns became either isolated, and often forgotten, crippled from being able to fight their own purposive battle, or were forced to retreat with the infantry, impossibly handicapped by their man-handled loads.[1] Errors of the first importance seem therefore to have been made by the army commander. Rigid lines of defence did not and could not produce the manœuvreability essential to meet the new German infiltration tactics, involving the exploitation in rotation of their light and heavy machine guns. The rigid British lines destroyed the co-ordination of machine guns, and prevented the use of ground to advantage. The subordination of machine guns to the infantry dispositions deprived the guns of their tactical and administrative organization ; and, even of more vital consequence, of positions and fields of fire which had been tested and upon which machine gun commanders were prepared to fight. The army commander, exercising such authority, rather than conceding it to the battle front commander, deprived the latter of initiative and power. The subordination of the framework, the vital body of the defence, the machine guns, to its clothing allowed first the tornado of the German attack to tear the clothing to rags and finally to dash the life out of the body. By so doing the army commander deprived both himself and his subordinates of reserves (*triarii*) with whom to make the counter-attack, the very heart of the defence. In effect, therefore, the Fifth Army fought as without machine guns, clearly because the principles of their tactical use had not been comprehended.

[1] To Major-General Sir Ernest Swinton belongs the credit not only for conceiving the Tank—" the machine gun destroyer "—but, also, in the face of War Office opposition, for impressing upon Mr. Lloyd George's mind the need both for machine guns and for men to serve them. The detailed story of Colonel Swinton's contribution is contained in his own book, " Eyewitness," pp. 181-183.

CHAPTER X

1918

Authority of the Official History of the Great War—A machine gun
battalion in action in a defensive battle—The battle of the Lys—
Defence of Meteren, 12th-18th April 1918, by the 33rd Bn.
Machine Gun Corps—A broken front—Value of trained scouts
—Admirable field of fire obtained—Improvisation of signallers
—Infantry as machine gun escorts—Transport in action—
Retirement " section by section and gun by gun with covering
fire "—German casualties—Testimony to British machine gun
fire—Recommendations by battalion commander after the action.

THE year 1918 is a momentous one in the annals of
machine gunnery. The whole of the experimental
work had been successfully concluded, the text works
revised, and the working tools carried to a higher stage
of perfection. The principle that only a personnel
possessed of high intelligence and good physique could
be recruited for the Machine Gun Corps had been well
established, and its ranks weeded of those who did
not conform to the required standard. The battalion
organization was adopted early in the year. The corps
was called upon to fight both the greatest defensive and
offensive battles in the history of the world.

[1] " Saul slew his thousands, and David his ten thousands " (1 Samuel
xxix. 5). This inscription appears below the figure of David, sculp-
tured in classic style, upon the Machine Gun Corps War Memorial,
Hyde Park Corner, London.

The conduct of the battles of 1918 is, therefore, of the greatest possible interest and importance. Some of the actions will stand as epic in the history of the British army. These serve, therefore, as an essential part of the traditional foundation upon which a machine gun *esprit de corps* is founded. Lessons of the utmost value are to be learned from a careful study of these actions, which testify, also, to the qualities of courage, endurance, and self-sacrifice of men of British breed.

It would, however, be impracticable to recite the detailed story of the actions of every machine gun battalion. Certain battles, both of defence and attack, have been selected for description for the following main reasons. They are of historical importance, and are so regarded by the Historical Section of the Committee of Imperial Defence. They are typical. The information available was contributed by eye-witnesses at the time, and is set out in some detail in War diaries. The lessons to be obtained from them are valuable as affecting organization and tactical handling.

The first narrative of operations selected is marked in the Official History of the War with the following passage : " According to all accounts it was the " resolute handling of its machine gun battalion " which contributed most to holding the Germans " back from Meteren " (12th-18th April 1918).[1] The narrative which follows, almost word for word, is that communicated to 33rd divisional headquarters by the officer commanding the battalion within a few days after being withdrawn from the battle. The action is especially interesting because it illustrates the handling of a

[1] Official History of the War, " Military Operations, France and Belgium, 1918, March-April: Continuation of the German Offensives," p. 272.

machine gun battalion in a defensive battle against great odds. For two days the battalion suffered the serious handicap of separation from the horsed transport—in place of which mechanical means were dramatically improvised—the ever-present danger of ammunition supplies failing, heavy casualties, and a front of some three miles held with little infantry aid. The machine gun commander was afforded complete control of the battle area, placing his guns so as to form an unbroken belt of fire across its front, with guns disposed in depth, also, in order to meet infiltrations of the enemy by direct fire, and to contribute both overhead fire, directed by improvised signal, from observation posts, and indirect fire by means of map and instruments. The casualties inflicted upon the enemy, as ascertained from the German archives, were very severe, and a formidable attack in the full flood of success was brought to a standstill.

The infantry were subordinated to the machine gun defence scheme and tactical organization, being utilized to fill gaps between the guns, especially at night, to counter-attack and recapture positions momentarily lost, and to patrol between the gun positions. In a defensive battle such an arrangement, which upon the occasion described, had not been foreseen—that is to say, it was not designed by the General Staff—would appear to be ideal, allowing to the machine gun commander the fullest liberty in the disposal of his guns, allowing him to obtain from them the maximum effect.

Narrative of the battle of the Lys. Operations between Bailleul and Merris, 12th-18th April 1918.

" On the 21st March the storm broke on the front of " the Fifth Army. The division was withdrawn from " the line and we were moved by bus and train to

" Lattre St. Quentin.   Very little news filtered through
" except that the enemy had made attacks upon a
" stupendous scale ; and rolling up the Third and
" Fifth Armies had almost broken our line and that of
" the French ; and was now advancing rapidly on the
" road to Paris.

" We remained in our concentration area for two
" days ; but at 7 P.M. on the 10th April orders were
" received to proceed by tactical trains to the Caestre
" area.   My battalion, divested of its transport, but
" with all the guns and ammunition boxes, was hurried
" into wagons behind a snorting engine.   Near St. Pol,
" a great shell hit the train and killed forty of my men
" who were cooped up in one cattle wagon.

" We detrained at Meteren at 10 P.M. on the 11th
" April.   At 10.30 on the morning of the 12th, seated
" in a placid farm-house with my battalion bivouacked
" in a pasture among cows and poultry, I received
" orders from divisional headquarters to make a recon-
" naissance.   Taking three cyclist patrols, made up
" from my scouts, I hurried due south of Meteren to
" Outtersteene.   Here large numbers of both wounded
" and unwounded men were in full retreat.   I observed
" especially the men of one division, pouches still filled
" with ammunition, who had not fired a shot, but were
" running away in the face of the enemy, lacking order
" and organization.

" The military pattern of bicycle is both clumsy and
" heavy, but we pedalled laboriously farther on seeking
" the enemy.   Half a mile farther I came suddenly into
" view of groups of the enemy pushing forward under
" covering fire, behind them flaming homesteads.

" I rallied some straggling infantry and lined them
" out on a five hundred yards front as a screen so that

" the Casualty Clearing Station at Outtersteene might
" be evacuated. And at the gates of the C.C.S. I
" commandeered a Ford ambulance, instructing the
" driver to take me back to Meteren. I recollect some
" qualm of conscience concerning this misuse of the
" Red Cross, but no Ford ever went faster. I reported
" to the divisional commander, suggesting that my
" guns should be rushed to fill the breach and that the
" infantry should follow as soon as possible.

" In Meteren there stood an A.S.C. motor-lorry
" column. I requested the use of a lorry, but the officer
" in charge refused it. This was no time to stand on
" ceremony. I took charge, and instructed the driver, a
" bright young fellow who rendered yeoman assistance
" to the division during the ensuing days, to drive off.

" We halted at the farm-house, where I had installed
" my headquarters, and within a few minutes half a
" company of machine gunners, guns, and ammunition
" complete, had been packed into the lorry, while I
" myself, with my adjutant, sat beside the driver at the
" wheel, revolvers in hand. We drove straight towards
" the ridge on which stood the Hoegenacker Mill, and
" this became the fulcrum of the fighting. On the
" way we surprised the advance-guard of the enemy in
" a ditch. From our seat beside the driver my adju-
" tant and I loosed off our revolvers and killed the gun
" crew, German storm troops, and captured their
" machine gun.

" Upon the ridge which I had chosen as the line of
" defence, we came into contact with the scouts whom
" I had left behind. They, in close combat, were con-
" ducting a rifle duel with the enemy.

" Masses of British infantry with grave disorder, and
" often led on by their own officers, were retiring on

" Meteren.   At the revolver-point I halted one battalion
" led in retreat by its commanding officer, ordering the
" men to turn about and occupy the Hoegenacker Ridge.
" Three times I gave my order and put it also into writing.
" The men refused to move.   Finally I gave the officer,
" whose men said they would accept no order except
" through one of their own officers, two minutes in
" which to decide, with the alternative of being shot
" out of hand.   At the end of those two minutes I
" struck him ; and the regimental sergeant-major ex-
" claimed, ' That's what I've been waiting for all day,
" sir.'   He led the companies up to the ridge, though
" they proved but a feeble defence and dwindled away
" during the following night. . . .

    " My command was largely new, a host of untried
" youngsters, lads of eighteen and nineteen.   I had
" formed a little body of battalion scouts and mounted
" orderlies, sixteen scouts and eight mounted order-
" lies. . . .

    " I trained them diligently as scouts, and demanded
" their confidence and loyalty with every artifice of
" which a commander can make use, in order that in
" any part of a battlefield they should be my eyes telling
" me accurately what I must know without embroidery,
" but telling me also without an eye to the main chance
" —safety or glory.   And I knew each one individually,
" just for what he was worth.   Prior to Meteren, with
" a little weeding, I had proved them.   Throughout
" the battle, I know without question that where I
" went myself, there my scouts went also. . . .

    " I saw hundreds of British soldiers, rifles and
" ammunition intact, streaming down the roads, flying
" in the face of the enemy.   The roads were filled with
" them, if not actually running, all moving fast, bunched

" like sheep, and there were ambulances at the C.C.S.
" evacuating wounded and still bringing more in. The
" retreat, rout, panic, must have proceeded very fast.
" I asked some of the men where they were going. No
" one seemed to know. They said that swarms of
" Germans were behind and that everyone had been
" killed or captured. A captain said he was retiring to
" the hills behind. That would be at Cassel, or so far
" as he was concerned in his so obvious haste, at Calais.
" . . . Then I collected my handful of lads and we
" pedalled our bicycles farther south.

" We saw German soldiers from a meadow, but not
" an English soldier in sight. The enemy were about
" four hundred yards away, and turned a light machine
" gun on us. The boot of one of my lads was ripped
" and the front fork of my bicycle was so bent that the
" wheel refused to go round. I ran back to the C.C.S.;
" and it was there that I persuaded the young man with
" the Ford ambulance to motor me to Meteren. . . .

" My scouts, boys of eighteen and nineteen, showed
" extraordinary heroism, taking the leadership, and
" ordering the defence with uncommon coolness and
" initiative. I returned from the reconnaissance to my
" headquarters where the lorry was being loaded, and we
" made for the ridge. No sooner was the lorry halted
" than we came under heavy machine gun and rifle-fire.

" In a very few minutes eight guns were disposed on
" the crest of the hill, one of ' Hog's back ' formation,
" lying between the Steam Mill, west of Bailleul and
" the Meterenbecque by Merris, culminating in Belle
" Croix Farm and the Hoegenacker Windmill. The
" lorry returned, bringing two of my companies into
" action, and I disposed them over a three-mile front,
" absolutely naked of defence, and one which we held,

" almost unaided and alone, as will be seen, despite
" most heavy attacks and severe losses against the
" attacks of certainly six German divisions without
" relief for seven days.

" The importance which this slight rise of ground
" assumed on the morning of the 12th April and until
" nightfall on the 15th must be realized. Even as the
" Flers Ridge of the Somme battlefield is the only
" eminence between the great plain of Belgium and that
" of northern France, so upon a smaller scale the
" Hoegenacker Ridge is the only considerable rise in
" ground covering Hazebrouck and the approach to the
" Belgian hills, Kemmel, Mont Rouge, Mont Noir, and
" the Scherpenberg.

" Possessed of the Hoegenacker Ridge, with its all-
" round field of fire for upwards of 4000 yards to the
" south, a defending force can prevent the massing of
" troops for the assault, and can hamper all movement
" over a frontage of five miles and a depth of two miles.
" Conversely the capture of the ridge by the enemy not
" only gave to him valuable cover and concealment from
" observation as well as safety from direct fire, and free-
" dom to concentrate for the assault, but at the same time
" contributed observation facilities of the utmost value.

" As the ridge is possessed of an admirable field of
" fire to the south, so also there is a view, uninterrupted
" except for hedgerows and farmsteads, to the north
" and west, covering the southern and western ap-
" proaches to Meteren, commanding Flêtre, Merris, and
" Hazebrouck itself, a field of view and fire of exceptional
" advantage to attack.

" This point of such immensely valuable tactical
" importance to either side in the fight lay on the ex-
" treme right flank of the IXth Corps, and its frontage

" approximated to that of the XXIst Corps which on
" the 11th had evaporated in casualties and in a retreat
" of its remaining troops without rear-guard action.
" The IXth Corps itself, with every available man

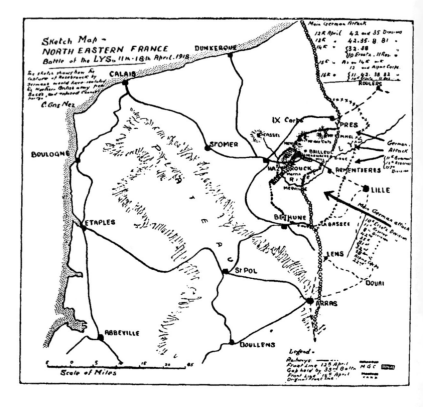

" capable of bearing arms, was strung out in a thin line,
" fighting desperately at every point against superior
" numbers, its resources wholly exhausted, not a
" platoon remaining which could be used to hold the
" ridge or to form a defensive flank on its right to the
" south of Meteren and Bailleul.
    " This was the situation at dawn on the 12th April.

" A gap, on a three-mile front, lay immediately before
" Hazebrouck, only four miles distant. With astonish-
" ing speed the Germans advanced with little or no
" resistance being offered. By 10.45 A.M., the hour at
" which in reconnaissance I came under fire by Outter-
" steene, the enemy had penetrated a depth of 5000
" yards, biting out a deep salient in the existing gap,
" with advanced troops armed with light machine guns
" spread out between Merris and the Steam Mill, south
" of Meteren.

" The right flank of the IXth Corps was in the air.
" The command of the Hoegenacker Ridge by the
" enemy would not only expose the corps line to being
" rolled up to the north through Neuve Eglise, but would
" prevent any further reserves, when brought up, from
" reaching the line, except at great risk in suffering
" heavy casualties before battle was joined, from direct
" fire from the ridge itself.

" The IXth Corps, indeed the whole front of the
" British army in Flanders, was, therefore, exposed to
" great peril. Hazebrouck itself was a rail-head and
" junction of strategic as well as tactical importance.
" Upon the town converged the British lateral com-
" munications, north and south, from the port of
" Dunkerque through Hazebrouck to Béthune, Arras,
" and St. Pol, and it was the focus of the railways from
" the coast at Dunkerque, Calais, and Boulogne. To
" the north of the Étaples–St. Pol–Arras line there is no
" other railway communication. The coast line be-
" tween Calais and Boulogne turns at right angles, east
" and south, at Cape Griz Nez. At the south-eastern
" corner of an approximate rectangle stands Haze-
" brouck, the other corners being Dunkerque, Calais,
" Boulogne. Dunkerque is only twenty-five miles

" distant, Calais, diagonally across the rectangle, thirty-
" two miles, Boulogne thirty-five miles. St. Omer
" itself, the convergence of important main roads, is a
" bare ten miles from Hazebrouck.

" Hazebrouck was, therefore, the key to the Channel
" ports, itself dominated by the Hoegenacker Mill
" ridge, a position on the morning of the 12th April of
" inestimable importance. The piercing of the line at
" this point, before the arrival of reinforcements to stem
" the tide, would break the British army in two,
" throwing the northern portion back on Dunkerque,
" Calais, and Boulogne, the southern army to form a
" new front facing north, with the loss of the Channel
" ports. Moreover, the loss of Hazebrouck would
" considerably increase the strategic danger to the
" ports themselves. Their loss involved a ready
" possibility for the intensification of the U-boat cam-
" paign, harassing cross-Channel communication. Al-
" though by the 12th French troops were on the move,
" these reinforcements could not arrive before the 14th
" or 15th, and, even then, should the Germans have
" broken through on the 12th, it is very doubtful
" whether the French could have contributed beyond
" assisting to form a new flank facing north, following
" the Boulogne–St. Omer road.

" To hold Hazebrouck at all costs was the vital
" necessity. To save Hazebrouck it was vital to retain
" the Hoegenacker Ridge until reinforcements, using the
" rail-head, had come into line and had filled the breach
" in strength.

" The 33rd Division detrained at Meteren at 10
" P.M. on the 11th. The 100th Brigade was sent up
" immediately to stem the tide at Neuve Église. The
" 98th Brigade was hurried north-east of Bailleul, each

" brigade with a company of machine guns. The 19th
" Brigade remained in reserve in Meteren, two com-
" panies of the 33rd Battalion Machine Gun Corps in
" farm buildings half a mile to the south. No one was
" aware of the débacle on the right of the IXth Corps, to
" which, with the exception of some small units of
" corps troops, hastily mobilized, the 33rd Division
" was the last available reserve. And of the division
" but one brigade and two machine gun companies
" remained on the morning of the 12th April.

" At 10.45 A.M. the reconnaissance had been made.
" At that moment the decision to hold the Hoegenacker
" Ridge had been taken. By 11.30 A.M. machine guns
" were in action from its summit sweeping the ap-
" proaches from the south. At this hour the ridge was
" held. With the exception of the loss of two gun
" positions rushed by the enemy on the 13th, whose gun
" teams died at their posts, the ridge was held until
" 7 P.M. on the 14th, after reinforcements had come into
" line, with French reserves in great numbers east of
" Hazebrouck, and after a trenched position, wired, had
" been constructed just south of Meteren.

" The particular incident of going into action on the
" Hoegenacker Ridge in the manner described is prob-
" ably the most thrilling in which organized machine
" gunners have ever participated. The rapidity of action;
" the extraordinary situation; the perfect discipline and
" drill; the setting of untouched farm-houses, copses, and
" quietly grazing cattle ; the flying civilians with their
" crazy carts piled high with household chattels and the
" retiring infantry behind ; the magnificent targets
" obtained ; and the complete grip of the situation by,
" and determination of, machine gunners—this action
" takes the highest place for all time in the history of the

" Machine Gun Corps, and is an epic of the tenacity
" and grit of the British soldier, well led by subordinate
" commanders with backs to the wall fighting against
" great odds.

" After an hour of the action, I made a very full
" reconnaissance with my adjutant. We discovered in
" the Belle Croix estaminet beside the mill a crowd of
" stragglers, fighting drunk. We routed them out, and,
" with a machine gun trained on them, sent them for-
" ward towards the enemy. They perished to a man.

" Then, as we ourselves left the inn, we found that
" the advancing Germans had infiltrated between our
" gun posts, and we came under a hot machine gun fire
" at close range. Why we were not immediately torn
" to ribbons passes my comprehension. We dropped
" to the ground on a field, fortunately heavily furrowed
" by fresh ploughing, and while machine gun bullets
" flicked past our ears and ripped the haversacks on our
" backs, we worked our way down the furrows as
" rapidly as possible, clawing at the earth as we
" travelled on our stomachs.

" About 1.30 P.M. the 1st Queen's [1] began to come into
" line from the direction of Meteren, but had no informa-
" tion whatever, and I disposed A Company in the line
" while my adjutant led D Company into position.

" With the commander of A Company I stormed
" the windmill which had fallen into the German hands,
" and we recaptured it in a hand-to-hand fight with
" German storm troops.

" The equipment for my signallers was with the
" transport, and I placed two men in the loft of the wind-
" mill with handkerchiefs tied to sticks, so that from
" the windows of its eminence they could watch the

[1] 1st Battalion, The Queen's Royal Regiment (West Surrey).

" moves of the enemy.   One man, a great hulking fellow
" from the Yorkshire moors, remained in the mill-top
" for three days until long after it had fallen into Ger-
" man hands, and finally escaped back to our lines
" attired in the uniform of a German soldier, after the
" mill had been blown down by our own artillery fire.

   " By two o'clock the left flank of the Queen's had
" been turned, the troops who were supposed to be
" in position, those stragglers whom I had collected,
" having dwindled away.   I could see large bodies of
" the enemy concentrating about fifteen hundred yards
" south-east of Meteren and in the copses by Outter-
" steene.   As they debouched we wracked them with
" machine gun fire, and could observe enormous losses
" inflicted among them.

   " I finally collected a party of many different units
" under a Cyclists' officer and disposed them to give
" local protection to my guns, especially on the left
" flank by the Steam Mill towards Bailleul.   Troops of
" every formation now began to dwindle into the line,
" rushed up in motor lorries from the headquarters of
" the IXth Corps.   Cooks, batmen, pioneers, even
" what seemed like a platoon of town majors under an
" area commandant.

   " By nightfall the line, though extremely thin, was
" continuous and held.

   " I entered a farm-yard in the village of Merris and
" found a foaming horse accoutred in the yard.   I was
" held in conversation by the farmer, who alleged the
" horse to be his own.   On leaving the house the horse
" was gone, so it then seemed that it must have be-
" longed to an enemy patrol.

   " Meanwhile, on my instruction, and following his
" own initiative, my good friend, the lorry driver, had

" made journey after journey through intense shell and
" machine gun fire, bringing ammunition, personnel,
" picks and shovels to my headquarters at the mill, and
" distributing tools round the Queen's outpost line.

" We worked feverishly during the night throwing
" out a wide stockade around the machine gun posts.
" But under cover of the mist, at dawn on the 13th, the
" enemy delivered a heavy attack on the centre of the
" line, at Belle Croix Farm. The Queen's gave way and
" two of my gun posts were rushed, both officers in
" charge being killed, and the company commander
" wounded. A company of the Queen's made two
" counter-attacks, and three times within one hour the
" mill passed from our hands to those of the enemy and
" back again. I was not ' at home ' in the mill during
" the first early morning assault, or without doubt I
" should have been killed, though I returned to join the
" second counter-attack, which re-won the mill.

" One of my sergeants went out to retrieve a gun
" which had fallen into enemy hands at dawn ; and a
" corporal penetrated the enemy lines to a distance of
" two hundred yards and brought back the other, which
" he got into action. Both men reported that the teams
" had died at their posts, having piled enemy dead
" before their guns.

" The early afternoon of the 13th was most critical.
" The enemy had courageously pressed forward. We
" were under continuous shell and machine gun fire,
" suffering casualties all the while, and the Queen's,
" who had only recently been reinforced by very young
" and inexperienced soldiers, began to weaken all along
" the line and retired from the ridge to a position about
" 800 yards to the north. The attack had been pressed
" hard on our left, and I feared that we should find

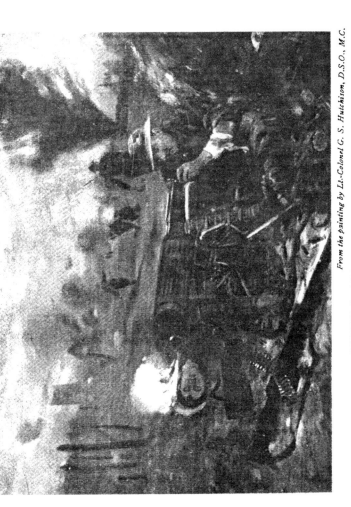

From the painting by Lt.-Colonel G. S. Hutchison, D.S.O., M.C.

"WITH BACKS TO THE WALL"

The 33rd Battalion Machine Gun Corps at Meteren, Battle of the Lys, 13th April 1918

" ourselves assaulted from the rear. So, with two
" horses which had been found, I rode with my orderly
" as far as Bailleul. There was not a soul in the streets
" of this once favourite billeting town. We galloped
" over the cobbles while shells fell among the masonry,
" and brick-dust filled the eyes and nostrils.

" I was able to establish touch with a brigade on our
" left and requested them to squeeze in to prevent the
" enemy from penetrating the village of Meteren. I
" did not now think it would be possible to maintain the
" line. We were running short of ammunition despite
" the exertion of the lorry driver, had no spare barrels,
" and with the exception of the Cameronians, no further
" reinforcements came to my long and scattered line.

" But at eight o'clock my transport officer arrived,
" and in a style reminiscent of the Royal Horse Artillery
" at an Aldershot field-day, the fighting limbers with
" belt-boxes and small-arms ammunition were galloped
" through a hail of shell and machine gun fire to our
" gun positions ; and my mounted orderlies, too, had
" arrived to be with me as far-seeing eyes and quick
" messengers to give me information from, or to carry
" orders to, any part of the line.

" In the late afternoon German cavalry galloped out
" from the cover of the copses to the south-east of
" Meteren, but were decimated by our fire.

" Apparently an order had been issued by the G.O.C.
" 19th Brigade for a retirement of the infantry to a line
" 1000 yards north of the Hoegenacker Ridge on the
" late afternoon of the 13th. No such order was com-
" municated to me. Most of the troops had in fact so
" retired. Many had become casualties, due especially
" to lack of training in the use of cover and ground.
" The losses included many officers endeavouring to

" rally inexperienced soldiers who continually exposed
" themselves and suffered losses from an enemy who,
" creeping forward, made admirable use of every fold
" of ground and of each hedgerow and ditch. Despite
" this order, the commander of A Company of the
" Queen's with his remaining men remained an invalu-
" able escort to the machine guns, continually patrolling
" the gaps between them.

" By night a continuous hail of bullets was kept up
" from the ridge, cones of fire, interlaced, and enfilading
" the whole front.

" At dawn on the 14th a further very heavy attack
" was made on our positions, and wide gaps were made
" in the front covered by the Queen's and the Cameron-
" ians.

" The enemy exploited these gains to full advantage,
" pushing forward light machine guns with great
" rapidity. The Queen's were very much shaken, and
" with the Cameronians again began to recede from
" their positions. On this morning our line was
" definitely maintained by the splendid devotion to
" duty by my machine gunners, who suffered severe
" losses.

" I moved continually between my posts, sometimes
" on horse-back, and sometimes on foot, and witnessed
" the enemy dead piled before our guns. The heaviest
" losses were inflicted.

" So critical was the situation that I issued orders to
" my sergeants in charge of gun teams that at any time
" they saw British troops retiring they were to fire on
" them ; and from near the mill I saw one of my gunners
" destroy a platoon of one regiment which in its panic
" had taken to flight.

" Between 6 and 7 P.M. another determined attack

" was made on our front. I had sent back con-
" tinuous reports to the brigadier commanding the
" 19th Brigade, and so seriously did he regard the
" situation that he asked me to come to him in his
" headquarters in Meteren personally to report. He
" asked me whether it was possible for any line to be
" held south and east of Meteren pending the arrival of
" further reinforcements, none of which could be ex-
" pected immediately.

" I replied that this was possible. He turned over
" to my command two platoons of the 2nd New Zealand
" Entrenching Battalion. The line, 800 yards north of
" the Hoegenacker Ridge, which I had already caused
" to be trenched and wired, was that which up to the
" end of the operations on the 19th constituted our
" front line ; and this I now made our front line on the
" 14th. I could not have asked for or expected any
" better co-operation than that rendered by the New
" Zealanders. I immediately issued written orders for
" the withdrawal of my guns to this line, and for them
" to be disposed in depth behind it. ' The withdrawal
" ' to be carried out, section by section, and gun by
" ' gun, with covering fire.' No finer retirement could
" have been carried out. In the face of great enemy
" opposition, and in the teeth of heavy machine gun
" fire at its outset, it was carried out without loss to
" either personnel or material, and every gun was with-
" drawn by concealed approaches and with irreproach-
" able discipline to the line to which the infantry had
" retired with some disorder. . . .

" There is further evidence as to the tactical import-
" ance of the Hoegenacker Ridge to be found in its later
" history. In full realization of the command of
" ground to the north and west afforded by this emi-

" nence, prior to the forward drive of the Second
" Army as part of the general allied offensive, orders
" were issued for the capture of the ridge. It was
" necessary for this to be done in order that troops
" could be massed for the subsequent attack under
" cover from observation. The assault on the Hoege-
" nacker Ridge, a minor operation, was carried out by
" the 9th (Scottish) Division on the 18th of August.[1] It
" is significant that within four days of its capture by
" the British the Germans evacuated the whole of the
" Lys Salient with the object of releasing their own posts
" and movements from observation.

" By dawn on the 15th I had established a good line.
" To this returned my signallers from the loft of the
" Hoegenacker mill. On the morning of the 15th I
" called for a volunteer from among my mounted
" orderlies to reconnoitre the whole position. My
" groom, riding my big black horse, ' Old Bill,' fleet of
" foot and a magnificent jumper, rode the whole length
" of the line under a hail of fire for three miles along the
" front of our posts, while I, observing him, noted his
" trail upon my map, and thus was able to mark the
" whole of our front. As he rode past the front of the
" 1st Queen's, the men rose from the little trenches
" which they had dug and cheered him lustily, as they
" had done when the transport wagons had galloped
" through their lines delivering ammunition to my
" posts.

" Towards the end of the action on the 18th, when

[1] " History of 9th (Scottish) Division " (p. 331) : " The ground
secured was of real importance as it dominated the whole sector, and
unless the enemy had abandoned all hope of defence in this district he
was bound to counter-attack. . . . Four days after the capture of the
Hoegenacker Ridge the Germans commenced a retreat on this front
which did not close until they had abandoned the whole of the Lys
Salient."

" our line was firmly established, French troops were
" appearing as reinforcements. . . .

" We, who strove to break the Georgs Offensive in
" April, and succeeded, must also pay our tribute to the
" courage and tenacity of the German assault. Every
" intelligent German soldier must have realized from
" his knowledge of political events that the Georgs-
" Schlacht was Germany's last throw of the dice, the
" final chance for victory.

" South of Bailleul, the spear-point of the thrust
" towards Hazebrouck, was the Alpine Corps, com-
" manded by General von Epp, the cream of which was
" the Bavarian Life Guard Regiment.[1] The histories
" of the regiments composing the 6th German Army
" declare how battalion after battalion hurled them-
" selves into the battle-line against Meteren and south
" of Bailleul. They record, also, a tragic list of casu-
" alties.

" While we may recommend the courage of the
" assault, we may glory in the satisfaction that machine
" guns in the hands of men of toughest breed withstood
" every attack—fire-power, superior at the decisive
" point, supported by a morale no less high than that of
" the enemy. To the machine gun went the victory.

" By the 17th of April it was clear that the German
" attack had expended itself. Each hour the strength
" of our artillery, both 18-pounders and French 75's,
" supported by adequate heavier pieces, arrived to the
" defence. Ammunition was conveyed to the lines by
" pack animals and limbers during the night ; while the
" General Staff conveyed new machine guns and belt-
" boxes to my headquarters in the Divisional cars.

" The 14th Jager Regiment, fighting on the left of

[1] Das Königlich Bayerische Infanterie Leibregiment.

" the Alpine Corps, ' encountered murderous machine
" ' gun fire,' as is related in its Regimental history.

" The 10th Reserve Infantry Regiment of the 81st
" Division which stormed Belle Croix Farm reports
" losses in this battle of 30 officers and 631 men. Its
" history records that at ' 5.30 on the afternoon of the
" ' 12th a further attack was made against the English
" ' line, when the 3rd Battalion came under most heavy
" ' fire. It was reinforced between 6 and 7 by the 2nd
" ' Battalion, and later relieved.' There appears to have
" been no lack of energy in this assault, and these
" Landwehr men seem to have rejoiced in the English
" canteens and ' good French red wine ' which fell into
" their hands.

" The 35th and 42nd Division led the German
" attack against the Hoegenacker Ridge. The losses of
" the 35th Division, amongst its regiments the 61st,
" 141st, and 176th, were so heavy that the division was
" withdrawn on the 14th. Between the 12th and 16th
" April the 42nd Division, composed of the 17th, 131st,
" and 138th Regiments, lost 50 per cent of its total
" strength.

" On the 13th two further divisions, the 81st and
" 8th, were thrown into the attack. On the 13th a fresh
" assault was made by the 10th Ersatz Division, the
" 11th Reserve Division, the 32nd Saxon Division, and
" the 30th Division. On the 15th the 12th Division,
" with the Alpine Corps, was added. On the 16th the
" attack was made by the 11th Reserve Division, the
" Alpine Corps, the 38th Division, with the addition,
" also, of the 42nd Division ; while the 32nd Saxon and
" 10th Ersatz Divisions, which had suffered very heavily,
" were withdrawn to Reserve. On the 17th, three
" Divisions, the 81st, the 38th, and the Alpine Corps,

LESSONS FROM METEREN 255

" whose earlier attacks had been frustrated, were thrown
" into the battle, together with the new 22nd Division
" which had been hurried from Alsace.

" The attacks of these ten divisions broke down
" with the heaviest losses on the front held by the
" 33rd Battalion Machine Gun Corps between the
" south of Bailleul and Merris from the 12th to
" the morning of the 18th April. . . .

" Certain important lessons in organization were
" emphasized in the Meteren battle.

" In operations of a fluid character, where manœuvre
" over a comparatively wide area is possible, machine
" guns are most effective if organized under one control,
" with one centralized source of ammunition supply,
" feeding with reserve personnel, and replacement of
" damaged equipment.

" The officer ordering the tactical disposal of
" machine guns in the battle must not permit himself
" to become too closely involved in any one section of
" the fight. His command of weapons, capable of
" sustained accurate fire, implies his direction of the
" means to obtaining fire superiority. His duty is to be
" closely in touch with the infantry brigadiers and
" battalion commanders conducting operations, whether
" in attack or defence. Although since the War
" machine gun organization has reverted to the in-
" clusion of one machine gun company with each
" infantry battalion, it appears that, in operations on a
" large scale, the brigade and divisional machine guns
" must again be placed under the command of one senior
" officer governing their tactical disposal. Without
" such organization the brigade or divisional com-
" mander may be deprived of highly concentrated
" reserves of fire-power, immediately available, offering

" a small target to the enemy, essentially mobile, capable
" of delivering a shattering blow at any given point in
" the attack to assist infantry infiltration and progress,
" capable also of stemming the tide of an enemy success.
" The commander of a division, the largest tactical unit,
" requires such a weapon of force and reserve in his own
" hands.

" I note that prior to the Meteren operations train-
" ing had pursued the following lines : ' Concealment
" ' of guns and personnel when in position.   Study of
" ' ground and contour.   Depth in defence.   Siting of
" ' guns in order to obtain Cross Fire in front of Infantry
" ' Posts and Strong Points.   Bands of fire.   Close
" ' liaison of all ranks with Infantry.   Proportional
" ' value of Direct and Indirect fire whether for Barrage
" ' or Harassing purposes.   Use of Battalion Scouts.
" ' The value of curiosity as a military virtue (Continuous
" ' study of everything and anybody.   Why is it there ?
" ' Why not ? etc.).   Supply, dependence on the
" ' Battalion and a central source.'

" In the same diary, following Meteren, I find, also,
" the following observations, which remain of value :
" ' It would appear that the most efficient method of
" ' despatching a Division ready for fighting at a
" ' moment's notice, by Tactical Trains, is in the
" ' following sequence—One Brigade Group : Machine
" ' Gun Battalion (or 3 Battalion M.G. Companies, less
" ' 1 with the leading Brigade according to present
" ' organization) with " Fighting Limbers," i.e. 32 four-
" ' horse four-wheeled vehicles ; 64 animals of which
" ' 32 are provided with Pack saddles and can be used
" ' as Pack animals : one Brigade Group.   Divisional
" ' Headquarters and Signals as decided necessary.   (In
" ' present M.G. organization both the latter Brigades

" ' would be without their Machine Gun Companies.)

" ' Beyond question each Machine Gun Unit de-
" ' spatched by train must be accompanied by its
" ' " Fighting Limbers." It occurred in the operations
" ' under review that a M.G. Company marched to
" ' battle with its guns, tripods, and the few belt boxes,
" ' which could be carried by the gun team personnel,
" ' disposed in Field Kitchens of Infantry Battalions.
" ' Other Companies went into action carrying, besides
" ' guns and tripods, 6 or 8 belt boxes per gun (only)
" ' over great distances, being entirely cut off from their
" ' Transport, including adequate belt box supply, spare
" ' barrels, condensers, and ammunition.

" ' Without the " Fighting Limbers " the great
" ' power of the weapon is greatly circumscribed. The
" ' importance of Machine Gunners, guns, and "Fight-
" ' ing Limbers " going everywhere together is as great
" ' as the undenied importance of the guns, transport,
" ' and personnel of the R.F.A. proceeding together.

" ' In daylight a Machine Gun Unit, well disposed,
" ' can hold a line the length of which is determined by
" ' the size of the Unit and the contour of the ground,
" ' without Infantry support. During darkness or in
" ' thick mist this is not practicable. By his tactics of
" ' infiltration the enemy can easily penetrate a line thus
" ' held (the line is one of posts without patrols or
" ' connecting files).

" ' It would appear that a Machine Gun Unit with
" ' a proportion of Infantry, definitely attached to it, can
" ' hold a line against an enemy attack. Therefore,
" ' in order to save casualties and to provide an ade-
" ' quate reserve for counter-attack, the normal Brigade
" ' front can be held by a Machine Gun Company,
" ' disposed in depth, with one Infantry Battalion

S

" ' disposed as local protection for the guns, for obser-
" ' vation, and to deal with individual enemy scouts, etc.,
" ' leaving two Infantry Battalions intact, available for
" ' the counter-attack. The Commander of the forward
" ' Infantry Battalion and the Commander of the
" ' Machine Gun Company must be together. (The
" ' present M.G. organization might prove such an
" ' arrangement to be embarrassing to the two com-
" ' manders.)

" ' It seems that had the various unattached forma-
" ' tions thrown into the fight been definitely allotted
" ' to Machine Gun Units, that the line and its flanks
" ' would have been better safeguarded. Patrolling
" ' during darkness and on misty mornings would have
" ' been better carried out and the line more securely
" ' guarded ; while gaps in the line could have been
" ' better supplied.

" ' I cannot overestimate the value of employing
" ' Scouts and Mounted Orderlies with a Battalion
" ' Headquarters. The scouts must be specially
" ' trained, with a high *esprit de corps* peculiarly their
" ' own. They should form part of the establishment
" ' of the Battalion Headquarters, and should not be
" ' part of the Section (or platoon).

" ' There must be far greater co-operation and
" ' support between automatic rifle and machine guns,
" ' the Lewis and the Vickers. During these operations,
" ' the enemy again and again contributed fine examples
" ' of how the tactics of these two weapons can be
" ' blended. The " Battalion Snipers " seemed to be
" ' the only men whose duty it was to fire rifles. Every
" ' rifleman is a sniper.

" ' Some bombs with the spare numbers of each
" ' Machine Gun Team should invariably be carried

" ' for local protection. A number of surplus guns, it
" ' is suggested 6, should be definitely handed over to
" ' the Machine Gun Battalion Commander from Ord-
" ' nance as immediate reserve in case of casualties.
" ' The presence of a machine gun on the spot may save
" ' a situation.

" ' The Machine Gun Section, 4 guns, is the
" ' machine gun fighting Unit. This must be recog-
" ' nized by Infantry. One gun may prove to be a
" ' " white elephant."

" ' During the operations several farm-houses were
" ' loopholed by the Royal Engineers for the Machine
" ' Gun Corps. Such positions were not taken up.
" ' The enemy, with his preponderance of artillery, on
" ' every occasion proceeded to "knock-out" farmhouse
" ' after farmhouse, inflicting heavy casualties on the
" ' occupants. It was observed that the enemy only
" ' occupied buildings which we presumed to have been
" ' demolished. Buildings which appear to the enemy
" ' to be demolished by his artillery fire, especially those
" ' with cellars, must be fortified and occupied by us
" ' whenever possible.' "

Special Order No. 2 of the IXth Corps concerning
the operations between 12th and 19th April 1918, at
Meteren, includes the following : " The maintenance
" of our line was undoubtedly due to the splendid
" devotion to duty and initiative displayed by the
" machine gunners, whose losses were very severe.

" I was particularly interested in the very difficult
" situation at Meteren,[1] April 1918," wrote the Adjutant of the German Alpine Corps, admittedly among the

[1] This letter from Major Graf von Armansperg is reproduced in
the Official History of the Great War, " Military Operations, France
and Belgium, 1918. March-April: Continuation of the German
Offensives," p. 304.

finest enemy troops, after reading an account of the operation. " We were accustomed to definite success " in attaining our objective everywhere, in Serbia, in " front of Verdun, in Rumania and Italy. For the first " time on this 13th April we succeeded in gaining only " a few hundred metres of ground." The attack was against a position of three miles of front held by one machine gun battalion, reinforced later by a very weak brigade of infantry and two platoons of the New Zealand Entrenching Battalion. The machine gunners held the gateway to Hazebrouck for nearly a whole week against the repeated assaults of several German divisions which broke down. In the 33rd Division Narrative of Operations occurs this conclusive passage : " The bulk of the fighting was borne " by the M.G. Battalion, who accounted for many of " the enemy."

Captured Operation Orders showed an extensive attack all along the line by the Sixth German Army. " The leading waves," says the 33rd Division report, " were not able to leave their positions owing to the " intensity of our machine gun fire."

CHAPTER XI

MACHINE GUN BATTALIONS IN ACTION—THE
DEFENSIVE BATTLE—MARCH-APRIL 1918

Battalion organization considered—The views of G.H.Q.—Failure
of Army Commanders to implement higher orders—The Fifth
Army retreat—A " set piece " defence—Man-power and fire-
power—Deficiency of orders and instructions—Action of
machine gun battalions cited from War diaries—Lack of
machine gun co-ordination in the Fifth Army—" The most
lethal weapon of the war "—Experience of machine gun
battalions in Second Army—Failure to recognize the services
of the Machine Gun Corps in despatches—Difficulties of the
Official Historian—German evidence—Fire action by 31st
Battalion—Use of machine guns and automatic rifles—German
instructions for tactical employment of heavy and light guns—
" This excellent weapon "—Examination of Fifth Army use of
the machine gun arm—Various critics answered—Chaotic
thought—Detailed experience of several battalions in March
1918—Machine organization abandoned—The essentials to
good machine gunnery—Valuable memorandum by Third
Army—New Zealand organization—Lessons learned—Summary of employment of machine gun battalions in a defensive
battle—A famous Order—Sir James Edmonds reflects.

THE account of the action by the 33rd Bn. Machine Gun
Corps, in April, precedes that of the battles of March
because the operation was distinctive as a machine gun
battle fought in accordance with the new battalion
organization. In many respects, also, the action was
unique : at least in having available a detailed account

of what happened and of the tactics employed.

The lessons, too, are of vital importance. The roles of the brigadier in charge of the battle zone and of the machine gun commander were perfectly harmonized, the former very properly contributing the direction of the battle to his subordinates on the spot, supplying his needs, and building his defence upon the frame-work of the machine guns. The machine gun commander asked only infantry escort for his guns, and for local counter-attacks, where enemy infiltration had penetrated between his guns, and, if permitted so to remain, would have outflanked their positon and especially have prevented their movement and man-œuvreability. This was his tactical requirement. Beyond this, he needed only the material for the fight, ammunition, spare parts, guns to replace casualties, and additional men to help to fill belts and to carry ammunition. These were provided at call. Wherever a straggler was to be found, he was requisitioned and sent forward under the orders of the battle commander. The services rendered by the Divisional Ordnance Department (D.A.D.O.S.) were also of the greatest value. The Divisional Command functioned like a well-oiled machine, with its chain of command centred in furnishing the fight with its needs.

The machine gun battalion organization was being tested during March and April. We shall return, therefore, to examine how other battalions fared during the Battle of the Lys. For the present, the focus of attention will be directed to the defence of the Fifth Army.

The controversy which has raged around the conduct of the Retreat by General Sir Hubert Gough, with its charge and counter-charge, with its hair-splitting over phrases and its propagandist appeal to prejudice, seems to overlook certain vital matters. A regimental officer is helpless in the face of bad orders. In battle it often occurs that those who command cannot see, and that those who do see do not command. It can never be permissible to break off an engagement except as a manœuvre : a leader must be sure of the ability to manœuvre successfully before he is justified in ordering a retreat. No discipline, as such, exists in the firing line : there is only mutual consent. Discipline begins behind the lines. Among other things discipline implies good organization.

When G.H.Q. had, after careful, even perhaps too slow, consideration, decided to inaugurate the battalion organization of machine guns, the argument was set out in a memorandum on the 10th February 1918. The emphasis of this document was in the following terms :

" The fighting of the last two years had disclosed
" certain faults in the present organization which
" militates against the efficiency and *esprit de corps* of
" this service (Machine Gun Corps), and it is clear that,
" if full advantage is to be taken of the experience
" gained as to the tactical handling of machine guns in
" the field, it will be necessary to introduce an organiza-
" tion whereby the full power of machine guns can be
" developed and their *esprit de corps* increased.

" The present organization fails in the following
" respects :

" The guns in a division are organized in four
" separate self-contained units without a directing head.
" The result is diversity of opinion and method, and
" lack of uniformity. . . . This organization is too rigid
" and does not meet tactical requirements either in
" attack or defence. . . .

" The formation of battalions renders the organiza-

" tion flexible. The enhanced importance of machine
" guns, especially in defence, and the necessity of adopt-
" ing an organization which will permit of the full power
" being obtained from the machine guns is so urgent
" that I hope these proposals will be accepted forthwith."

That the decision was of first-class importance,
and that army and corps commanders were entirely
familiar with the arguments is suggested by the controversy which had brought the decision to a head. On
21st October 1917, G.H.Q. had issued a circular letter
upon the organization and establishment of machine
gun companies. This memorandum stated : " Great
" diversity of opinion exists as to the conditions such an
" organization should fulfil, and as to the tactical role of
" the machine gun in the field." A questionnaire
accompanying the memorandum seriously threatened
the existence of the corps, going so far as to enquire—
" Would it be preferable to select men from the infantry
" battalions in each division to maintain the machine
" gun companies of the division, replacing them in
" battalions by ordinary infantry drafts ? " presupposing,
as it appears, that no special training for machine
gunners in weapon, in technique, and in the use of
ground was necessary at all.

This memorandum had, however, directly paved
the way for the battalion organization ; and, even preceding the decision by G.H.Q., battalions had been
formed, in fact if not in name. The army commanders were, therefore, familiar with the reasons which
finally led G.H.Q. to settle upon the battalion organization, and on the 16th February the Army Council
" approved in principle so far as the battalion organiza-
" tion of machine guns is concerned."

" I trust," had written the Chief of Staff for Sir

Douglas Haig, " that approval in principle will be given " to these proposals as early as possible, as it is of the " greatest importance that any measure of reorganiza- " tion should be put into effect at once."

There was no delay. By 19th February, orders had been issued in the field, but preceding the final authorization, commanding officers, adjutants, transport officers and other appointments had assumed duty on the 19th January. The service of machine guns, brought to a higher state of administrative and tactical efficiency, was therefore available to army commanders more than a month prior to the German attack : nor was there any doubt that the onslaught would be delivered in the early spring.

There was ample time, therefore, in which to organize and co-ordinate the machine gun plan upon an Army basis. It had long been recognized that machine guns are the very fibre of a defence. British experience on the Somme, at Arras, Cambrai, Ypres had burned this lesson into the minds of the fighting troops. Yet, though the new organization, designed to produce greater tactical efficiency, was available, it was neglected. The machine guns were quite insufficiently disposed in depth. Both the Third and the Fifth Armies demonstrated this fault. No effective machine gun barrage scheme was organized. Few concrete emplacements were available : and, if machine guns are the framework of defence, all available labour should have been turned to provide such strongholds of defence. There was insufficient ammunition at the machine gun posts. No instructions were given to infantry as escorts for the machine gun teams, even after general orders for retreat had been given. This last omission was disastrous. The machine guns remained to cover the retirement, and were then left to carry their heavy burdens with depleted gun-teams and with no kind of local protection : while, except in rare instances, the essential transport had been sent miles away.

The mist of the morning of 21st March enabled the German troops, under cover of a furious bombardment, to approach close to the British lines, and in consequence direct fire from forward guns was limited. This development should not have mattered very much : for in the known circumstances it was neither desirable nor necessary to hold large numbers of infantry in the front defensive zone. It was, in fact, held by posts. There were, however, sufficient machine guns available for a scheme of indirect barrage fire which, if organized, might have thrown the mass of the German attack into confusion and inflicted the heaviest casualties upon them : while the infantry brigades were held for counter-attack.

Such guns, disposed in depth, should have been located in concrete strongholds, disposed in depth, organized in pairs, controlled in batteries, immensely supplied with ammunition, protected by small bodies of infantry under resolute leadership. If and when the attack passed through the first barrage zone, the outpost line should have made signal by telephone and runners to indicate the fact, so that range could be shortened to the second barrage line. Should the enemy have penetrated the second barrage curtain, then, while some guns remained, with infantry escort, to cover the retirement, the other guns would be retired by transport to secondary positions, organized in the same manner as the first. It is no condition of such organization that the grouping of machine guns in pairs, linked together as batteries with a common target based upon interlacing cones of fire at the longer ranges, should restrict individual action and initiative. Quite the contrary. To appreciate the dual role of machine guns is to understand how flexible can be their disposition and manœuvreability provided that gun positions are not bound by divisional areas and trench lines.

The defence plan was a " set piece," and there appears to have been no difficulty in its organization. Mr. Lloyd George, in a statement issued on 20th March 1937, exonerates General Gough[1] for all blame in " organization." He refers to " The refusal of the " Fifth Army to run away even when it was broken." When an Army is broken it implies surely that the control has passed beyond the domain of generalship. No one has doubted the courage and endurance of the average British citizen soldier : what has been held in criticism—and most rightly so by military critics, if the lessons of history are to be of any value to the future— has been the generalship. The attack began on the early morning of the 21st March : by the evening of the 22nd the Fifth Army had been driven in some places, or had retired by orders of alarmists, completely beyond its battle zone and half the Army was beyond its last prescribed defensive line. Mr. Lloyd George continues with the assertion : " It was not the fault of the " Fifth Army nor of their gallant General that although " the attack had been anticipated for weeks the line was " so thinly held at that point."[2] Resistance is not a matter of man-power but of fire-power. The questions at issue are whether the fire-power available was sufficient to prevent a retreat which, as a " broken army " without leadership, sometimes dissolved into

---

[1] The Index to " The Fifth Army," by General Sir Hubert Gough, contains no mention of machine guns.
[2] From a letter sent to the Fifth Army Dinner, London, 1937.

disorganized rout: and whether this fire-power was used to the best advantage.

Throughout the whole of the Fifth Army there is no record of a machine gun battalion having been permitted to fight as a battalion. Thus the " full power of " machine guns was not developed." No scheme for co-ordinating machine guns along the Army front was arranged. Hence the organization was not rendered flexible. Neither was there any concerted machine gun barrage : nor were the guns disposed in sufficient depth. No orders were given to the infantry as to their co-operation with machine guns. Having regard to the paucity of men of which Mr. Lloyd George makes much, the clearest and most definite instructions should have been given to all infantry commanders as to the purpose of the new machine gun organization, and as to their own role in building upon its framework. Nothing of the kind was done. This was in striking contrast with the general experience of the Second Army at the battle of the Lys.

Excerpts from the War diaries of machine gun battalions disclose the following illuminating points :

The 12th Battalion was " divorced from its transport. " The men carried all their belt-boxes (16 per gun), guns " and gun equipment." The battalion commander expresses in his report : " The importance of not " separating a M.G. Battn. from its transport cannot be " over-emphasized."

The 36th Battalion notes that it was " impossible to " see 100 yards." Yet, contrary to instructions which laid down that machine guns were not to be placed in the trenches, a proportion of the guns available were so disposed. The battalion commander records that " the enemy bombed down the trenches and captured " the guns when the infantry retired."

The 22nd Battalion, which met with some local success in inflicting casualties, states : " Great difficulty " was experienced in obtaining sufficient S.A.A. [am- " munition] for refilling belts, but this was overcome by " collecting spare bandoliers." In a " set piece " defence and " planned retirement," which the Fifth Army retreat is alleged to have been, there seems no reason why sufficient ammunition should not have been available and provision made for it ; especially to machine guns.

The 4th Battalion " retired with the infantry." In this instance the battalion commander was successful in retaining a part of his transport. " The guns were " mounted on limbers and galloped back to take up " new positions." But the infantry again retired.

The 8th Battalion placed its companies at the disposal of brigades, contrary to instructions.

The 21st Battalion, commanded by Lieutenant-Colonel Reginald Settle, D.S.O., M.C., was admirably organized. On the night of the 21st-22nd it covered counter-attacks by the 2nd Lincolns and 7th Leicesters. The battalion " remained in action, its commanding " officer killed, until ordered to withdraw or over- " whelmed."

The 18th Battalion, too, fought with great gallantry. " The guns organized in depth and disposed to be " mutually supporting." There was, however, no Army scheme to co-ordinate divisional machine gun battalions, so that, in the result, the depth and mutual support attained in the 18th Division was lost by continual outflanking, where such proper disposition of machine guns did not exist.

The 30th Battalion, which brought 10 guns successfully into action in defence of Ham, was " greatly

270 MACHINE GUN BATTALIONS IN ACTION

" outnumbered and surrounded " and " compelled to
" evacuate." The battalion retired with the infantry :
but at the time of evacuation had sustained only one
officer casualty. No infantry escort was provided for
the guns. Had this been available it is doubtful whether
a retirement was at all necessary. Mr. W. P. Andrew,
who was taken prisoner on 21st March, wrote, " The
" front line was a skeleton consisting of isolated Lewis
" gun posts, to say nothing of inexperienced personnel.
" . . . Not more than 3 or 4 Vickers guns were in con-
" crete positions." While he was firing to his front the
enemy " sent a strong bombing-party to the rear . . . the
" first Hun bomber got within 20 yards before I turned."

The 24th Battalion reports that on the 26th " No
" order was given to the battalion at all. We remained
" in position and covered the retirement of the 1st
" Royal Fusiliers."

The records of other battalions engaged, although
sometimes showing heavy casualties—the 61st lost 14
officers and 320 other ranks missing ; the 8th, 16
officers and 300 men—and giving accounts of local
actions wherein severe casualties were inflicted upon the
massed advance of the enemy, in no instance demonstrate
a clearly conceived plan of defence, wherein machine
guns were the key-points, co-ordinated so as to be
mutually supporting ; and disposed in depth throughout the Army defensive zone, in order to prevent the
turning of flanks.

Where a division made a stand it found its flanks
exposed by others falling back. The machine guns
upon which a new flexibility and manœuvreability had
been endowed by G.H.Q. were forced to correspond
with the general retreat ordered by Sir Hubert Gough
on the night of the 22nd.

It is the contention here that had the Fifth Army commander co-ordinated his machine gun defence,[1] well supplied with ammunition and positioned in concrete, and, further, had he issued incontrovertible orders that machine guns were to be regarded as the framework of defence, the machine gun positions " to be defended at all costs," then no disorderly retirement would have been the sequel even of his precipitate order to retreat. Indeed, it is conceivable that the German attack on this front would have been crushed, without its enormous prizes in prisoners and material, and no doubt with the heaviest casualties to the enemy. The accomplishment of one machine gun battalion at Meteren, holding a three-miles front against the attacks of several German divisions, could surely have been repeated on the Somme. As Mr. Lloyd George wrote in his Memoirs, " the machine gun was the most lethal " weapon of the war."

The criticism here is of the tactical ordering. This is not to say that there were not many instances of superb gallantry by machine gunners, most of which must go unrecorded. In the 21st Battalion, the War diary states : " Only one message received from 2nd " Lieut. Dalzell. This was timed 10.0 A.M. and " stated : ' Enemy through, numbers unknown, am " ' knocking hell out of them.' " In the same battalion, Corporal Livesey was captured, but almost immediately escaped, and then hid. During the darkness he observed a German cycling along a track beside him. He shot the German with a revolver which he had picked up, and retraced his steps through the German lines, rejoining his own battalion, and continuing the fight.

The action of the machine gun battalions in the

[1] Compare footnote 2, p. 305.

Second Army under Sir Herbert Plumer at the battle of the Lys, April 1918, has already been instanced. The performances of other battalions, though not so spectacular, provide several valuable lessons and serve to corroborate those of the Somme battles in the preceding month.

The 25th Battalion was heavily engaged, east of Bailleul, from 10th April, on which date Lieutenant-Colonel J. D. Deane Drummond, D.S.O., M.C., was wounded. Command was taken by Major W. W. Ashcroft, who, in taking part in a counter-attack on the 11th, was killed. Between this date and the 14th, the battalion suffered further heavy casualties among its officers and N.C.O.'s. Temporarily withdrawn from the battle, the battalion was again in action upon Mont Noir, and before the month was out the casualties had mounted to 4 officers killed, 15 wounded, and 9 missing, and a total of 475 other ranks. The services rendered by this battalion in desperate situations were of the highest possible value.

The 49th Battalion, fighting as a tactical unit astride the Bailleul–Armentières road, rendered yeoman service, and similarly suffered severe casualties among its officers. The battalion was noted as " specially dis-" tinguished in the recent fighting." Instances of its work are that " 2nd Lieutenant Marshall with his two " guns advanced by short rushes under heavy fire, and " drove the enemy over the railway." 2nd Lieutenant Bentley " engaged a large party of the enemy at 600 " yards range : good observation was obtained and the " strike of the bullets was seen right in the middle " of the party and heavy casualties were seen." Another gun, having fired at 500 yards, advanced and " collected one light machine gun, 6 unwounded and " 12 wounded prisoners and counted 25 dead of the

" 107th Saxon Regt." On 17th April, many good targets were obtained. " Telescopic observations " showed that heavy casualties were inflicted and the " consternation caused could be distinctly seen." By the 18th, after heavy fighting only 13 guns remained intact. There is no doubt that the guns of this battalion gave solidity to a defence which from time to time was about to break, yet the lack of any kind of appreciation of its work seems to be expressed in a special order issued by the 147th Brigade after the operations—" All " ranks can be proud that they have shown that with " rifle and bayonet the Boche can be defeated."

The 59th Battalion, part of which was fighting at Neuve Eglise, reports that " The 4 M.G.S. were able " to pulverize the attack at short range and inflict very " heavy casualties." Nevertheless, the infantry withdrew. In recording his observations after the fight, the commanding officer noted : " A small infantry escort " of picked men should be attached to each pair of " guns. . . . It is hard to fight one's way back and at " the same time carry guns and belt-boxes."

Such was the general experience of nearly every battalion engaged in the March and April battles. In the Fifth Army, upon one sector, a machine gun company remained to cover the retirement of an infantry brigade. No one was left behind to assist with the loads or to give protection to the machine gun teams. When they retired, almost surrounded, they found that stockades of wire had been thrown out by the infantry ; and under heavy hostile fire were forced to crawl through the barricades, suffering severe casualties in so doing and losing many of their weapons and much material.

Lack of appreciation of the work accomplished by

T

machine gunners was subsequently noted by Colonel G. Lindsay, First Army machine gun officer, always zealous for the well-being of the corps which had been so much his child, in a report to G.H.Q. on 14th May 1918. He wrote : " Steps to be taken to obtain proper " recognition in Special Orders, Despatches, etc., for " the Machine Gun Corps. The omission to do this " has caused much disappointment to all ranks, and is " very detrimental to *esprit de corps*." It must be remembered that the Machine Gun Corps was a picked body of men. The reports by inspecting officers invariably noticed " the fine bearing and physique " of the men." With only seven exceptions these reports also pay high tribute to the admirable state of discipline and efficiency found throughout the battalions of the corps. These battalions, it should be emphasized, were considerably larger than were those of infantry, the transport equalled that of a brigade, while the tactical responsibility, covering a divisional front, far exceeded that of an infantry battalion. Nevertheless, brigade and divisional commanders frequently ignored the existence of machine gun battalions and companies, and seldom bestowed a compliment, far less a decoration, upon the machine gunners. The action fought by the 33rd Battalion has been contributed at some length. The Official History of the War (" Military Operations, France and Belgium, 1918," March and April) refers to the action of this battalion in six pages and notes, " For this and its action on the succeed- " ing days until 19th April, the 33rd Battalion Machine " Gun Corps received a 'record' from the IXth Corps,"[1]

---

[1] Official History of the Great War, " Military Operations, France and Belgium, 1918. March-April: Continuation of the German Offensives," pp. 270-72.

of which only six were awarded throughout the battle. Yet the War diaries of the 19th Brigade and 1st Queen's do not suggest that machine guns ever existed. But an order of the 1st Queen's, dated 16th April, paragraph (i), begins : " Platoon commanders " will ascertain from the men's paybooks the number " of men inoculated within the last 12 months," a suggestion as to the relative importance of two matters during the fiercest fighting in history.

In regard to this latter, recommendations for "Im- " mediate Awards " were scaled down. The Machine Gun Corps, possessing no influential personages at headquarters promoted to the higher ranks, had no one of authority zealous for its proper recognition, as had such corps as the Royal Engineers and the Royal Regiment of Artillery. The Machine Gun Corps was without Territorial affiliations and so did not have the advantage of the advocacy of members of Parliament and others interested in sustaining local prestige. As the result, decorations and awards were often con- tributed tardily and without sufficient appreciation of the services rendered by a body of men whose perform- ance should naturally have been of that excellence to be expected of a *corps d'élite*.

Negligence on this matter was, however, not uni- versal, and one such letter of appreciation addressed to Lieutenant-Colonel F. G. Chalmer, D.S.O., is published hereunder :

" *To O.C., 9th Divisional Machine Gun Battalion.*

" I have been trying to find out for the past week " particulars of officers of your battalion who did " particularly good work with my battalion at St. Eloi " on 25/4/1918.

" It is difficult to get full details, as everyone was
" very busy at their own job on that day, and impossible
" to get names, as we had only gone into the line a few
" hours before the attack took place. Two officers,
" however, appear to have stood out, one who had guns
" at the crater and was killed later in the day, and an-
" other who had guns at Piccadilly Farm who though
" severely wounded worked his guns until the last.

" It is impossible to speak too highly of the conduct of
" these two officers, who throughout the day fought their
" guns with the greatest daring and disregard of danger.

" The whole work of the machine guns was mag-
" nificent ; all ranks are loud in their praise and
" unanimous in saying that they were mainly instru-
" mental in breaking up with heavy losses the numerous
" attacks that the enemy launched on the position, under
" probably the hardest conditions in which men have
" ever had to fight.

" (*Sgd.*) J. INGLES, Lieut.-Col.

" Commanding 5th Cameron Hrs."
4/5/1918.

Those responsible for the compilation of the Official
History of the War have always been presented with
peculiar difficulties when presenting an account in
sequence of such wide-flung battles as were those of
March and April 1918, wherein, moreover, formations
and units often became inextricably mixed together.
The task is not easier when it is considered that some of
those who bore the brunt of the battles perished fighting
their own directed, individual battle against great odds.
Their last history is unknown beyond the tale of the
steady staccato of their guns when all else had retired.
It is rare, indeed, that the War diary of any higher

formation assists. Regiments with historic names received their "mentions," while the Machine Gun Corps was often forgotten.

Nevertheless from the German side we have overwhelming evidence of the effectiveness of machine gun fire and of the fight made by machine gunners. General Ludendorff specifically warned his troops of the danger to be expected from the British machine gun nests. A German order of the 13th Reserve Division dated 23/4/18, found on a captured prisoner, stated: " It must be taken into consideration that, even during " the heaviest artillery preparation, hostile machine " gun nests will remain in action," a sufficient testimony to the courage of the Machine Gun Corps.

The following are typical of the reports of prisoners. Captured south-east of Vierstraat on 26th April, a prisoner from the 39th R.I.R., 13th Reserve Division stated, " the losses of the 3rd Battalion from M.G. fire " were so severe on the first day, especially at the opening " of the attack, that during the night of 25th-26th April " the battalion was organized into one strong company " of about 190 men. The 12th Company had 18 men " and one *Leutnant* left out of a previous strength of 88."

The anticipations of the divisional order had been realized.

The 21st Division Summary, No. 17, of 27th April 1918 stated : " All prisoners agree that their heaviest " casualties have been from M.G. fire. Several prisoners " taken yesterday state that M.G. fire seemed to come " from all directions, both on the morning of the 25th " and 26th, and the resistance made by our M.G.s has " had a strong moral effect on the German infantry."

The report upon the fighting in the battle of the Lys by Lieutenant-Colonel V. L. S. Cowley, D.S.O., M.C., commanding the 31st Battalion, is of great interest. The battalion was admirably organized, while its tactical handling showed both boldness and a fine understanding of the task. Prisoners reported in respect of a local counter-attack covered by the battalion that " owing to the accuracy of machine gun fire they could " not put their heads above the trench and so were " captured without a fight." The raiding party captured 22 unwounded and 3 wounded prisoners. For its part the 31st Battalion received the congratulations of the army commander. A further counter-attack by the 93rd Brigade was accompanied by 2 machine guns with the third wave of each battalion, the teams carrying 8 belt-boxes apiece. The advance was admirably timed and the machine gunners suffered no casualties. The attack was covered by a machine gun barrage on the final objective, which caught the enemy and caused them severe casualties.

Lieutenant-Colonel Cowley reports that on the 12th April, " the infantry made no attempt to fire at parties " of enemy walking down hedges. . . . Although no " pressure was being put on them by the enemy they " continued to fall back in disorganized bunches, thereby " leaving machine guns in isolated positions . . . 4000 " rounds were fired before ammunition ran out, when " it became necessary to withdraw, the machine " gunners being practically surrounded, though heavy " casualties had been inflicted on the enemy."

In summarizing the operations, the commanding officer states : " The outstanding feature has been the " inability of the Lewis gunners to carry out their role " of covering infantry and fighting rearguard actions. " This work had to be taken over by machine guns. " Though great success was attained, it was achieved

" only through the heroic behaviour of officers and men
" alike, and with the loss of a large amount of valuable
" gun equipment and unnecessary casualties and fatigue.
" . . . There were but few cases, except in the Guards
" Brigade, when the infantry gave any thought to the
" people who were so valiantly enabling them to get
" back. . . . If Lewis guns are not to be used, it is
" essential that escorts of stout-hearted men be provided
" for machine guns. . . . The right place for the officer
" commanding the machine gun battalion in active
" operations is at the forward brigade headquarters."
This report confirms those of other machine gun
battalion commanders, and emphasizes the thesis as to
the respective roles of machine guns and automatic
rifles propounded in Chapter IX.[1]   No clear instructions had ever been issued on the subject ; nor is there
any evidence that machine gun units and infantry conducted combined schemes while in rest areas.   Even
at the Machine Gun Training Centres at Grantham
and Camiers, no publication seems to have appeared
defining the tactical employment of two different
weapons whose mechanism alone superficially suggested
the similarity.[2]
The Germans, however, not only understood the
essential difference between the two weapons, but from
Fourth Army headquarters on 11th June 1917 were
issued detailed instructions for the " tactical employment " of the ·08/'15 light machine gun, excerpts of
which serve to corroborate the view which it is suggested
leaves no alternative :
" The ·08/'15 machine guns should be employed

[1] Chapter IX, pp. 225-233.
[2] Tactical Summary of Machine Gun Operations, No. 2,
November-December 1917 (SS. 201), p. 11, contributes brief suggestions only.

" independently of the ·08 machine guns [heavy,
" corresponding to the Vickers guns of the Machine
" Gun Corps] of the machine gun companies, and
" should be sited accordingly. They should be posted
" in the front line, either in shell-holes or in one of a
" number of alternative positions reconnoitred in ad-
" vance. They need not be distributed by platoons,
" but particular stress should be laid on flanking and
" cross fire. They should not fire over the heads of
" infantry. . . . Good results can be obtained against
" reconnoitring patrols and troops moving to the
" assault. . . ."

In presenting something of a narrative of the
defensive operations during March and April 1918, it
has not been possible to include accounts of the actions
fought by machine gun battalions of the First and
Third Armies. In the latter, the action of the Guards
machine gun battalion was especially distinguished.
This history must necessarily concern itself primarily
with the tactical development and use of machine
guns ; and, in consequence, the operations of certain
battalions of the Second and Fifth Armies, for reasons
which are self-evident, have received the greater notice.

As already quoted,[1] a critic of "machine guns (heavy)"
suggests : " Was ever a most useful weapon so mis-
" handled, and on some occasions even forgotten, as was
" the machine gun ? . . . When one remembers coming
" across earnest machine gun teams in the back areas
" studiously firing into the night one is still apt to feel
" very sad. I never knew what became of their bullets,
" but I never read that the enemy had suffered."[2] If men

[1] See p. 111.
[2] 'Weapon and Target,' by Lieutenant-Colonel N. J. Macky,
M.C., A.D.C., N.Z. Military Forces, "Army Quarterly," January
1937.

will ignore the evidence they are bound to arrive at false conclusions.   Clearly, it would be disastrous for future organization if ill-informed criticism of this character should be permitted to govern vital decisions.   The writer exclaims : " We have perhaps not got a proper " perspective of our weapons . . . we can realize what " sheer waste of organization we indulged in."   Views of almost precisely the same nature were in vogue after the failure of the Montigny *mitrailleuse* in 1870-1 ; and while, after the Manchurian War of 1904-5, Germany rapidly armed with machine guns, very little progress was made in the British army.   Even up till late in 1918, corps, divisional, and brigade commanders and other staffs often showed that they possessed no " proper perspective " of the machine gun, and were often unable to understand its characteristics, beyond repeating the senseless slogan—"a weapon of oppor- tunity."   In consequence, everything possible seems often to have been done to render the organization non-effective.   During the winter 1917-18, machine gun organization was being closely considered by the War Office and G.H.Q.   The final conclusion was set out in G.H.Q. memorandum of 10th February 1918 as follows : " If full advantage is to be taken of the " experience gained as to the tactical handling of " machine guns in the field, it will be necessary to " introduce organization whereby the full power of " machine guns can be developed."   This memoran- dum, immediately circulated, introduced the machine gun battalion organization.   Actually, except in name, machine guns had been so organized in several divisions, including the 33rd, since the autumn of the preceding year.   Yet, a IIIrd Corps memorandum of 27th May 1918 contains the following amazing statement :

" The question ' who is responsible for the tactical
" ' handling of M.G.s ? ' is at present rather difficult to
" answer as divisions differ greatly in their methods of
" employing their M.G. Battns. . . . There is the case
" of one battalion, which has guns in three divisional
" areas, where all three divisions have different ideas
" on the tactical handling of machine guns." In the
same memorandum, apparently to placate everyone,
while ignoring the orders of the commander-in-
chief, the following appears : " It should be an axiom
" that every brigadier disposes himself of (a) in attack
" not less than 8 guns ; (b) in defence not less than
" 4 guns." One may well ask why ? By what
principle ?

Having considered all the available information
concerning the dispositions of the enemy, the disposal
of machine guns should be determined by the topo-
graphical nature of the ground. This is the first and
final principle affecting their tactical handling. Divisional " areas " can have nothing whatever to do with
the selection of sites for machine guns from which, by
direct or indirect fire, or both, they can most effectively
contribute the maximum of fire-effect, in attack or
defence. To deny this doctrine is to misunderstand
completely the definite characteristics of the machine
gun and the cardinal principles which govern its tactical
uses. Writing of the operations of the last week of
March 1918, the commander of the Guards machine
gun battalion states : " The battalion organization
" was particularly justified at this period. Brigade
" boundaries were continually being altered ; and where-
" as in the old days of independent machine gun com-
" panies this would have involved a great deal of work
" for the personnel of the companies by having to

" comply with these changes of boundary, we as a
" battalion took little more than an official and academic
" interest."

In contradiction to the chaotic thought upon
machine guns which dominated the Army, while several
corps and divisions were active in trying to upset the
orders of the Commander-in-Chief, the Canadian
Corps, on 10th May 1918, launched a positive
memorandum, " for the guidance of all officers." The
memorandum contains such vital passages as : " There
" is no similarity between infantry battalions and
" machine gun battalions either as regards administra-
" tion or tactics. A machine gun battalion can be
" more closely compared to a divisional artillery both
" in its organization and in its tactical distribution.
" The machine gun service must be regarded as a
" distinctive arm with tactics of its own."

On the 10th May the First Army also issued a
memorandum, No. 1958 (G), addressed to the 1st, 10th,
11th, 13th, 17th, 18th and Canadian Corps, in which
the army commander " emphasized the following
" points :

" (a) The organization of the Machine Gun Corps
" into battalions has proved even more successful than
" was anticipated.

" (b) The discipline, training, standard of interior
" economy, and general fighting efficiency of machine
" gun units has increased enormously since the re-
" organization, and the work of the Corps during the
" recent fighting has been of the highest order."

I suggest that the foregoing, incidentally a mere
fraction of the evidence, is a sufficient answer to Colonel
Macky. The fact, however, that a staff officer can
found a thesis as to the proper use of weapons upon total

misconceptions suggests that possibly others remain in ignorance of the tactical possibilities of the machine gun. Colonel Macky falls into the same error as did the military critics after the Franco-German War of 1870. He writes : " The great problem is to get a " machine gun up close and keep it moving. . . . If " they (machine guns) were to form an integral part of " the attacking troops, they could and would be well " fought." These are examples of the suggestions which ought to be applied to automatic rifles. But automatic rifles are classified as " Machine gun (light and automatic)," showing errors of understanding and classification which are bound to lead to further muddled thinking. He continues : " to be covering troops in " whom they are not directly interested is wasting a " human factor which is valuable." Here the " divisional area " argument reappears, but now disguised as a moral factor. Could any argument be less well founded ? Not only the later organization, but, in 1914, machine gun teams served any infantry unit with equal zeal. At Omdurman in 1897, the machine gun batteries with the Sudanese and Egyptian troops were drawn from the Staffordshires and Connaught Rangers, and the execution was immense. After 1871, every authority came to agree that machine guns are a distinct arm, their tactics prescribed by the nature of the weapon. They share nothing in common with the automatic rifle, except mechanical loading and ejection. Colonel Macky even tells us that " at night or with " smoke the field of fire must be contemplated as " beginning within twenty yards of our positions. " Machine guns became singularly useless at this " range." Apart from the achievements by barrage batteries set on S O S lines, the fixed platform makes the machine gun, *par excellence*, the ideal weapon for night fighting.

The siting of machine guns for attack should be considered solely from the point of view of forcing the enemy to keep his head down—in addition of course to the infliction of casualties—and preventing him from bringing up his reserves while the infantry advance, a lesson first learned in the Russo-Japanese War, and accentuated by our failure to exploit machine guns in support of attacking waves of infantry in the battle of the Somme, 1916. Overhead and indirect fire are contributed with the object of achieving the foregoing result. At the longer ranges the angle of fall of the bullet enables fire to fall actually into entrenchments where the flat trajectory of short ranges would miss the mark. Moreover, the effective beaten zone for one or more guns is known with mathematical precision. The machine gun must be fought, vigorously, performing a dual role, frequently in one engagement, that of direct individual fire and of indirect collective fire.

In summarizing the battle of the Somme, 1916, the Official History of the War declares : " The prime " causes of general failure were the strength and " depth of the German position." It is generally admitted that the German machine guns contributed mostly both to the strength and depth of the position. The casualties of the Fourth Army and VIIIth Corps of the Third Army amounted to 2438 officers and 55,032 other ranks, of whom 993 officers and 18,247 men were killed. The figures are a sufficient testimony to the efficacy of machine gun fire, in a defence of strength and of depth.

The disposition of the 33rd Bn., M.G.C. at Meteren, although improvised on the spot at a moment's notice under fire, was one of the strength of 48 guns only, but one of considerable depth. The IXth Corps Special Order, already quoted, contains the following : " In " spite of the hard fighting of the two previous days, " night harassing fire was maintained during the night " of the 13th-14th. . . . This line was held by machine " guns in face of great odds until ordered to withdraw " on the evening of 14th instant, this withdrawal being " carried out in the most creditable manner, without " further loss, either to personnel or material, showing " the excellent state of training and efficiency within " the battalion."

Such " harassing fire " is described by Colonel Macky as " studiously firing into the night." The fact that machine gunners understood their weapon, instruments, maps, and the use of ground, necessarily involved that " study " of which this critic complains. He regards the organization of machine guns as " sheer waste." The whole weight of evidence is against him.

Let us see then what happened at the same period, March-April 1918, when the new machine gun battalion organization was abandoned. The narrative of operations from 21st-27th March 1918 of the 9th Battalion Machine Gun Corps provides one illustration. The commanding officer reports : " It had long been " known that a German attack was impending, and it " came in no sense as a surprise. The S O S barrage " had been carefully co-ordinated with the artillery— " it was not too ambitious, and was undoubtedly of " adequate density. It was placed where the 18-pdr. " barrage was thin or non-existent, covering the valley " between Gonnelieu and Villers-Guislain. At neither " of these two places did the enemy succeed in pene- " trating our line until after our troops had been with-

" drawn.   The guns of the battalion were distributed
" in depth. . . . Although all positions had been selected
" primarily for direct fire over the sights up to ranges of
" 1000 yards and over, each gun had been where poss-
" ible given an indirect S O S line on to ground in
" front of our front line.   The fields of fire were in
" all cases good—in many excellent—and the protec-
" tion for gun teams fair.   The ground between the
" Yellow and Brown systems had been carefully
" reconnoitred. . . ."

Here then is evidence of the careful preparations
which both time provided and the most serious nature
of the threatened attack demanded.   Yet the narrative
continues :   " It is a matter for regret that no oppor-
" tunity was afforded for testing these defences, which
" would I think have provided the enemy with a difficult
" nut to crack."   The whole story is one of hasty
retreat ;   the fruitless and purposeless abandonment of
carefully chosen positions ;   of guns stripped of ammunition limbers, ordered to positions miles behind
because of " congestion on the roads " ; of machine guns
maintained in action with denuded teams—beggared of
their mobility, deprived of the means to fight.   In
desperation the commanding officer continues under
date 27th March :   " It was reported that the infantry
" had been ordered to retire as the enemy were through
" on their flanks ;   as there appeared to be nothing to
" justify such a move it was decided to remain and stop
" all infantry possible."   And here they remained.   At
this period of the War everyone knew that machine guns
were the backbone of any system of defence.   Without
entering into the familiar Haig–Gough–Lloyd George
controversy, one matter is clear.   There was a sufficiency of machine guns, together with the proved and

authorized organization, to provide both " strength and depth for the defence." The Germans did not rely upon great numbers of men packed into the firing lines, but upon fire-power, disposed in depth. At the moment of test, machine gun battalions were ordered to abandon their positions and join a retreat, when in fact they considered the enemy could be checked and the retreat was unnecessary. That the 9th Battalion, though eager, was little engaged at the most crucial moment of the greatest battle of history, is proven from its casualties for the whole period, amounting to 7 officers and 119 other ranks of whom more than one-third were taken prisoners, wounded and surrounded after ammunition had run out. This surely is the old story of " Order, Counter-order, Disorder," or of organization carefully planned, being jettisoned.

The 47th M.G. Battalion in front of Equancourt in the Fifth Army suffered almost the same fate. The battalion lost most of the guns ; one company, deprived of transport, failed even to save the tripods and a single belt-box. The commanding officer wrote : " I think " some more guns might have been saved if fighting " limbers had been kept within reach, at least within " two miles." A first principle of machine gun or-ganization is that the " transport " constitutes an inseparable part of the fighting unit, the M.G. Section (Platoon) and Company. An officer of this battalion, captured, writing from Mainz in July 1918, reports : " we were surrounded at Bus after two hours' fight and " all ammunition gone, one officer badly wounded in " the knee, another in the stomach." After a detailed and documented description of the obstinacy of the Higher Command in face of the demand for machine guns, Mr. Lloyd George concludes with the observa-

tion : " One is astounded at the tardiness with which
" our military leaders came to any realization of the
" power of the most lethal weapon of the war." [1]

The utility of the machine gun depends upon
ammunition supply, and thereafter upon its mobility,
which consists of a sufficiency of man-power and
of horsed, wheel or pack, or mechanical transport.
Mobile covering fire of density within the infantry
front is provided by automatic rifles. Machine guns,
by their nature, fulfil a different task.

The Guards Machine Gun Battalion in the same
battle, near Boiry St. Martin, suffered similar experiences. The officer commanding reported : " No.
" 3 Company, true to the tradition of the 3rd Guards'
" Brigade, was divided up amongst the battalions
" of the brigade irrespective of whether a section of
" Vickers guns could be efficiently disposed in each
" battalion front. Little attempt at distribution in
" depth had been made." Finally, we have the guards-
man's cynical reference to " wind up " in the Higher
Command, on the 3rd, 13th, and finally 22nd March,
when he was prepared to fight from prepared positions
to the death. Planned retreat ? There was no plan :
the retreat skipped from one coloured line to another,
while good men in whom was the spirit of the fight,
bound hand and foot as the result of ignorance and
prejudice, remained to die. The machine gun organization, so perfectly created, was abandoned at the
very moment when it would have proved of the highest
possible value.

The whole history of the Fifth Army retreat might
perhaps be reconsidered in the light of the disposition
and organization of machine guns. The test is not one

[1] " War Memoirs of David Lloyd George," p. 599 *et seq.*

which the Fifth Army need fear. If the main props of any structure upon which it has relied are taken away or stripped of their power, the whole edifice collapses. Human beings in the herd are even more prone to be swayed by alarmist talk and orders than they are in accepting those of confidence and faith. An orderly planned retirement, such as was suggested by the 9th M.G. Battalion's intention in respect of the Brown and Yellow Lines, or as was carried out by the 33rd M.G. Battalion on the 14th April at Meteren, is a tactical movement, devised by a commander of ripe knowledge, clear perceptions, firm grasp of military principles, and of courage which communicates itself to his subordinates. Retreat is a different matter.

When a defensive position is subjected to attack, the duty of a commander is to hold his infantry for that counter-attack which is the soul of defence. The main attack should be allowed to be met by machine guns co-ordinated to plan : these constitute the frame-work of defence. The M.G. battalion organization had been recognized as the necessary co-ordinating factor. In division after division in the Fifth Army the organization appears to have been ignored; except in isolated places there was little show of defence for several days. Retreat is not a word upon which to build the morale necessary to counter-attack. Machine guns failed because the power to fight was taken from them. Panic among those relying upon a deficient mainstay of the defence often followed.

The early prophets gained little of honours as they preached the gospel of " the Devil's watering-pots." Officers of each arm are inclined to view ground from the point of view of their own arm. The infantry officer, with his weapons of rifle and automatic rifle, views ground from a standpoint vastly different from that of the machine gunner, because of the different nature of the respective weapons. This is the point to press. If we are to speak of " Weapon and Target," we must first understand the nature and capacity of the weapon, and the type of target which it can best engage. Thereafter we can enunciate tactical principles whereby, in attack and defence, the weapon can most effectively be used and the target most economically and speedily destroyed.

In a small " professional " army, sufficiently large to provide avenues of promotion within the several arms, the tendency is that the views of both officers and men will become more strictly circumscribed by the needs and tactics of the arm in which they serve, with all the rivalries which arise therefrom, as " gunners," " sappers," " footsloggers," cavalry. In battle, officers, especially in the higher ranks, have need of a capacity to view and visualize ground from the point of view of artillery, cavalry, machine gunners, infantry, the tank, and the air. The failure of tanks, notably at Ypres in 1917, was also due to the failure of the Higher Command to visualize ground from the viewpoint of the tank officer. The striking success at Cambrai was due to a choice of battleground determined by tank officers.

From the outset let it be insisted that machine gunnery demands both high intelligence and strong physique. Only those cadets from the Military Colleges showing special aptitude in map-reading and mathematics should be posted to machine gun units. The rank and file must be carefully selected from the available pool of recruits, and posted for training to machine gun units. Before appointment to command

292 MACHINE GUN BATTALIONS IN ACTION

of an infantry battalion, each officer should have served for a period of at least one year in command of a machine gun company. Such suggestions perhaps envisage an army recruited upon a different basis and a closer co-ordination of mechanical and non-mechanical units. At least, so far, it has been demonstrated from the experience of the Great War that where machine guns were rightly handled, with that freedom of tactical control and leadership permitted to machine gun commanders which the characteristics of the weapon demanded, their success was invariably of the highest order.

" The ·08/'15 *light* machine gun is only a means " whereby the *infantry* can increase their volume of " fire.

" For mobile defence, the ·08/'15 light machine " gun is indispensable. It is posted either in the fore- " most line, or in front of the latter in nests and in shell- " holes.

" In the attack, when skilfully handled and judi- " ciously posted, the ·08/'15 light machine gun con- " tributes a valuable increase to the volume of fire. It " can advance with the first wave of the assault and " engage portions of the enemy's trenches where our " attack is held up. This demands initiative. . . . " Command, as regards both tactical employment and " ammunition supply, should be exercised by the " infantry company commander. . . .

" Only under the above conditions can full use be " made of *this very excellent weapon.*"

This document was captured, translated, and issued to the British army (SS. 579, General Staff (Intelligence) General Headquarters). Unfortunately its importance was not emphasized, or it may have been buried beneath the spate of literature upon every conceivable subject which often harassed fighting commanders. It is not merely a tale that runners were sent during the crisis of battle through enemy bombardments to enquire of battalion commanders the number of tins of apple jam issued and consumed during the preceding month !

Lieutenant-Colonel Cowley confirms also the view held by every machine gun commander possessed of the fighting spirit and of true tactical understanding. The place of the machine gun commander is in the forefront of the battle, directing operations, in close touch with the brigadier (K.T.K.) commanding the forward sector, a view which corresponds with the German tactics, already reviewed.[1] But how he condemns " the fatigue caused by push-biking 30-50 miles " a day " upon a G.S. cycle !

The actions fought by battalion, companies, and sections of the Machine Gun Corps during the battles of March and April should, many of them, find a place in this history. The canvas is, however, too small. Mention must, however, be made of certain of these actions. The 24th Battalion with the 8th Queen's " made a desperate defence " on 22nd March " at Le " Verguier. . . . A very weak battalion with some " machine guns held up two German divisions for " some hours and then slipped away unmolested." The Germans had planned to capture Le Verguier twenty-four hours earlier.

On the Lys, the 31st Battalion with one and a half companies on 11th April drove the enemy from La Becque in a notable action. The 58th Battalion, on 25th April, was attacked by German tanks, attempting to approach Cachy. " The concentrated fire of 6 guns put

[1] See pp. 225-233.

" the tank crew out of action and it then surrendered."
Two tanks were left in the battlefield, the German
casualties being 1 officer and 8 men killed, and 3
officers and 50 men wounded.

As a final summary of the employment of machine
gun battalions, during the operations of March and
April 1918—the test of the new organization in defence
—it appears that the following conclusions are wholly
borne out by the weight of evidence :

The Fifth Army, awaiting an assault which it had
anticipated for several weeks, had issued no co-
ordinated plan of machine gun defence. The positions
were often ill-chosen. Machine guns were not disposed
in sufficient depth. The machine gun battalion, not
being regarded as a tactical unit, was deprived both of
its power and resources : the machine gun commander
was not enabled to exercise his command. Few concrete
positions were available. The supply of ammunition
was deficient. After the retreat was ordered, the
transport forming an integral part of the tactical unit
had in most cases been ordered far from the scene of
operations.

Had an Army Machine Gun Scheme been devised
when the retreat was ordered, the machine guns would
presumably have fallen back to previously reconnoitred
positions at which dumps of ammunition were ready :
presuming that the orders were passed to machine gun
battalions, which was not always so in practice, and
that the machine guns were afforded infantry escorts
in retirement after they had covered the main retreat.
There was no such plan. Machine gunners, depleted
in their teams by casualties, were left, often without
orders from the brigades to which they were attached,
to carry back their heavy loads ; and, almost surrounded,

to fight their way back as best they could, salving as much of their essential fighting material as was possible. The Official History of the Great War [1] notes : " There was little artillery to support the German ad- " vance and without it the German infantry did not seem " inclined to face fire. They seemed, however, as ready " as ever to take advantage of weak spots in the line." Thus it would appear that the main reason for the Fifth Army retreat, and consequent losses, was the failure to base the defence upon machine guns dis- posed in depth. This could only have been achieved by utilizing the battalion organization introduced for this very purpose, and inaugurated, moreover, with expedi- tion, because General Headquarters fully realized the urgency of the need. General Gough, not alone, failed to implement the new scheme. Machine guns were virtually ignored, while the proper role of the automatic rifle had never been definitively explained to Army Commands.

That a machine gun battalion co-ordinated and dis- posed in depth and using its ground for manœuvre can withstand infantry attacks, especially those with weak artillery support as was the case on the Somme, 1916, after the preliminary bombardment, is proved by the success achieved by the 33rd Bn. Machine Gun Corps, and elsewhere. Sufficient machine guns were available with the Fifth Army for the purpose. As it was, the machine gunners, fighting individual battles with desperation and heroism, were abandoned by an Army retreating under orders in their rear. Unable to carry their loads and come again effectively into

[1] Official History of the Great War, " Military Operations, France and Belgium, 1918 : The German March Offensive and its Prelimin- aries."

action, incurring heavy casualties through lack of local protection, the machine gunners frequently found themselves without weapons with which to fight. The infantry, observing what they had been accustomed to regard as the focal points of the defence often without the means to fight and out of action, continued to retreat, frequently without any serious pressure from the enemy.

The Fifth Army on 23rd March was by no means exhausted. There is no such thing as an army which needs a rest. There is only an army that needs a leader.

On 29th September 1918 the Third Army issued an order which clearly emphasized the integrity of the machine gun battalion as a tactical unit. The order stated " that it was again necessary to emphasize that " the officer commanding a machine gun battalion is " a fighting commander who directs and controls his " units in the same manner as any other commander " of a formation—with the exception that his operations " are dependent on and subsidiary to those of infantry. " His own aim is to assist the infantry in reaching the " objective and maintaining it there : he must therefore " not be tied to Divisional Headquarters during battle, " but forward with his report centre at or in the vicinity " of one of the Infantry Brigade Headquarters which is " actually conducting the operations, where he is in the " main line of divisional signal communication and " from which he can handle his machine gun battalion " tactically in accordance with the plan of the divisional " commander. In this position he can by the use of " his reserves influence the fight ; that is to say, according " to the situation he must be able to—

" (a) Concentrate in order to obtain superiority of " fire where required ;

" (b) Arrange for flank penetrations ;

" (c) Harass the enemy when in retreat ;

" (d) Reorganize in depth for a further advance ;

" (e) Occupy ground gained so as to consolidate
"   in depth ;

" (f) Relieve troops with fresh ones ;

" (g) Keep a reserve as long as possible, so as to be
"   able to influence the forefight."

In short, the machine gun battalion is, and must function as, a fighting formation and not as a pool for supplying machine gun units to other formations.

The brigade commander, " actually conducting the operations," corresponds with " Kampf Truppen Kommandeur " of the new German tactics; and closely allied with him in control of the battle proper must be the machine gun commander conducting the fire fight. For the purpose of the battle, all formations must come under the immediate command of the battle zone commander, the machine gun commander manœuvring his guns for the purpose of obtaining the results outlined in the Third Army Memorandum.

In analysing the machine gun battalion organization the Official History of the New Zealand Machine Gun Corps [1] declares : " If the divisional and brigade " commanders had realized the true tactical significance " of the machine gun battalion formation, it is possible " that much of the opposition to it would have dis-" appeared. It is submitted that on active service the " machine gun battalion is the true formation. The " tremendous influence the machine gun has upon the " fire fight renders it absolutely necessary that the whole " of the divisional guns be under a separate command,

[1] " With the Machine Gunners in France and Palestine," by Major J. H. Luxford, N.Z., M.G.C.

" so that the reserves may be employed solely in con-
" formity with the tactical situation. If companies or
" sections form part of brigades or battalions they are
" very often in places where they are not required and
" cannot be brought into action without such delay
" as may very easily render their assistance useless.
" Machine gun work is a specialized branch of the
" service."

Before March 1918, be it noted, General Headquarters had emphasized the necessity for co-operation
between machine guns themselves and between machine
guns and infantry. " Co-operation is the foundation
" upon which successful machine gun tactics rest. To
" ensure it, the closest possible liaison must be main-
" tained between machine gun units themselves, and
" between machine gun units and other arms. The
" intentions of a commander for any operation should
" be communicated to the senior machine gun officer
" in the form of general instructions. . . . The machine
" gun battalion is, and must be employed as, a tactical
" unit, and the machine gun commander is a tactical
" commander. . . ."[1] The Fifth Army failed to carry
out the orders.

In summarizing the lessons learned between 21st
March and the end of April 1918, the following points
may be re-emphasized :

Guns must be sited for direct fire, which is their
primary task. Positions, capable of long-range fire,
with a wide traverse, must be chosen. The Section
(Platoon) of 4 guns, with its fighting limbers, is the
fighting unit : it must not be broken.

Sections, generally, must be grouped within their
companies for the performance of the secondary

[1] SS. 192 : The Tactical Employment of Machine Guns.

machine gun task—barrage, "S O S Line," harassing
fire. This implies that machine gun positions and their
alternatives must be well furnished with ammunition.
Nevertheless, machine gun teams must not be un-
necessarily wearied with barrage fire, this fire being
conceived to break up enemy concentrations and in
support of the counter-attack, where possible with
observation. The latter may be obtained by posting
scouts in the forward zone, under orders to command
fire by means of a prearranged code of visual signals,
flag, lamp, or rockets. Fighting limbers must be kept
close up to the guns.

The systems of trenches, or defensive lines shown
upon operation maps, in an army, corps or divisional
sector, must not be regarded as a mere series of successive defence lines to be held one after the other but
as a single defended area, the protection of which is laid
out upon a definite, co-ordinated plan according to the
nature of the ground. The plan adopted should be
such as to render the divisional sector capable of resistance to attacks from any direction. The disposal of
machine guns within this plan presupposes their direction as a tactical unit by a tactical commander. The
machine guns within the divisional sector are the
framework of the defence, within which the divisional
commander holds and manœuvres his infantry and
tanks for the counter-attack, and orders the lines of
artillery fire. The defence of the forward zone should
be entrusted to automatic rifles, mortars, snipers and
bombers, assisted from the rear by artillery. The
machine gun barrage will be directed to prevent reinforcement to an enemy attack, and the forward move of
artillery and transport. Machine guns in the forward
zone should be in rear of the front line or defences, but

capable, where possible, of sweeping No Man's Land with direct fire. Their main task is to engage the enemy with direct fire at the shorter ranges, between 500 and 1000 yards, should he succeed in penetrating the front line.

The rear guns must be grouped in batteries, echeloned in depth, their fire-plan carefully worked out and prescribed in any " set piece " defensive plan. Alternative positions must be prearranged so that, in the event of an attack penetrating the front line, the rear guns are available for manœuvre, or to provide barrage fire in covering the counter-attack. Should the flanks of the divisional sector fall back, the duty of the rear guns is to provide a defensive flank with direct enfilade fire. They must not fall back in line with any retreat on the flank ; but, on the contrary, in co-operation with the machine guns manœuvring within the weakened front must present a stout framework of resistance. The enemy will find himself possessed of a dangerous salient, and within the zone held by machine guns, the divisional commander can concentrate infantry to counter-attack for the relief of those occupying the zone of the threatened flank. Unless machine guns are co-ordinated upon a corps, and army, plan, they cannot fulfil this their most important role in defence : nor can success be achieved unless the machine gun battalion, or unit, is handled as a tactical unit, with its maximum of fire-power. Though machine guns cannot actually gain ground, they can hold ground ; but only if the fire-plan has been so carefully co-ordinated as to leave no gaps, and when provision has been made for ammunition supply and infantry escorts to machine gun teams.

These principles will result from a zone of machine gun defence, organized in depth, equipped for the fight, rather than from a series of positions covering, and limited to, successive trench lines. The purpose of placing machine guns in depth is to ensure the enemy being engaged effectively, irrespective of the direction of his attack; but the guns must not be dotted indiscriminately over the zone, as they will not then be capable of manœuvre, nor of contributing barrage and harassing fire.

The machine gun is almost inexhaustible. Machine guns are not retired from battle unless short of the means to fight. No machine gun must be considered to be out of action unless destroyed by hostile fire or unless deficient of ammunition.

The Official History of the Great War (" 1918," 2nd Volume) records the orders issued by a subaltern, as demonstrating the spirit of the troops resisting the German onslaught. This order is here reprinted, together with the personal narrative of the officer who issued it. The order became famous and was widely circulated throughout the British army. In the American force copies were mimeographed and distributed as " an admirable model of all that a set of standing orders " should be." [1]

" Special Orders No. 1 Section 13.3.18.

" (1) This position will be held, and the Section will remain here until relieved.

" (2) The enemy cannot be allowed to interfere with this position.

" (3) If the Section cannot remain here alive, it will remain here dead, but in any case it will remain here.

" (4) Should any man through shell-shock or other cause attempt to surrender, he will remain here dead.

[1] The narrative, by Captain F. P. Bethune, M.C., is reproduced by courtesy of " Reveille," the Official Journal of the N.S.W. Branch of the R.S.S.I.L.A.

" (5) Should all guns be blown up, the Section will use
   Mills Grenades and other novelties.
" (6) Finally, the position, as stated, will be held.

" F. P. BETHUNE, Lt.,

" O/C No. 1 Section

   " Towards the end of February 1918, the 3rd
" Machine Gun Company, of which I had the honour
" to command No. 1 Section, was moving into the line,
" upon its accustomed business, and, as the custom was,
" two officers—on this occasion, Lieuts. Fred Archer
" and Arthur Baker-Finch—were sent forward to re-
" connoitre the position where a couple of forward
" guns were to be sited.   On their return, Baker-Finch
" informed me that the position to which they had been
" sent was, from a machine gunner's point of view,
" quite a hopeless one, with a field of fire of about six
" yards, which meant that, if the enemy attacked, the
" guns' crews would be scuppered from cover at short
" range, before they could fire a shot.   This was bad
" indeed from any point of view, and, in addition, I
" knew that in the ordinary rotation of duty it would be
" my especial chum, Lieut. J. C. Hoge, who would be
" in charge of the guns.

   " As second-in-command of the company, I went to
" our C.O. and protested against men being sent to a
" position where they would be useless if the enemy did
" not attack, and both useless and dead if he did.   As
" this protest was of no avail, I pointed out to the C.O.
" that I would feel that my honour was involved unless
" I were put in charge of the guns, so got the job.   The
" next step was to select the crews for the guns, and it
" seemed only fair to put the situation squarely before
" the men, for, though one is justified in claiming the
" things that appertain to his honour as a soldier, it is

" quite evident that he has not the right to order others
" to risk their lives in the same quarrel.

" Accordingly, I ordered No. 1 Section to be fallen
" in, and, having told them that I was taking the guns to
" a position where there was no field of fire, etc., I asked
" for volunteers to take a step forward. The only result
" of this request was that the whole section, with
" soldierly precision, advanced one step forward, so I
" was forced to make my own selection. I find in my
" diary for 1st March 1918, the following : ' Am taking
" ' in three good men and three new ones, as I do not
" ' want too many of the old section to get scuppered if
" ' we get it in the neck, while at the same time we must
" ' be good enough to exact payment before we are blown
" ' out, and there are plenty of Mills grenades for the
" ' final flutter.'

" Next day we left for the position, but on the way
" we were overtaken by a runner, with orders for me, to
" say that the intended position was to be abandoned,
" and I was to take my men and guns to a place called
" Buff Bank, which I found a very excellent position
" for a gun fight, for though in most places in the line
" it was possible to die, at Buff Bank one could have
" died very expensively.

" So we placed our guns in position, loaded all spare
" belts, placed our 10,000 rounds per gun ready to hand,
" and sat down to wait for three weeks, with nothing to
" pass the time except an occasional gas miasma from
" Fritz, and, of course, the usual line ration of rather
" noisy explosives, and a little jesting in No Man's
" Land, which, poor Fritz could not understand, was
" for the nonce regarded by us as land held by us in
" the name of King George of England, and upon
" which all trespassing was forbidden. When we first

" moved in, there were infantry to strengthen our
" hands, but after a few days there was talk of a
" massed attack developing, and the infantry were
" moved back much against their will, to safeguard
" a second line of defence.

" Under the circumstances, it seemed indicated that
" as things were now entirely in our hands, each man
" should have written orders that should make abso-
" lutely clear to him exactly what our job was, so that,
" if he had to die, he should die in his own lighthearted
" fashion, in goodly company. So the battle orders
" quoted above were issued on 13th March."

In the very valuable and masterly summary of the
Operations of March and April 1918, which concludes
the volumes of the Official History of the Great War
dealing with these events, Sir James Edmonds writes :

" Actually, very small bodies (of Germans), by
" infiltration brought about retirements, as we have
" seen. On the other hand, the New Armies, in their
" valour, very often held on too long ; but, accustomed
" to fight in line, they tried to retire in line, and were
" in the highest degree sensitive with regard to their
" flanks, a fact which was only too well exploited by
" the enemy. Lack of appreciation of the necessity
" of strengthening the flanks of gaps made by small
" local penetrations was responsible for many with-
" drawals from tactical points, the possession of which
" was essential to prevent the continuation of his
" advance. Too much reliance was placed on main-
" taining a continuous line at the expense of the true
" principles of the use of ground." [1]

---

[1] Official History of the Great War, " Military Operations, France
and Belgium, 1918, March-April: Continuation of the German Offensives," p. 480.

As we have seen, except where machine gun battalions were permitted to manœuvre as tactical units, they too were forced to conform to the rigid infantry line : and the retiring infantry frequently left the machine guns to defend fronts and flanks which had disappeared. Further, the co-ordination of the machine gun defence upon a corps or army plan prior to the expected attack would have ensured adequate depth, the cardinal principle in ordering machine guns for defence. Such depth would have been the means of sketching new lines upon which a retiring infantry might rally. General Edmonds makes the additional point that retreat had never been re-hearsed, a factor which it is stated led to confusion. There can be no doubt of this. Nevertheless, a proper understanding of the role of the machine gun and of its tactical handling in regard to ground [1] would, it certainly appears, have produced the necessary stiffen-ing after the front had been broken on 21st March, even if sufficient troops were not readily available for serving the counter-attack.

The Official Historian summarizes the contribution of the Machine Gun Corps in the following telling sentence : " The machine gunners were everywhere, " and contributed to every German repulse." [2]

[1] Official History of the Great War, " Military Operations, France and Belgium, 1918, March-April: Continuation of the German Offen-sives," p. 471. " The Lewis gun was little more than a cumbrous, heavy and not too reliable automatic rifle—in fact, the fire-power of infantry battalions and brigades had just been lessened by the re-organization of the machine gun companies into divisional battalions."

[2] *Ibid.* p. 485

X

CHAPTER XII

MACHINE GUN BATTALIONS IN ATTACK
AUGUST–NOVEMBER 1918

Recoil of an army—Scarcity of records—The Guards machine gun
battalion—Tales of gallantry—Captain Liddell Hart on machine
guns—Machine gunners as " Storm troops "—The passage of
the river Sambre—Offensive power, the distinguishing feature
of machine guns—Motorized machine guns—The Canadian
Corps — Science revolutionizes tactics — Attack tactics summarized—Machine gun battalion organization a natural evolution — Speculations as to the future — G.H.Q. summary,
January 1919—Machine gun armament, 1918—Use in the air—
von Richthofen—A *corps d'élite*—The role of the British army—
Testimony of the Chief of the Imperial General Staff—Virtues
of the machine gunner.

IF the historian of the future has no experience of
war conducted with such prodigal loss of life and
material as were the battles from 1916 until the
Armistice, he will find some difficulty in understanding
how the British army after its stupendous losses and
hammering by the German offensives of March and
April 1918, and again in May and June, was able itself
to assume an offensive which, without cessation, was
pursued for more than three months of terrific fighting,
culminating in victory. The whole Army recoiled to
action as does the perfected mechanism of the machine
gun. Young troops, with an incredibly small stiffening

of tried regimental officers and N.C.O.'s, leaped to the attack and drove in the most formidable bastions of the German defence. The British Cabinet, so critical of Sir Douglas Haig, was overwhelmed with astonishment: the Generalissimo, Marshal Foch, so tardy in practical assistance, so frigid in his recognition of the achievements of British troops, most unusually sent his personal congratulations to the British Field-Marshal, whose troops again bore the brunt of the battle.

The attack was opened by Rawlinson's Fourth Army on 8th August. On the 22nd, Byng's Third Army came into action ; and, on the 28th, Horne's First Army joined the fray. An action, on 4th July, which Ludendorff has since stated to have given the first fatal shock to the military power of Germany, preceded the main offensive ; it was carried out by the Australian Corps, attached to which was the 33rd American Division. It is not practicable to follow the operations of most of the machine gun battalions taking part in this gigantic battle. It is sufficient to say that the traditions of the Machine Gun Corps were nobly upheld—traditions short-lived, yet filled with the most sublime epics of a soldier's duty. Each day saw fought out its Waterloo, its Balaklava, its Rorke's Drift.

The most remarkable factor to be found in these vast swift-moving operations is the manner in which the new machine gun battalions adapted themselves to offensive battle in open country, as self-contained tactical units.

No records by army or corps machine gun officers, beyond the carefully detailed narratives of Colonel N. K. Charteris, Fourth Army Machine Gun Officer, are available. The unit histories, for the most part, assist very little. It is clear, however, that machine guns were fought with energy, adapting themselves to their dual role, and rendering the greatest services to the attacking infantry, both by covering fire and by giving protection to the flanks.

The officer commanding the Guards Machine Gun Battalion, Lieutenant-Colonel R. C. Bingham, D.S.O., in the Third Army, writes : " A triumph of secrecy " was attained concerning these operations. The " discipline in the division was so strict that the troops " who had been holding the line up to zero night heard " of the attack for the first time on arrival in camp on " relief by the attacking troops.

" The 2nd Guards Brigade was detached for the " attack and No. 3 Company was attached to the " brigade for the operations. The company was " divided into attacking guns and consolidation guns, " technically called ' Forward ' and ' Rear ' guns. " The attacking guns were given a roving commission " within certain areas, roughly those of the attacking " battalions, though with the duty uppermost in their " minds of assisting the battalion's advance when " possible and filling gaps where touch might be lost. " . . . The brigadier twice during the three days the " brigade was in action expressed his gratification at " the rapidity with which teams moved into their " appointed place. . . . Great determination was shown " by Lieutenant Mungall and the men of his subsec- " tion in working forward under machine gun fire " to a position from where they were able to silence " a hostile machine gun. . . . On the 25th, during a " counter-attack, 2nd Lieutenant R. W. Daniels ' very " ' gallantly covered the withdrawal of a Guards " ' Company inflicting severe casualties on the enemy.'

" Great bravery and ability was shown during these

" operations by Lance-Corporal A. Cruickshanks,
" limber corporal, in keeping his section supplied with
" ammunition. This N.C.O. made several journeys
" up to his gun positions always through artillery fire
" and more often than not under machine gun fire."
No. 2 Company succeeded in silencing a battery of
three hostile trench mortars at a range of 1000 yards.
The casualties among the gunners were everywhere
heavy : but commensurate with the work accomplished.
" On one gun Lance-Corporal Fegan was left the sole
" survivor of his team. With the help of an orderly
" he managed to collect ammunition and kit for two
" guns, by dint of crawling about all day under fire."

On 27th August the 1st Guards Brigade " ran into
" a position strongly held by the enemy and intense
" machine gun fire stopped the attack dead. As the
" leading line climbed to the top of the bank of the
" sunken road from which they started some of the men
" actually fell back wounded among their comrades
" waiting their turn to go over.

" It was at this juncture that 2nd Lieutenant
" Stewart was badly wounded in placing his section
" on a flank in such a position that they were able to
" modify the hostile machine gun fire." He was
killed later. " 2nd Lieutenant Connolly assumed
" command of the section, but had already been twice
" wounded while reconnoitring positions from whence
" he could best help the infantry advance. With the
" greatest indifference to pain he remained at duty and
" showed an example to his men of the greatest value
" at the time. He, too, was killed during the morning.

" Command of the Section devolved on Sergeant
" S. T. Kirkham, and, as the hostile machine gun fire
" had created a gap between our right and the next

" division, he led his section forwards to Banks
" Trench, where he met the Adjutant, Captain Wright.
" Between them, and with the help of Lance-Corporal
" J. Flennon, all four guns were got into position
" effectually covering the exposed flank of the division.
" . . . Sergeant Kirkham and Lance-Corporal Flennon
" were awarded the D.C.M.

 " The leading wave of the left attacking battalion
" was practically annihilated after going a short distance,
" but one of the companies in support managed to
" advance a little further and two guns under Sergeant
" W. Taylor, the athletic champion of the battalion,
" and a gallant soldier, got up to their line, but it was
" not long before one of his guns was put out of action
" and all but two of the team became casualties. At
" this juncture the Germans showed an inclination to
" counter-attack and before long had almost sur-
" rounded the company. Sergeant Taylor held them
" in order to allow the infantry to extricate themselves.
" He was one of the last to escape the Germans'
" encircling movement. . . . The chief feature of this
" action was the co-operation between the infantry and
" the machine gunners."

 Later, on 15th September, when the Guards
Division attacked the outlying trenches leading to the
Hindenburg Line, the machine gun battalion provided a barrage with two and a half companies.
" Preparations for the barrage were begun on X-Y
" night, ammunition being taken up and slits dug,
" etc. The work, which was carefully camouflaged,
" was continued on Z night and finished three hours
" before Zero. Gun positions had been pegged out and
" lines laid out before dusk the evening before." One
half-company moved forward with the 1st Guards

Brigade, and suffered heavily during the initial advance.
" In Soap Trench, the grenadiers were being seriously
" harassed by machine gun fire from Bull Gun Pits
" and neighbouring trenches, and the officer com-
" manding the battalion asked the section officer to
" deal with them. Sergeant A. E. Fox was ordered to
" get two guns into position in Owen Support. One
" gun was taken across very exposed open ground to
" the selected position where an abandoned German
" machine gun was found with numerous filled belts
" near by. Sergeant Fox wisely decided that it would
" be better to use this German machine gun as a pair
" to his own rather than risk the other gun team
" joining them across the open. Signals were therefore
" made countermanding the second gun. The hostile
" machine gun fire was silenced after firing 3500 rounds
" and two or three German guns put out of action.
" This enabled the grenadiers to move forward again."
    In some arresting comments in his survey of
infantry action,[1] Captain Liddell Hart notes that, after
a few weeks in 1914, " The armies were held fast in
" the grip of Hiram Maxim. The history of the years
" that followed is one of ceaselessly renewed frontal
" onslaughts on entrenched lines held in reality by
" machine guns, if nominally by infantry. . . . There
" were two possible means of reviving movement on the
" battlefield. One was to make men bullet-proof by
" putting them in armoured vehicles. The other was
" to teach men to evade bullets by a revival of stalking
" methods. The British were pioneers of the first,
" the Germans of the second method "—infiltration
tactics. The command and training of machine gun
battalions on the whole was undoubtedly higher than

[1] Captain B. H. Liddell Hart, " The Future of Infantry," pp. 26-27.

that of most infantry battalions, while the severe casualties inflicted upon machine gun companies attacking on the Somme in 1916, and at Ypres in 1917, had taught machine gunners the lessons of scouting and of the " stalking method." The British infantry, after their heavy casualties and reinforcement by largely untrained soldiers, had not learned how to use the automatic rifles at their disposal. Their casualties would undoubtedly have been less had they been able to exploit automatic rifles as did the Germans in March and April 1918.

Captain Liddell Hart continues : " Great as was the " success that attended these new tactics, one should " remember that it was achieved under a great handicap. " The new tactics had to be learned and applied by a " vast residue, whereas it was essentially the method " for a carefully picked and highly trained *élite*. The " Germans showed their recognition of this fact in " confiding the application of these tactics to special " ' storm-troops,' but time was short, and the 1918 " vintage had to be uncorked before it had matured. " Hence even the results of 1918 do not provide a fair " measure of its possibilities."[1] The Machine Gun Corps itself was a " carefully picked and highly trained *élite*," though perhaps largely immature. Nevertheless, although handicapped by the weight of their weapons, the corresponding role of " storm troops " became that of machine gunners. The burden was recognized, and where battalion commanders were afforded freedom in tactical control, and machine gun units complete with transport were kept intact in the open warfare which followed, the handicap helped to develop the use of transport, especially the half-limber in action, so that

[1] Captain B. H. Liddell Hart, " The Future of Infantry," p. 28.

in consequence machine gunners were frequently more mobile than infantry.

A striking instance of such mobility is afforded by the illustration of the 33rd Machine Gun Battalion leading the way of its division through the Fôret de Mormal to its farther extremity, approaching the river Sambre on 5th November 1918. Only one road, often obstacled, was available, and the only practical way of getting the guns forward was to make use of the road prior to its congestion with other traffic. The scheme worked admirably. The machine guns were able to render prompt action when opposition was met at the villages of Sart Bara and Berlaimont. When the river was reached, it was found to be unfordable, the bridges destroyed, and the enemy strongly posted on the farther side. The machine gunners were able to give heavy overhead fire in support of the Royal Engineers and infantry constructing bridges, thus subduing the enemy fire. Nor was that all.

Scouts were sent forward to test the depth of the river. It was found that if limbers were driven into the river, and anchored to the bed, temporary bridges could be improvised in order to afford the passage of machine guns, with which, from among buildings on the farther bank, direct fire could be brought to bear upon the enemy positions upon the rising ground beyond. Volunteer drivers were called for to undertake the hazardous journey through a storm of machine gun fire. Two sections, one after the other, were driven at break-neck speed towards the river. The casualties were heavy, but two drivers succeeded in plunging animals and limbers into the river, where the mules were cut loose, and the limbers dragged into position to form a footway. Within a short while machine gunners were able to creep forward with guns and ammunition, cross the improvised bridge, and maintain a steady fire upon the German positions until a more stable bridge had been completed by the Royal Engineers.

The General Staff had properly foreseen the power of the machine gun in offensive warfare, for in the memorandum of January 1918 [1] it was stated : " Next " to the artillery, the machine gun is the most effective " weapon employed in modern war, and against troops " in the open at suitable ranges it is proportionately " even more effective than artillery. . . . The distin- " guishing feature of modern machine gunnery is its " offensive power. . . . Modern machine gunnery has " reversed the passive tendency."

The role of " storm troops " which fell, naturally enough, upon the Machine Gun Corps added both to its burdens and casualties, but there is no instance recorded of any flinching by the personnel of the corps in the fulfilment of their task.

Experiments—little more—in motorizing machine guns had been made since 1914. But on 9th May 1918 the Minister for the Overseas Military Forces of Canada duly sanctioned the organization of two Canadian Motor Machine Gun Brigades, and one Canadian Motor Machine Gun M.T. Company. The motor machine gun brigade consisted of 64 guns of eight 8-gun batteries, divided into two wings. During Haig's vast drive to the east, the Canadian Corps " attacked with great boldness, especially the Canadian " Motor Machine Gun Brigade. Motor cyclist patrols " operated as far as 2000 yards behind the German " front line, while motor lorries and armoured cars, " carrying machine guns and their teams, on several

[1] SS. 192.

" occasions went clean through the enemy front,
" dropping guns and teams where required as they
" went. . . . The 17th Armoured Car Unit were sent
" forward down the main St. Quentin Road and assisted
" in adding to demoralization. They found the staff
" of a German Corps Headquarters at breakfast in
" Framerville and shot many of them through the win-
" dows of the house in which they were sitting. Before
" the cars opened fire, German officers came out to
" speak to the drivers, thinking they were German
" cars." [1] Here is a vision of the warfare of the petrol
age.

Elsewhere the mobility, dash, and fire-effect of
machine gunners in attack is well illustrated. On 22nd
August the 3rd Australian Machine Gun Battalion
played an important part in the attack on Bray-sur-
Somme. Sixty guns covered the infantry advance,
firing 420,000 rounds in three hours, during which the
attack was highly successful. On the 25th, on another
part of the front where the attack continued on Mon-
tauban, the infantry advance was rapid. Good use was
made of limbers and pack animals which enabled the
machine guns to keep pace with the infantry. On
the 27th, after Trones Wood had been recaptured, the
Fourth Army Intelligence Summary records : " The
" success of our attack in the evening as stated by
" prisoners was largely due to our machine gun fire, which
" succeeded in keeping down the heads of the enemy."
This information served to corroborate the examination
of prisoners captured by the 7th Australian Infantry
Brigade, east of Villers-Bretonneux, on the night of
17th-18th July, who stated that " A large number of

[1] Report by Colonel N. K. Charteris, C.M.G., D.S.O., Fourth
Army Machine Gun Officer.

" casualties were caused to our troops in close support
" by machine gun fire, but few from artillery." A
prisoner of the 152 Infantry Regiment, 41st Division,
taken on 26th July, stated that " owing to the number of
" casualties in his battalion, caused mainly by machine
" gun fire, all four companies of his battalion were in
" the line with one platoon in support to each."

In short, scientific machine gunnery, tactically
ordered by an officer skilled in machine gun technique,
served to embarrass and finally to overwhelm the new
German defensive tactics. This is not, however, to
suggest that the German machine guns failed. Quite
the contrary. The casualties sustained by the British
during each month of the Final Offensive were almost
as heavy as those of any period of the War. The
effect of British machine gun fire was to prevent the
massing of troops for counter-attack and to force the
defending infantry to keep their heads down.[1] As
Captain Liddell Hart so aptly states, " The armies were
" held fast in the grip of Hiram Maxim." Later in his
chapter upon the " Revival of Infantry," he suggests :
" I believe that machine gun stalking—in suitable
" country—offers possibilities that few soldiers have
" yet realized." This role actually fell to the Machine
Gun Corps between August and November 1918, but,
as elsewhere suggested, it is pre-eminently that of the
automatic rifle man. It is because of the danger to
the machine gunner from infiltration by stalking that
it is essential for machine gun teams to have infantry
escorts, or, better, marksmen scouts, whose duties are
to protect the gun team against stalkers.

After the Armistice, 11th November 1918, the

---

[1] " The defensive is merely a particular case of the offensive."—
Archimedes in " The Times," 9th November 1937.

General Staff reissued its publication " The Tactical
Employment of Machine Guns " (SS. 192) in January
1919. This document represents, therefore, the final
considerations, definitions, and determinations following more than four years of war. That epoch had
witnessed amazing developments in the science of war.
For the first time not only had aircraft been used,
but the combatants had built great fleets of aircraft,
whose pilots had added immensely to the arts of flying
itself. Mechanization had become a new factor in war,
the most notable element in which was the introduction
of the tank. Transport itself was on the eve of revolutionary changes. The cavalry arm played an insigni-
ficant role—indeed, almost none at all—in the great
struggles in the European sphere, although it was valuable in Palestine, Mesopotamia, in minor operations in
the Sinai Peninsula, and for patrol work on the Indian
frontier. Artillery had been multiplied upon a prodigious scale ; while new scientific discoveries in tele-
phony and wireless were quickly adapted for military
uses. Chemistry had introduced the new factor of the
gas attack, with anti-gas measures and expedients.

The infantry arm, however, had borne the brunt
of the battles ; and among all the belligerents the
machine gun had come to be regarded as the most
deadly weapon both in defence and attack. Owing to
the confusion of the battlefield, the more so perhaps
in warfare in which a high proportion of the warriors
had been untutored in the use of arms prior to the
outbreak of hostilities, the infantry arms received less
attention, and in consequence made less scientific
progress, than the more spectacular results obtained
from such novelties as aircraft, gas, and the tank.
Preconceived notions as to the tactical employment of

infantry and their weapons governed the minds of the British High Command until the close of operations.

The German " Lehre von Kampf " had insisted, " The offensive battle should take the form of a " succession of waves which progressively swamp the " enemy's positions until the objective is gained, or " until he is too weak and lacks time to oppose a dam to " the tide of the attack." This theory of the attack, to which the British rigidly adhered until the end of the War, was discarded by the Germans in favour of the infiltration tactics introduced for the 1918 offensive ; in the same way that Germany had revolutionized the tactics of the defensive battle, elaborated in a textwork and issued to all German divisions on 1st December 1917,[1] while the British clung to a defensive theory which, but for stout resistance at certain points, the mismanagement of Ludendorff's strategy, and the fact that the German advance overran communication and supplies, would have meant no less than a rout of the British army on the Western Front in March and April 1918.

The German method of attack against troops of weaker morale was overwhelmingly successful, at Caporetto against the Italians, against the Roumanians throughout, and against the Russians at Riga on the river Dwina on 1st September 1917. It is true, of course, that the German High Command was not concerned alone with the stalemate of the Western

[1] ' The German Defensive Battle, 1917,' is critically examined, under this title, by Captain G. C. Wynne of the Historical Section (Military) Committee of Imperial Defence, in the " Army Quarterly," April, July, October 1937. The article is particularly well-informed and carefully documented. Captain Wynne states that the German defensive tactics preceding the ' new model ' were closely imitated by the British Armies, and were " in great measure responsible for the disaster to the Fifth Army " on 21st March 1918.

Front, and most of the German divisions possessed fighting experience from other fronts, where manœuvre was possible and the various arms could be exploited to the fullest advantage in new ways. Nevertheless, being well supplied with information by the Intelligence Service, G.H.Q. was in no way ignorant of the changes in German tactical technique. Rather were the modifications and changes in tactical information both in attack and defence ignored.

Nowhere was ignorance and the stubborn adherence to preconceived notions more marked than in the matter of machine gun organization and distribution. Machine guns had been multiplied from 24 per division in 1914 to 64 by August 1917, and for special operations to a figure much in excess of this number. Yet, both in defence, with notable exceptions as affecting certain divisions, and in the attack, machine guns were frequently subordinated to roles for which they were ill-adapted and wherein they were unable to give anything approaching their full fire-value.

During the last eighteen months of the War the science of machine gunnery made strides beyond all measure ; in technique, organization, and tactical disposition. This was not, as some claim, because the stagnation of the battlefields of France and Belgium produced such unusual phenomena that special and exceptional organization was necessary to meet it ; that in fact the rigid defensive lines of the Western Front provided the *raison d'être* for the Machine Gun Corps. Quite the contrary : the corps and battalion organization were a natural evolution because machine gun technique had so advanced as to demand new tactical principles for governing their disposition in the defensive and attack battles. For, once quit of the shell-torn zones—pounded into a quagmire, over which neither transport of any kind nor men could move except by almost superhuman effort—and when both movement and manœuvre again became possible, whether in defence or attack, machine guns were able to exploit to the fullest advantage both the enriched technique and large group organization under a single command.

After the battles of March and April 1918 the British High Command had come to regard the machine gun pre-eminently as a defensive weapon, and was inclined to subordinate its use to this role, although contrary to the letter of its own memoranda. In fact, as was to be demonstrated in the battles which, commencing in August 1918, continued with hammer-blow success until the Armistice, not only is the machine gun a supreme offensive weapon, but, organized in battalions under one command, it was also a decisive weapon.

The tasks of machine guns in the attack may be summarized as being to cover the infantry during their advance ; to grip on to all ground won—machine guns are the claws of the offence ; to cover a further advance. The attack itself consists either of a " set piece " operation, or a continued advance, perhaps with pauses, in open warfare.

The " set piece " attack demands that guns will be used both for direct and indirect fire. In order to decide the number of guns to be allotted to each task, it is necessary to consider the tasks and objectives of the main attacking force, whether infantry or cavalry, mechanized infantry, tanks, or a mixed force consisting of various arms and various forms of mobility. The second consideration is the nature of the ground, and the third the ammunition supply. The Forward Guns will ordinarily use direct fire, rarely combined sights. Their duties are to watch for opportunities for covering fire during the advance, to protect the attacking force during consolidation, and to break up counter-attacks.

In this role too many machine guns should not be used, nor can they be profitably employed. The organization of ammunition supply is both exception-ally hazardous and arduous : though, not only with mechanical means but also with the half limber and horse transport, great boldness and dash can always be employed. To use too many guns will usually be to duplicate the work of automatic rifles with weapons less suitable. This has been emphasized. The result will be to waste highly trained men, as during the Great War, and to lessen the offensive power of the remainder of the guns. Machine guns should never be used in groups of less than two. The success of a machine gun advance accompanying the early stages of the assault depends upon careful pre-liminary arrangements being made for an exhaustive reconnaissance, the allotting to each gun its special role, location, and route; and the use of initiative by machine gunners in the use of ground, instead of blindly follow-ing the first waves of attack. Upon arrival at the final position, machine guns must be sited in depth, and from such positions contribute a wide and long field of fire. The forward guns should never undertake barrage fire.

Batteries of opportunity, consisting of four guns, have also been used with high success. Their role must be an independent one, being held in reserve by the machine gun commander until a moment arises—either when the attack is held up, or to exploit a success—when the battery can be released. There-after the battery, complete as a tactical unit, becomes an

Y

independent force whose duty it is to subdue the enemy resistance by manœuvre and fire-power, or to harass his communications and reserves. The successful use of forward guns and batteries of opportunity depends upon preliminary training with infantry and other assault arms.

The task of the rear guns in a ' set piece ' offensive will be barrage fire. The maximum frontage for each such gun should not exceed 50 yards. The barrage necessitates skill in organization and familiarity with machine gun mathematics. Co-ordination between brigades, divisions, corps, even armies, is necessary. As many as 350 machine guns have been used and up to 2,000,000 rounds have been fired in a large ' set piece ' operation. Carefully arranged plans and definite orders are necessary to a successful barrage. Concealment of batteries must not be overlooked : the use of nets is a simple and admirable camouflage.

Protection of machine gunners against aircraft action will tend to increase. Various expedients were employed during the Great War for the purpose of obtaining an ' air cone of fire,' for groups of guns, specially mounted for anti-aircraft work. Tracer bullets, with a directing gun, or placed as to one in twelve in belts, have been found useful. An experiment carried out in April 1937 demonstrated that considerable advances had been made both in directional fire and its control in anti-aircraft work.

In open fighting, especially where the advance is rapid, more reliance will have to be placed on machine guns. The Fourth Army No. M.G. 23/19 dated 12.6.18, issued by the General Staff, laid down : " Although working in the closest combination with the " infantry, machine guns are complementary to but not

" part of the infantry and must not be considered as
" such. . . . It is seldom desirable to detach machine
" guns to lower formations than infantry brigades,
" unless for some specific tactical purpose, such as
" infantry on a detached mission. . . . The brigadier
" will exercise command of the machine guns in his
" brigade through the machine gun group commander.

" Machine guns, capable of long-range accurate
" fire, will go forward by bounds, their objectives
" being positions from which overhead or flanking fire
" can be brought to bear. As in retirement, so in
" advancing, machine guns will advance by alternate
" sections, one section being always ready for fire-
" action. The machine gun commander must watch
" the infantry, tanks, and other movements of his own
" troops in the advance, and conform his plans to the
" requirements. The purpose of machine gun fire is
" that by fire-action the advance shall be enabled and
" attack withheld.

" In the advance, task after task will spring up,
" depending upon the tactical situation and merging
" into one another, all of which must be carried out by
" machine gunners on their own initiative within the
" sector allotted to them." In these words G.H.Q.
summed up machine gunnery.

The absolute correctness of the assertion made by
G.H.Q. that machine guns have tactics of their own
which are neither those of " the infantry nor of the
artillery " is well illustrated from the following. In the
Fourth Army,[1] during the Final Operations, there were
certainly six different instances in which machine guns
were allotted to infantry battalions, and where the

[1] From Reports by Colonel N. K. Charteris, Fourth Army Machine
Gun Officer.

machine gunners received no orders whatever from the infantry battalion commanders. An infantry battalion C.O. ordered *one* machine gun to cover the advance of his battalion with an indirect *barrage*. Another infantry battalion C.O. ordered 3 guns to go to three points on the map. The field of fire from one of these points was only 20 yards, but yet the same authority would not permit the machine gunners to move to a more suitable position.

Many admirable illustrations of the correct employment of machine guns in the attack battle during the last phase of the Great War are available. For example, the 18th Machine Gun Battalion, in the attack on St. Pierre Vaast Wood on 1st October 1918, employed 40 guns to cover the valley running north-east from Combles. Definite areas in the valley were sub-allotted to the participating machine gun companies. During the action the artillery confined its fire to shelling the high ground in the flanks and drove the Germans into the machine gun fire in the valley. The 7th " Buffs " (East Kent Regiment) closed the exit to the valley and captured 500 prisoners.

On 28th August, 8 guns of the 50th Machine Gun Battalion put down a barrage in rear of Pommiers Redoubt and prevented the escape of 2 officers and 50 other ranks, who surrendered.

On the 9th August, the 4th Australian Machine Gun Battalion, advancing in depth, formed a defensive flank covering 3000 yards and successfully kept down the fire of 22 German field guns, severely harassing the attack, until our own artillery came into action and destroyed the hostile guns.

The 12th Machine Gun Battalion, on 22nd August, so successfully covered the infantry attack with direct overhead fire at 2000 yards range that when the infantry reached their objective with low casualties they found 30 German machine guns which could not be withdrawn and many dead and wounded on the captured ridge.

Such instances well illustrate the variety of tasks undertaken by machine guns in the attack battle. Such successes were secured only when guns were used for collective action in numbers varying from 8 to 60 ; when guns advanced in depth ; where machine gun officers were permitted freedom of action within the tactical scheme and to use their own initiative. In order, therefore, to use machine guns rightly these are the required desiderata : first, weight of fire-power ; second, collective action ; third, freedom of action ; and fourthly, use of initiative. Finally, let it be repeated that to obtain the most from machine guns they must be fought with boldness, nor will mere bravery suffice without that essential organization and study of ground without which this nerveless weapon cannot function. Given ability, courage of a high order, and knowledge of the tactical uses of the weapon, then no weapon has so far been evolved which has proved itself to be so effective as the machine gun in offensive operations.

Since the history of early development little has been said concerning mechanical improvements. In fact, Maxim and Hotchkiss had said the last word on mechanical efficiency. Vickers improved upon the Maxim gun, but altered none of its mechanical principles. Such additions as were produced during the Great War period were usually designed to suit the peculiar character of a campaign largely of trench warfare, and affected the packaging of ammunition, the material for belts, and the organization of spare parts. All this experience may prove valuable for campaigns and " police work " in the varied climate and conditions of a wide-flung Empire. Only one new fact emerged which is of permanent usefulness, namely, that the machine gun should never enter action without a minimum of 5000 rounds of ammunition, ready in belts for use. This rule should apply to actions of all kinds.

Speculation as to the tactical changes in land warfare which may be necessitated by the introduction of troop-carrying aircraft and aerial operations designed to prevent concentrations of troops must continue until the matter is tested by war. The experiences of the Italian-Abyssinian Campaign and Indian Frontier Operations (1936–7), where the defence was ill-matched in arms and possessed of no air arm, form no criteria for judgment. Nor is the Civil War in Spain of any value as a basis for forming opinion in this respect, for the numbers of aircraft engaged on either side are comparatively few, their numbers having been grossly exaggerated by the propagandist press of both sides. Apart from operations conducted by definitely mechanized forces, the same reasoning applies to the use of tanks and other mechanized means for the transport of material and men. Major-General J. F. C. Fuller, a specialist in mechanized warfare, after a visit to the Spanish front, entered a considered disclaimer,[1] pointing out that in no instance had there been any engagement which could be described as mechanized, while the close confinement of the small tanks tended to lower morale because their cramped conditions resemble that " of a coffin." Though mechanized means increased, up till November 1937 there had been no mechanized battles.

[1] " The Times," 7th April 1937.

Mechanized land war-machines, however, will undoubtedly be armed with machine guns.

It is not possible to hazard what measures may in the future be adopted for the purpose of neutralizing tanks, though it is evident that the tank teams, being confined within the moving fortress, possess power only so long as the engines function and the casement remains intact. Anti-tank guns and bombs have already been evolved and will always be found to equate with both the density of the plating and the speed of the tanks. Nevertheless, the speed now attained by tanks provides unique possibilities for the exploitation of the element of surprise: while the moral effect of a large concentration of tanks in attack will certainly prove formidable. It is, however, difficult to foresee how ground gained can be held except by men on foot. No one can be certain of the effects of arms, of new inventions, or indeed of the roles of an entire arm. There are no casualties on manœuvres. A war upon one terrain conducted by two types of belligerents may be quite unlike any other war. Prior to the Great War, if any soldier had suggested any one of the following propositions he would have been damned eternally : that cavalry would have no role in a modern European war ; that controlled rifle-fire would disappear and machine guns and automatic rifles take its place ; that bayonets would be preferred as toasting-forks and superseded by bombs as weapons ; that troops could face 50 per cent casualties and more and yet go on— yet these things happened.

Of tactics, we cannot be certain. Strategy, however, is a different matter : and if we cannot be sure how new forms of mobility may transform the tactics of the battlefield, we can be certain that our marvellous world mobility is an asset of incalculable value which must not again, as in the Great War, be neglected. That mobility has been contributed by our command of the sea; by our genius for flight; by air and sea ports all the world over; and by Empire populations of immense resources and of high fighting qualities, available and ready to render service in the defence of a common cultural and material heritage. As has been demonstrated in warfare of all kinds up to 1938, the machine gun remains unrivalled both in attack and defence, a weapon possessed of overwhelming potentiality which, used with skill, cunning, and daring, can evade the tank and master other arms.

During the last phases of the Great War the Machine Gun Corps demonstrated with renewed certainty the value of the new battalion organization for offensive warfare in open country. The great drive to the East was surging upon its course when, on 15th October 1918, His Majesty King George V, writing from Buckingham Palace and accepting the Colonelcy of the corps, said : " I have received your telegram with " much pleasure. Please assure all ranks how proud I " am to be Colonel-in-Chief of the Machine Gun " Corps, which has gained so high a reputation for " efficiency and gallantry in the field. I shall always " follow their doings with the greatest interest. GEORGE " R.I., Colonel-in-Chief."

General Headquarters finally laid down its considered views as to the tactical employment and organization of machine guns in January 1919.[1] The most important points from this document, summarizing the whole experience of the Great War, are given hereunder.

[1] SS. 192, January 1919.

" The machine gun must be regarded as a distinctive
" weapon with tactics of its own, which are neither
" those of the infantry nor of the artillery, but inter-
" mediate between the two.

" Its value in attack is as great as in defence, and
" in every operation the offensive possibilities of the
" machine gun must be developed to the full.

" Fire over the heads of friendly troops may be
" carried out with complete safety. Effective fire is
" possible at long ranges.

" The only point in common between the machine
" gun and the field gun is that both weapons are fired
" from a steady mounting. . . . The machine gun can
" only provide effective fire up to 2900 yards.

" The material and moral results obtained by
" machine gun fire opened unexpectedly on suitable
" targets cannot be over-estimated, and every oppor-
" tunity for securing surprise effect must be sought.

" A high standard of training in reconnaissance is
" necessary for machine gunners.

" Tactical units must be kept intact. The maximum
" fire-effect is obtained by the employment of collect-
" ive fire from a number of guns operating under
" one control.

" Disposition in depth is essential ; and must be
" the guiding principle in machine gun tactics.

" The transport is essentially a fighting portion of
" the battalion.

" The machine gun battalion is, and must be
" employed as, a tactical unit, and the machine gun
" battalion commander is a tactical commander."

The machine gun strength of the Allies on the
French and Belgian Front, in 1918, numbered 21,436,
together with 79,258 automatic rifles or light machine

guns. The total of the British machine guns was 3816, compared with less than 200 in 1914. The former figure must be regarded as approximate, and does not include machine guns used for training or in the Ordnance workshops for repair. The French possessed 15,400 heavy and 59,786 light machine guns; the Belgians, 1100 heavy and 3014 light; and the American Army, 1120 Vickers guns and 3840 automatic rifles. The proportion of rifles to heavy machine guns in the British army was 138; that of the French 43, of the Belgians 53, and of the Americans (5 divisions) 54.

In the British army, after the German Offensive of March and April 1918, when certain divisions were reduced to cadres, but on the other hand, Army machine gun battalions were organized, the machine units on the Western Front were 54 machine gun battalions with 64 guns each; 9 machine gun squadrons with 12 guns each; 5 motor machine gun batteries with 6 guns each; the Canadian Machine Gun Brigade (5 batteries of 6 guns each); 3 Army machine gun battalions with 64 guns each.

In the French army the fourth company of each infantry battalion was a Machine Gun Company of 12 guns, except in the instance of certain Chasseur battalions. The French, in 1918, had 921 battalions and 27 Chasseur battalions of 5 companies and 16 of 6 companies. The Chasseur 5-company battalions possessed a Machine Gun Company of 6 sections and 18 machine guns; and the 6-company battalions, 2 machine gun companies of 24 guns each: 4 each of the six cavalry divisions had 24 machine guns. There were also 175 machine gun companies *de position*, separate units, not moving from one part of the front to another, with 8 guns to each company; and with the artillery, also, a large number of guns were allotted. The machine guns were Hotchkiss.

In the Belgian army the fourth company of each battalion was a Machine Gun Company, each with 8 guns. In a regiment of infantry, the 1st and 2nd battalions were armed with Colt machine guns and the 3rd battalion with the Hotchkiss. The machine gun squadron of cavalry was armed with 4 machine guns and with one or two motor guns. The divisions of the United States of America included four infantry regiments, each with its machine gun company of 16 guns. Each of the two infantry brigades within the division possessed its machine gun battalion of 96 guns; while each division also had its divisional machine gun battalion, motorized with 32 guns.

Germany and Austria had made vast strides in machine gunnery, both in equipment and technique. Not only did each battalion possess its Machine Gun Company; but continuously further unattached machine gun companies were formed, at the disposal of Army Commanders. To the end, when the German Empire was tottering to its ruin, in rear of the retreating army, the German machine gunners fought to the last man and round of ammunition, valiantly upholding the traditions of the spirit of the gun.

A history of machine guns would be incomplete without reference to the air. The machine gun is the weapon of the air. At the beginning of the Great War observers exchanged shots with pistols, carbines, and shot-guns. Later the machine gun was taken aloft and mounted on a swivel. Then Constantinesco turned his inventive skill to the problem, and produced a gear which permitted the pilot to fire between the blades of his whirling propeller. The guns were bolted to the body of the plane and the pilot aimed by pointing his whole machine. This enormously increased the efficiency of the plane, and a good pilot was as deadly a shot as a sharpshooter on the ground. The gear did not, however, always function perfectly, and many a pilot came to grief by shooting off his own propeller.

In order to assist the pilot in aiming, tracer bullets were introduced. These were bullets filled with black powder which ignited from friction as they reached the gun muzzle and sparkled as they went through the air. They also set fire to anything they hit. An even more lethal bullet was known as the Buckingham, which was filled with phosphorus instead of powder. Both sides used them against balloons. The machine gun bullets were held together in belts of aluminium links, each round and each link being carefully tested on the ground before the pilot set off.

The machine gunnery of the air was a high art, for it involved the whole science of flying. " Chasing tails " is part of that art ; while the instruction given to those who aspired to shooting down two-seaters was : " Come up underneath so close that you can " wear the wheels of his undercarriage as ear-rings, and " then fire ! "

In describing one of the successful flights of the famous Rittmeister Baron von Richthofen, Floyd Gibbons wrote : " He pulled up on the stick sharply " and, with his motor roaring under a wide-open " throttle, zoomed upwards under the dark red belly " of the English plane. In a flash of a few seconds he " was within thirty yards of his quarry, and his twin " machine guns were trained on the bottom of the " plane. His finger pressed the trigger button, and " then the speeded-up Spandaus poured forth a stream

" of lead which raked the under-belly of the British
" machine from nose to tail. . . . After delivering the
" burst of lead . . . Richthofen found himself so close
" under the plane that he had to swerve suddenly to
" avoid colliding with it. . . . The disabled plane
" plunged downwards in a mad spiral towards the
" earth—almost two miles below."

The British were armed with Vickers, the Germans
with Spandaus. The story of their fighting is that of
flying itself.

The organization of machine guns in an army so
uniquely recruited and utilized as is that of Great
Britain has for long taxed the brains of the Higher
Command. Before any other consideration, however,
it may be urged that machine gunners be specially
recruited as machine gunners, a separate arm, a *corps
d'élite*. In a mechanized age, wherein every youngster
is under the spell of speed and the marvels of machinery,
it is suggested that the best among the available pool of
recruits would be attracted by an arm which contributes
a romanticism not less than the mechanics of the air.

The British army performs a dual role, that of an
Empire police and that of a cadre on which to build a
national army in case of emergency: perhaps also that of
a highly skilled mechanized expeditionary force, as an
auxiliary to an ally, or to be made use of in some
theatre of war, in exploitation of our unique imperial
mobility, whereas the main British contribution might
be in the air and by sea.

No matter how the Army might be utilized and
expanded for war, it would seem that all experience
teaches that the machine gun battalion is the only
organization which stands up to the varied tests to
which machine gunnery must be put. Morally, in the

development of *esprit de corps*, the battalion organization best will serve. For purposes of training, especially in the selection and training of experts such as scouts and of officers in the control of numbers of guns, the battalion organization again is the only one possible. Companies may be detached for garrison duty, as is often done with infantry battalions.

Carrying these considerations further, however, it seems that the time has come when infantry battalions should be transformed into machine gun battalions, each of which would consist of three machine gun companies of 16 guns apiece, with 16 guns as spares ; and one company, as a Headquarters Company, consisting of trained scouts, gun escorts, bombers, trench mortar section, signallers.

Tanks and mechanized light infantry (the Rifle Regiments) should fulfil the role previously held by infantry of the line. Machine gun battalions should in principle be mechanized, but in any such scheme of reorganization it must be recognized that a mechanized battalion relies upon its oil supply, involving columns of wheeled oil-tanks, confined to roads, and of trains ; whereas, in the last resort, a mule can feed almost upon anything. These factors depend also upon the theatre of war, and the normal duties of garrison and its potentialities; and are matters which go beyond the scope of this volume.

Much of the history of the development of the machine gun and of its tactics is identified with that period of the War classified as " Trench Warfare." It must be emphasized that in such operations the role of the machine gun cannot be fully developed, nor its tactics exploited. Trench warfare may admirably suit both heavy artillery and mortars but not the machine gun. The characteristics of mobility, highly concentrated fire-action, and accuracy at long range clearly suggest that this is so. Pre-eminently the machine gun adapts itself to conditions of open fighting, whether in European warfare or in battling with turbulent tribes-men.

In open warfare of the future field guns may be able to move by covered ways, but no matter what assist-ance may be contributed by them or by heavy guns, it would appear that progress will depend upon the lighter weapons. These will be able to attack by short rushes, by crawling and stalking.

The latest German Infantry Training Manual (" Ausbildungs Vorschrift für die Infanterie ") appears to be improved as a result of the German failure to defeat the Russians decisively in 1915, 1916, and 1917 because the tactics adopted were too slow. When the Russians halted, the Germans, completely failing to realize the power of organized machine gun fire, brought up artillery, and even delayed until heavy guns had been brought into action.

The new text-book organizes the Rifle Company into three *Züge*, each containing three smaller *Gruppen*. In each *Gruppe* there is a rifle section of eight to ten men, and a light machine gun section of four men. The *Gruppe* is the basis of tactics, providing the " fire and movement " of our pre-war regulations. The riflemen push forward, covered, if necessary, by the machine guns (light guns, *i.e.* automatic rifles) of the *Gruppe*, until they are stopped ; when, if required, heavy machine guns or trench mortars and, later, field artillery come to their aid.

In 1922 the War Office took the weighty decision to disband the Machine Gun Corps. The establish-ment of British infantry battalions was made to coincide with that of Germany, namely, one machine gun company with each infantry regiment. In 1936 a fresh decision was made when 13 Line battalions and one battalion of the Guards were converted into machine gun battalions, thereby, in effect, recreating the Machine Gun Corps.

Machine guns remain as the Army's first line of defence and its most potent weapon in following up an attack. Thus will the machine gunners of the future keep alive " the spirit of the gun."

The machine gunner, endowed with a well-balanced physique, an open and agile mind, his weapon as familiar to his hand as is the keyboard of his instrument to a skilled pianist, may seem to possess all the qualities necessary to make him a model, even able to train and to command. But this is not so. The machine gunner, as all the history of his success in battle proves, must be possessed of a keen desire for action ; a predilection, governed by reason, for contact and risk, a temerity and natural bent for responsibility, and above all faith, the flame which inspires the whole. The instinct for taking responsibility implies a quick initiative, so necessary to a weapon ready for opportunity ; faith is that confidence which lies near to the heart of courage. " Even foolhardiness," wrote von Clausewitz, " that is not to be despised." [1] Courage, endurance, sacrifice—these also are the soldier's qualities.

It may be thought that these attributes are only to be found in a man of rare gifts, in the man born to rule and lead. In the average human being there are qualities which are acquired by toil and by the efforts

---

[1] " Vom Krieg."

of daily life. This being so, no amount of effort, consideration, test, and experiment, of man and machine in training,[1] can be regarded as wasted. Both deliberation and judgment in such matters fall to the responsibility of the officer.

Nevertheless, despite the injunction of von Clausewitz, those called upon to fight at the most critical points in the vanguard of the attack battle, and to remain " with backs to the wall " facing fearful odds when all else seems lost, must consider, also, the lines which demark prudence and temerity, courage and character, discipline and initiative, abnegation and faith. Heedlessness robs an act of bravery of every vestige of worth ; prudence gives it all value. Prudence is, therefore, an attribute of mind which foresees and measures the obstacle in order the better to overcome it. If prudence is conducive to estimating the difficulty, and daring of undertaking the fight to overcome the obstacle, courage is necessary to defeat the difficulty : courage, which is itself fortified by that interior force, character. Mere bravery, that victory of man over his instincts in the face of danger, is but an elementary attribute for an officer. The machine gun officer who lacks bravery is no leader.

Courage is something else : it is a virtue of peace time as well as of war ; a virtue of daily life ; a will to master difficulties ; a virtue composed of celerity of mind, grasp of facts, *sang-froid*, will-power. Strength of mind is that which upholds courage and masters chance. Even as strength of body is attained by purposive physical training, so fortitude of mind may be acquired by training, both by individual exercise

---

[1] ' Man and Mechanics : Training a Soldier,' by Lieut.-Colonel G. S. Hutchison, D.S.O., M.C., "Army Quarterly," January 1938.

and through good leadership. Abnegation, that is the sacrifice of self in the cause of an ideal, which may be an intangible or may be found in that very homely and intimate relationship of comradeship, is an attribute of true greatness. Above all, there must be faith, the virtue without which no great work can be accom-·plished. To hold the beleaguered trench, to storm the citadel of the enemy, can be counted as no mean labour. The accomplishment of either may save an army, even a nation, from defeat. Faith is the imponderable which spreads as rapidly as terror, and to it, according to report, we owe the recovery before the Channel ports and in front of Amiens in 1918.

The tradition of the machine gunner is vested in his gun. Its spirit, that of invincibility at the moment of opportunity in the attack, that of impregnable resistance in defence, is the guide for the gunner. Yet, he cannot serve that spirit unless he conforms to those precepts which alone can make him master of weapon and opportunity, and which steel him even to the death.

AWARD OF THE VICTORIA CROSS
TO THE MACHINE GUN CORPS

Lieut. J. R. N. GRAHAM, 9th Bn. Argyll and Sutherland Highlanders, attd. 136th Co. Machine Gun Corps	*Gazette* 14.9.17	Istabulat, Mesopotamia	*Deed* 22.4.17

For most conspicuous bravery, coolness, and resource when in command of a Machine Gun Section.

Lieut. Graham accompanied his guns across open ground, under very heavy rifle and machine gun fire, and when his men became casualties, he assisted in carrying the ammunition.

Although twice wounded he continued during the advance to control his guns and was able, with one gun, to open an accurate fire on the enemy, who were massing for a counter-attack. This gun was put out of action by the enemy's rifle fire, and he was again wounded. The advancing enemy forced him to retire, but before doing so he further disabled his gun, rendering it useless.

He then brought a Lewis gun into action with excellent effect till all the ammunition was expended. He was again severely wounded, and forced through loss of blood to retire.

His valour and skilful handling of his guns held up a strong counter-attack which threatened to roll up the left flank of the Brigade, and thus averted what might have been a very critical situation.

L/Cpl. H. MUGFORD, 8th Sqdn. Machine Gun Corps	*Gazette* 26.11.17	Monchy-le-Preux, France	*Deed* 11.4.17

For most conspicuous bravery and devotion to duty when, under intense shell and machine gun fire, L/Cpl. Mugford succeeded in getting his machine gun into a forward and very exposed position. From this point he was able to deal most effectively with the enemy, who were massing for counter-attack. His No. 2 was killed almost immediately, and at the same moment he himself was severely wounded. He was then ordered to a new position, and told to go to a dressing-station as soon as the position was occupied. He refused to go to the dressing-station, but continued on duty with his gun, inflicting severe loss on the enemy.

Soon after he was again wounded, a shell breaking both of his legs. He still remained with his gun, begging his comrades to leave him and take cover.

Shortly afterwards this non-commissioned officer was removed to the dressing-station, where he was again wounded in the arm.

The valour and initiative displayed by L/Cpl. Mugford was instrumental in breaking up the impending counter-attack of the enemy.

Pte. H. G. COLUMBINE, 9th Sqdn. Machine Gun Corps (Posthumous)	*Gazette* 3.5.18	Hervilly Wood, France	*Deed* 22.3.18

For most conspicuous bravery and self-sacrifice displayed, when, owing to casualties, Pte. Columbine took over command of a gun and kept it firing from 9 A.M. till 1 P.M. in an isolated position with no wire in front. During this time wave after wave of the enemy failed to get up to him. Owing to his being attacked by a low-flying aeroplane the enemy at last gained a strong footing in the trench on either side. The position being untenable he ordered the two remaining men to get away, and, though being bombed from either side, kept his gun firing and inflicting tremendous losses. He was eventually killed by a bomb which blew up him and his gun. He showed throughout the highest valour, determination, and self-sacrifice.

Pte. (A. L/Cpl.) A. H. CROSS, 40th Bn. Machine Gun Corps.	*Gazette* 4.6.18	Ervillers, France	*Deed* 25.3.18

For most conspicuous bravery and initiative. L/Cpl. Cross volunteered to make a reconnaissance of the position of two machine guns which had been captured by the enemy. He advanced single-handed to the enemy trench and with his revolver forced seven of the enemy to surrender and carry the machine guns with their tripods and ammunition to our lines. He then handed over his prisoners, collected teams for his guns which he brought into action with exceptional dash and skill, annihilating a very heavy attack by the enemy.

It is impossible to speak too highly of the extreme gallantry and dash displayed by this N.C.O., who showed throughout four days of operations supreme devotion to duty.

| T. 2nd Lieut. W. A. WHITE, 38th Bn. Machine Gun Corps | *Gazette* 15.11.18 | Gouzeaucourt, France | *Deed* 18.9.18 |

For most conspicuous bravery and initiative in attack.

When the advance of the infantry was being delayed by an enemy machine gun, he rushed the gun position single-handed, shot the three gunners, and captured the gun. Later, in similar circumstances, he attacked a gun accompanied by two men, but both of the latter were immediately shot down. He went on alone to the gun position and bayoneted or shot the team of five men and captured the gun. On a third occasion, when the advance was held up by hostile fire from an enemy position, he collected a small party and rushed the position, inflicting heavy losses on the garrison.

Subsequently, in consolidating the position by the skilful use of captured enemy and his own machine guns, he inflicted severe casualties on the enemy. His example of fearless and unhesitating devotion to duty under circumstances of great personal danger greatly inspired the neighbouring troops, and his action had a marked effect on the operations.

| Lieut. A. E. KER, 3rd Bn. Gordon Highlanders, attd. 61st Bn. Machine Gun Corps | *Gazette* 4.9.19 | Nr. St. Quentin | *Deed* 21.3.18 |

For most conspicuous bravery and devotion to duty. On the 21st March 1918, near St. Quentin, after a very heavy bombardment, the enemy penetrated our line, and the flank of the 61st Division became exposed. Lieutenant Ker with one Vickers gun succeeded in engaging the enemy's infantry, approaching under cover of dead ground, and held up the attack, inflicting many casualties. He then sent back word to his Battalion Headquarters that he had determined to stop with his Sergeant and several men who had been badly wounded and fight until a counter-attack could be launched to relieve him. Just as ammunition failed his party were attacked from behind by the enemy, with bombs, machine guns, and with the bayonet. Several bayonet attacks were delivered, but each time they were repulsed by Lieut. Ker and his companions with their revolvers, the Vickers gun having by this time been destroyed. The wounded were collected into a small shelter, and it was decided to defend them to the last and to hold up the enemy as long as possible. In one of the many hand-to-hand encounters a German rifle and bayonet and a small supply of ammunition was secured, and subsequently used with good effect against the enemy. Although Lieut. Ker was very exhausted from want of food and gas-poisoning and from the supreme exertions he had made during ten hours of the most severe bombardment, fighting, and attending to the wounded, he refused to surrender until all his ammunition was exhausted and his position was rushed by large numbers of the enemy. His behaviour throughout the day was absolutely cool and fearless, and by his determination he was materially instrumental in engaging and holding up for three hours more than 500 of the enemy.

| Lieut. D. S. McGREGOR, 6th Bn. Royal Scots (T.F.), attd. 29th Bn. Machine Gun Corps (Posthumous) | *Gazette* 14.12.18 | Nr. Hoogemolen, Belgium | *Deed* 22.10.18 |

For most conspicuous bravery and devotion to duty near Hoogemolen on the 22nd of October 1918, when in command of a section of machine guns attached to the right flank platoon of the assaulting battalion.

Immediately the troops advanced they were subjected to intense enfilade machine gun fire from Hill 66 on the right flank. Lieut. McGregor fearlessly went forward and located the enemy guns, and realized that it was impossible to get his guns carried forward either by pack or by hand without great delay, as the ground was absolutely bare and fire-swept. Ordering his men to follow by a more covered route, he mounted the limber and galloped forward under intense fire for about 600 yards to cover.

The driver, horses, and limber were all hit, but Lieut. McGregor succeeded in getting the guns into action, effectively engaging the enemy, subduing their fire and enabling the advance to be resumed. With the utmost gallantry he continued to expose himself in order to direct and control the fire of his guns, until, about an hour later, he was killed. His great gallantry and supreme devotion to duty were the admiration of all ranks.

INDEX

Abyssinia War (1936), 156, 326
Aircraft, machine guns mounted on,
    33, 198, 216-17, 331-3
Alt, Colonel (1884), 51
American Civil War (1861–5), 7, 8
American 30th M.G. Battalion
    (Charleston, N.C.), 7
Ammunition, 201, 204-5, 213, 289
Anderson, Major D. D. (1887), 61
Andrew, Lieut. W. P., 270
Applin, Lieut.-Colonel R. V. K.,
    106-8, 112, 116
Arbuthnot, Major-General (1887), 62
Archer, Lieut. Fred (A.I.F.), 302
Armament :
    Armoured cars, 33
    Artillery, 12-13, 26, 73-4, 75-6,
      196, 199, 203, 204, 207, 211,
      216, 224
Armit, Captain (1885), 53
Ashanti War (1874), 38
Ashcroft, Major W. W., 272
Atteridge, Captain A. Hilliard, 106
Augezd gun, 79, 99
Australians, 169, 302-4, 313, 315, 324
Automatic rifles, 85-6, 110, 112, 115,
    138, 141, 151-2, 161, 229-32,
    279, 295 (and see under Lewis
    gun)

Baker-Carr, Brigadier-General
    D. D'A., 130, 136-7
Baker-Finch, Lieut. (A.I.F.), 302
Balck, Colonel, 112
Ball, Major, 190
Battery formation, machine guns in,
    198, 207
Battles, actions, and engagements :
    Alexandria, bombardment of
      (1882), 43

Amiens (8th August 1918), 307
Arras (1917), 172-6
Atbara (1897), 68
Cambrai (1917), 217-22
Chitral (1895), 65
Gravelotte (1870), 15, 17, 21-4, 25
Gumbat (1895), 65
Le Maisnil (1914), 129
Le Mans (1871), 26
Loos (25th Sept. 1915), 141-3
Lys (April 1918), 123, 223, 234-60,
    271-5
Meteren (12th-18th April), 235-60
Malakand Pass (1895), 65
March 1918, 229, 261-70
Mars la Tour (1871), 29
Messines (June 1917), 176
Meudon (1869), 10
Mons (1914), 120-23
Montigny la Grange (1870), 14,
    18, 20-21
Mukden (1904), 91-2
Nanshan (1904), 15
Omdurman (1897), 67-70, 284
Piccardina (1467), 5
Ravenna (1512), 5
Saarbrücken (1870), 14
Santiago (1899), 73
Somme (1916), 122, 126, 165-8,
    171, 324
    Flers-Courcelette (15th Sept.),
      126, 163
    Gommecourt (1st July), 158
    High Wood (16th July), 49, 165 ;
      (24th August), 122, 185
Spicheren (1870), 13
Weissenberg (1870), 13
Vimy Ridge (1917), 175
Ypres (1917), 182, 184, 186, 197,
    201-7, 223

Battleships, machine guns mounted on, 43
Bazaine, Marshal (1871), 16
Beckmann, Captain von, 91
Beith, Major (Ian Hay), 190
Belt-loading, 66, 222
Belts, metal, 134
Benson, Lieut. G. E. (1887), 61
Beresford, Admiral Lord Charles, 40, 43, 44, 45-6, 62
Bergman, Lieut. O. W. (1890), 79
Bergman gun, 98
Bethune, Captain F. P. (A.I.F.), 301-304
Bidder, Lieut.-Colonel H. F., 215
Bingham, Lieut.-Colonel R. C., 308
Bird, Major-General Sir Wilkinson, 96
Bloomfield, C.Q.M.S., 131
Boraston, Lieut.-Colonel J. H., 165
Bostock, Sergt.-Major, 116
Boult, A. J. (1900–12), 79
Brabazon, Lieut.-Colonel J. P., 55
British South Africa Company (1893), 62-3
Browning gun, 99
B.S.A.P., 63
Burmese War (1885–7), 45

Camiers, base, 145 ; school, 189, 191, 193
Campbell, Major-General J., 112
Canadians, 175, 224, 314
Cartridges, 7, 50
Casualties, 17, 115, 164, 171, 185, 298, 230, 243, 277, 285, 294
Cavalry, 33, 34, 35 ; school, 59
Chalmer, Lieut.-Colonel F. G., 275
Characteristics, machine gun, 26, 47, 56, 57, 58, 116, 122-6, 197, 199, 204-5, 217, 221, 282
Charles Salvator, Archduke, 104
Charleston (S.C.), 7
Charteris, Colonel N. K., 117-18, 192, 307, 315, 323
Chelmsford, Lord, 39
Chetwode, Field-Marshal Sir P., 119
China, opposition to machine guns in, 56

Clarke, Lieut.-Colonel R. G., 116, 118, 187
Claxton, Colonel (1868), 38
Clery, General Sir F., quoted, 19
Cochrane, Colonel J. K., 189
Coleoni, General (1467), 5
Colt gun, 98, 99
Columbine, Pte. H. G., V.C., 340
Command :
    Divisional machine gun officer, 180-84 ; Corps machine gun officer, 187, 215 ; 224, 226-8, 231-2, 236, 253
Conference, ix
Connolly, 2nd Lieut., 309
Co-ordination of light fire-arms, 153, 217
Corsellis, Captain D. H., 192
Cowley, Lieut.-Colonel V. L. S., 277-9, 293
Cox, Major, 190
Cross, Lance-Cpl. A. H., V.C., 340
Cruickshanks, Lance-Cpl., 309

" Daily News," quoted, 63-4
Dalzell, 2nd Lieut., 271
Daniels, 2nd Lieut R. W., 308
Da Vinci, Leonardo, 127
Dawson, Sir Trevor, Bt., 66, 98, 99
Dean, Major P., 186, 216
Deane Drummond, Lieut.-Colonel J. D., 272
Defended area, 299
Defensive battle tactics, 236, 256
De Montbrisson (1904), 78
de Montherlant, Henri, quoted, 24
Denny, Major M. E., 190
de Reffye, Colonel (1870), 12, 25, 29, 120
Dionysius of Syracuse, 3-4, 6, 127
Diplock, Mr., 127
Discipline, 263
Dormus, Major von, 104
Douay, General (1870), 13
Du Peyré, Lieut. (1912), 98
Dupuis, Mr. (1863), 38

Edmonds, Brigadier-General Sir J. E., quoted, 304
Elcho, Lord (Earl of Wemyss), 36, 52
Elles, Lieut.-General Sir H., 217
Epp, General von, 253

Error, factors of, 196-8
Esprit de corps, 140, 171, 235, 263, 274
Fafschamps, Captain (1851), 9
Fegan, Lance-Cpl., 309
Feld gun, 29
Field Service Regulations, 97
Fielding, Colonel (1870), 30-31
Fire :
    barrage, 110 ; organization for, 177-8 ; 185-9, 193-5, 208, 215, 217
    control, 15, 197
    covering, 199-200
    discipline, 107-8, 109, 121
    effect, 19, 56, 57, 58, 76-7, 102-3
    harassing, 190-91, 256, 286
    indirect, 76, 80, 256
    overhead, 76, 92, 93, 113, 116, 150
    power, 3, 10, 123, 220
    volume, 4-6, 15, 36, 124
Fitzgerald gun, 98
Fixed platform, 123, 197-8
Fleck, Captain von (1906), 98, 112
Fletcher, Colonel (1872), 30
Forbes, Major (1893), 63
Foreign Powers, armament of, 100, 101, 102, 104
Fort Victoria, 63
Fortress, defence of, 88-91
Forward guns, 180, 308, 321
Fosbury, Major G. V., V.C. (1870), 10-11 ; (1882), 36, 43
Fox, Sergt. A. E., 311
France, naval adoption of Hotchkiss gun, 37
Franco-German War, 8, 11-16, 17-18, 19, 20, 21-4, 26-7
Fuller, Major-General J. F. C., 23, 113-14, 116, 217

Gallipoli (1915), 169-71
Gardner, Mr. W. (1884-5), 56, 64
Gardner guns, 43, 44, 45
Gatling, Dr. (1862), 8
Gatling guns, at Le Mans (1871), 26 ; adopted in U.K., 30-31 ; in Russia, 32 ; in Ashanti War (1874), 38 ; in Zulu War (1879), 39 ; in Peruvian-Chili War (1879), 40 ; adopted in Royal Navy, 40, 43, 45

Gelsthorpe, Captain A. M., 214
Generalship, 21-4, 81, 267
Gorloff, Colonel (1877), 32
Gorloff guns, 32-3
Gough, General Sir H., 219, 267
Graham, Lieut. J. R. N., V.C., 339
Grantham, Machine Gun Training Centre, 49, 143-6, 189, 191
Ground, topography, 282 ; visualizing, 291, 305 ; Australians, 313
Gunpowder, 4

Haig, Field-Marshal Earl, 165, 193, 216
Haldane, Lieut.-General Sir A., 84, 87
Hamilton, General Sir Ian, 84-5, 170
Hamley, General Sir E. B., *quoted*, 16
Haslingen, Lieut.-General G., 112
Henderson, Colonel G. F. R., *quoted*, 16
Hetherington, Captain, 127
Hetthey, Major, 215
Hewitt, Captain R. G., 118
Hoening, Captain F. (1904), 95
Hoge, Lieut. J. C., 302
Honours and Awards, 273
Hotchkiss, Mr. B. B., 37, 99
Hotchkiss gun, invention of, 37, 42, 66, 85, 87, 91 ; described, 99-100, 101 ; adopted in French Army and Navy, 100
Hutchison, Lieut.-Colonel G. S., 133, 165-8
Hyperscope, 133-4
Hythe School of Musketry, experimental work on machine guns, 71-2, 97, 105, 108, 109, 112, 116, 117

Immediate action, 116
Infantry, 110, 317
Infiltration, 232, 311
Instruction :
    British, G.H.Q., 136, 137, 159, 160, 195, 217, 220-21, 263-5, 281, 298, 328, 330 ; First Army, 283 ; Fourth Army (1916), 160-62 ; (1918), 322-323 ; Third Army, 296 ; Canadian, 283
    French, 159

Instruction—*continued*
  German, 15, 148-9, 220-21, 279-
    280, 292, 335

James, Captain W. H. (1880), 36
Japanese use of machine guns, 92
Jardine, Captain, 86

Kampf, Truppen Kommandeur, 293
Ker, Lieut. A. E., V.C., 341
Khalifa, Abdullahi (1897), 68, 69
Kiesling, Captain H. von, 112
King George V, H.M., 188 ; Colonel-
    in-Chief Machine Gun Corps,
    328
Kirkham, Sergt. S. T., 309-10
Kitchener, Field-Marshal Lord, 67,
    118, 131
Kretschner, Lieut., 112
Kuropatkin, General (1904), 19

Lavau, Commandant J. C. (1908–10),
    98, 120
Lawrence, General Hon. Sir H., 264-5
Leadership, 209
Lewis guns, 79, 86 ; establishment
    in 1915, 143 ; true role of,
    151, 152, 217, 221 ; Fourth
    Army instructions on hand-
    ling (1916), 161
Li Hung Chang, 55
Liddell, 2nd Lieut. Aidan, V.C., 129
Liddell Hart, Captain B. H., *quoted*,
    311-12, 316
Limbers, 256-7, 299
Lindsay, Colonel G. M., 118, 131,
    145, 189, 274
Livesley, Cpl., 271
Lloyd, Captain W. N., 45
Lloyd George, Rt. Hon. D., 135-7,
    144, 233, 267, 271, 288-9
Loading belts, 66
Loading clips, 66
Lobengula, 63
Longstaff, Captain F. V., 106
Ludendorff, General, 193, 277
Ludwick, Captain, 132
Luxford, Major J. H., 297

Macdonald, General Sir Hector, 68
McGregor, Lieut. D. S., V.C., 342
Macky, Lieut.-Colonel N. J., 280-84,
    286

McLean, Kaid (1905), 100
McLean, Lieut. A. J., 191-2
McMahon, Lieut.-Colonel N. R.
    (1907), 97
MacMahon, Maréchal (1870), 18
Machine Gun Corps :
  Personnel, viii ; first suggested, 53,
    62, 131 ; formed, 141 ; strength
    in June 1916, 146 ; in Novem-
    ber 1918, 330 ; H.M. King
    George V Colonel-in-Chief,
    328 ; disbanded in 1922, 335 ;
    War Memorial, 260
Machine Gun School, at St. Omer,
    130 ; at Wisques, 131 ; at
    Camiers, 189
Machine Guns :
  Cycles of development, vii, 27 ;
    function in modern warfare,
    2-3 ; failure as artillery weapon,
    12-13, 18 ; success as cavalry
    weapon, 32-5 ; adopted as
    infantry weapon, 47, 58-9,
    61, 74-5
Machine tools, 7
Madsen gun, 79, 98, 101
Manœuvreability, 232-3
Martin, Colonel (1860), 38
Marwitz, General von der, 219, 220
Matabele War (1893), 44, 63-4
Mathematics, 1, 189, 192, 196-7
Maxim gun, 17 ; invention of and
    improvements in, 48-9, 64,
    66 ; mechanism explained, 50,
    53, 54, 55, 99, 101
Maxim-Nordenfeldt gun, 66-7
Maxim, Sir Hiram, 48-9, 50, 56, 66,
    82
Mayne, Lieut.-Colonel C. B., 80
Mechanization, 2, 33, 114-15
Meckel, General, 81
Medway, H.M.S., 42
Metal-clip loading, 66
Military colleges, 110
Mitrailleuses (Montigny), origin of,
    9 ; in Franco-German War,
    9-15 ; invention of, 10-11 ;
    misuse of as artillery, 12-13 ;
    examples of success, 14, 20-
    21, 26 ; organization, 26-7 ;
    failure, 27, 29 ; experiments
    in England, 30

Mobility, 57, 59, 74, 76, 115, 125-6, 224
Moltke, General von (1870), 15, 16
Montagnon, Lieut. B. C., 224
Montigny, Monsieur (1869), 9, 10, 11-12
Motor machine guns, 189, 314-15
Mouceaux, Monsieur (1867), 38
Mountings, 12, 15 ; early difficulties, 38, 46 ; tripod, 59, 62, 99 ; Mark IV Tripod, 118, 125, 197-8 ; fixed platform, 123, 197-8
Mugford, Lance-Cpl. H., V.C., 339
Mungall, Lieut., 308
Musketry, high quality in B.E.F., 120 (and see under Hythe School of Musketry)

Napier, Field-Marshal Sir C., 52
Navarro, Pedro (1512), 5-6
Navy, Royal, adoption of Gatling gun, 40, of machine gun on torpedo boats and battleships, 41-3, 46
Nile Expedition (1886), 44
Nogi, Marshal (1904), 16
Nordenfeldt, Mr. T., 37, 64, 66, 82
Nordenfeldt gun, 37, 42, 43, 45 (and see under Maxim-Nordenfeldt)
Norregaard, M. W., quoted, 88-9, 90-91
North-West Frontier (1895), 64-5 ; (1936), 326

Odkolek von Augezd, Baron A., 79, 99
Officers, instruction of, 72 ; selection of, 171-2
Official History :
difficulty, 271 ; quoted, 295, 301, 304, 305
Opposition, 8, 38, 40, 45-6
Organization :
Austrian, 331
Belgian (November 1918), 330-31
British, Gatling gun in, 1871, 31 ; Battalion, 74, 195, 234, 256, 261-7, 268, 286, 290 ; Brigade, 139 ; Company, 141, 171, 180 ; in November 1918, 330

Canadian, 175
French, artillery mitrailleuses (1870–71), 12-13, 26 ; in November 1918, 330
German (1908), 96 ; (1914), 103 ; (1915), 147-50 ; (1917), 194-195 ; (1918), 225-33, 331
Japanese (1904), 91
Russian (1904), 91
United States, in November 1918 331
Orgues, 5
Orpen, Sir William, 114
Owen, Captain J. F. (1874), 36
Oxford and Asquith, Earl of, 131

Pachmari, School of Musketry, 105
Palmcrantz (see under Nordenfeldt)
Palmer, Mr. (1663), 6-7
Palmer, Mr. (1862), 38
Parker, Lieut. J. H. (1899), quoted, 73-8
Patents, machine gun, 37, 49-50, 66, 79, 98-9
Perino, G. (1890), 79
Perino gun adopted in Italy (1908), 101
Perkins, Mr. (1830), 38
Personnel, training of, 170
Physical qualities, 1, 6, 73-4, 77, 337-339
Pierce, Major W. (A.E.F.), 8
Pinney, Major-General R. J., 173
Plumer, Field-Marshal Sir H., 135, 216
Politicians, 25, 100
Polybolos, 3-4, 127
Pom-pom gun, 54, 72, 92
Port Arthur, 15, 84, 88-91
Prisoners, testimony of, 194
Psychology, 1-2, 6, 73-4, 77-8, 337-339

Rathbone, Major, 190, 192
Rawlinson, General Sir Henry, Bt., 150, 160-62
Read, Mr. Handley, 189
Reconnaissance, 243, 245
Reinforcement Camp, Camiers, Base, 145
Repeating weapons, 6

Requa, Dr. Joseph (American Civil War), 7
Rexer rifle, 79, 86
Ribaudequins (*see under* Orgues)
Richthofen, Baron von, 332
Riflemen, role of, 194
Rifles, automatic (*see under* Lewis gun *and* Automatic rifles)
Rifles, early repeating, 67
Rifling, 10-11
Robertson, Field-Marshal Sir W., 151, 155
Rogers, Captain E. (1875), 36
Rohne, General von (1901), 96
Rolfe, Commander, R.N., 43
Roman Legion compared with German defensive system, 225-31
Russo-Japanese War, 15-16, 17, 27, 33-5, 80-94, 185

Satow, Major G. F. H., 190
School, Machine Gun, first mooted, 61
Schouboe, M. (Denmark), 79
Schulz, Major, 112
Schwarz, Bernard, 4
Schwarzloss gun, 98, 99, 101, 104
Scouts, 222, 239, 240, 252, 256, 258, 313
Settle, Lieut.-Colonel R., 269
Sights, Zeiss telescopic, 96
Signallers, 252
Silverman, Mr. J. (1898), 66
Siting, machine guns, 110, 298
Skoda guns, in Austria, 98, 104
Smith, Major W. W. M., 61
Sokolov, Colonel, 104
Soldiers, duties of, 27
Somme, German defensive system on 1st July 1916, 148-50
South African War (1899-1902), 72, 92
Spandaus gun, 332-3
Spanish Civil War (1936), 90, 157
Spanish-American War (1899), 73
Stessel, General (1904), 15, 16
Storm troops, 312
Strategical considerations, 243-4
Strength of Machine Gun Corps, (March 1916), 146, 319 ; at end of Great War, 330
Sudan (1897), 6, 7

Supporting guns, 180, 308, 321-2
Swinton, Major-General Sir E. D., 127, 233

Tactical employment:
  German instructions (1914-18), 14-15 ; misuse, 17 ; Parker and other theories, 73-8 ; Applin theory, 106-8 ; German disposition (1917), 225-33
Tanks, 10, 18, 33, 126-7, 156 ; at Cambrai (Nov. 1917), 217-19, 291
Taylor, Sergt. W., 310
Technique, 319
Territorial Force, 52
" The Times," *quoted*, 33-5
Thesiger, Major-General G. H., 142
Torpedo boats, machine guns mounted on, 40
Training, 78, 131, 170, 291
Trench warfare, 132-3
Tripod, 59, 62, 99 ; Mark IV, 118, 125, 197-8
Tulloch, Major T. G., 127

Ullrich, Herr, *quoted*, 92
Unwin, Captain E., V.C., R.N., 171

Valbrègue, General (1870), 13
Vandenburgh, Mr. (1862), 38
Vickers gun, 62, 86 ; Vickers R.C.A.M., 118
Vickers-Maxim gun, 99
Victoria Cross, award of, to machine gunners, 339-42
Villiers, Mr. Frederick, *quoted*, 89
Volunteer, adoption of machine gun, 51, 52-3
Vuilleumier, Colonel (1904), 78
Vulnerability, 13, 57, 60, 125

War Office, special committee (1870), 30 ; opposition, 40, 45
Ward, C.Q.M.S. Instructor, 131
Warlow, Mr., 38
Wellington, Duke of, *quoted*, 22
West, Major M. R., 47
White, 2nd Lieut. W. A., V.C., 341
Wilhelm II, Kaiser, 55
Wilson, Field-Marshal Sir Henry, 83
Wilson, Major (1893), 63
Wingate, Sir Francis, 69

INDEX

Wolseley, Field-Marshal, 54

Wray, Colonel (1870), 30

Wright, Captain, 310

Wright, Major R. M., 163-4, 190-91, 199

Wynne, Captain G. C., *quoted*, 225, 318

Yamata, Colonel (1904), 87

Yate, Captain C. A. L., 84

Zaharoff, Basil, 40-41, 66, 82

Zaleski, Colonel, 35

Zeiss telescopic sights, 96

Zulu War (1879), 39

INDEX TO FORMATIONS AND UNITS

Divisions: 4th, 187 ; 8th, 165 ; 9th (Scottish), 141-2 ; 11th (Northern), 170 ; 23rd, 205 ; 33rd, 173, 202, 214, 244

Infantry Brigades: 100th, 186 ; 7th Australian, 315 ; 12th Canadian, 223

Infantry Regiments: 1st Queen's, 167, 246 ; 7th Buffs, 324 ; 1st Middlesex, 211-13 ; 16th K.R.R.C., 165 ; 2nd Argylls, 211-13 ; Artists' Rifles, 130 ; 72nd Canadian Infantry, 223-4

Machine Gun Units—

Guards Machine Gun Regiment, 111, 162-4

100th Machine Gun Company, 49, 122, 165-8, 173-4, 185, 186, 188, 201-14 (*and see under* 33rd Machine Gun Battalion)

Battalions : Guards, 111, 289, 308 ; 4th, 269 ; 8th, 269 ; 9th, 286 ; 12th, 268, 324 ; 18th, 269, 324 ; 21st, 269, 271, 277 ; 24th, 270, 293 ; 25th, 272 ; 30th, 269 ; 31st, 278, 293 ; 33rd, 123, 222, 234, 274, 285 ; 36th, 268 ; 47th, 284 ; 49th, 272 ; 50th, 324 ; 59th, 273 ; 3rd Australian, 302-4, 315 ; 4th Australian, 324 ; 4th Canadian, 224

THE END

Printed in Great Britain by R. & R. CLARK, LIMITED, *Edinburgh.*

Printed in the United Kingdom by
Lightning Source UK Ltd., Milton Keynes
140089UK00001B/3/A